RHEUMATIC DISEASE CLINICS OF NORTH AMERICA

Immunology for the Rheumatologist

GUEST EDITOR
Bruce N. Cronstein, MD

February 2004 • Volume 30 • Number 1

SAUNDERS

An Imprint of Elsevier, Inc.
PHILADELPHIA   LONDON   TORONTO   MONTREAL   SYDNEY   TOKYO

W.B. SAUNDERS COMPANY
A Division of Elsevier Inc.

The Curtis Center • Independence Square West • Philadelphia, Pennsylvania 19106

http://www.TheClinics.com

RHEUMATIC DISEASE
CLINICS OF NORTH AMERICA   Volume 30, Number 1
February 2004   ISSN 0889-857X
Editor: Barton Dudlick

The ideas and opinions expressed in *Rheumatic Disease Clinics of North America* do not necessarily reflect those of the Publisher. The Publisher does not assume any responsibility for any injury and/or damage to persons or property arising out of or related to any use of the material contained in this periodical. The reader is advised to check the appropriate medical literature and the product information currently provided by the manufacturer of each drug to be administered to verify the dosage, the method and duration of administration, or contraindications. It is the responsibility of the treating physician or other health care professional, relying on independent experience and knowledge of the patient, to determine drug dosages and the best treatment for the patient. Mention of any product in this issue should not be construed as endorsement by the contributors, editors, or the Publisher of the product or manufacturers' claims.

Rheumatic Disease Clinics of North America (ISSN 0889-857X) is published quarterly by Elsevier. Corporate and editorial offices: 170 S Independence Mall W 300 E, Philadelphia, PA 19106-3399. Accounting and circulation offices: 6277 Sea Harbor Drive, Orlando, FL 32887-4800. Periodicals postage paid at Orlando, FL 32862, and additional mailing offices. Subscription prices are USD 167 per year for US individuals, USD 250 per year for US institutions, USD 83 per year for US students and residents, USD 198 per year for Canadian individuals, USD 303 per year for Canadian institutions, USD 219 per year for international individuals, USD 303 per year for international institutions and USD 110 per year for Canadian and foreign students/residents. To receive student/resident rate, orders must be accompanied by name of affiliated institution, date of term, and the *signature* of program/residency coordinator on institution letterhead. Orders will be billed at individual rate until proof of status received. Foreign air speed delivery is included in all *Clinics* subscription prices. All prices are subject to change without notice. POSTMASTER: Send address changes to *Rheumatic Disease Clinics of North America*, W.B. Saunders Company, Periodicals Fulfillment, Orlando, FL 32887-4800. **Customer Service: 1-800-654-2452 (US). From outside of the US, call 1-407-345-4000. E-mail: hhspcs@harcourt.com.**

Reprints. For copies of 100 or more of articles in this publication, please contact the Commercial Reprints Department, Elsevier Inc., 360 Park Avenue South, New York, New York, 10010-1710; phone: (212) 633-3813, fax: (212) 633-3820, and e-mail: reprints@elsevier.com.

Rheumatic Disease Clinics of North America is covered in *Index Medicus, Current Contents/ Clinical Medicine, Science Citation Index, ISI/BIOMED,* and *EMBASE/Excerpta Medica.*

Printed in the United States of America.

GUEST EDITOR

BRUCE N. CRONSTEIN, MD, Professor, Departments of Medicine, Pathology, and Pharmacology; and Director, Division of Clinical Pharmacology, New York University School of Medicine, New York, New York

CONTRIBUTORS

JOSEPH M. AHEARN, MD, Associate Professor, Division of Rheumatology and Clinical Immunology, Department of Medicine; and Co-Director, University of Pittsburgh School of Medicine-Lupus Center of Excellence, University of Pittsburgh Schools of the Health Sciences, Pittsburgh, Pennsylvania

WILLIAM P. AREND, MD, Professor, Division of Rheumatology, University of Colorado Health Sciences Center, Denver, Colorado

NAN CHIANG, MD, The Center for Experimental Therapeutics and Reperfusion Injury, Department of Anesthesiology, Perioperative and Pain Medicine, Brigham and Women's Hospital, Harvard Medical School, Boston, Massachusetts

MARY K. CROW, MD, Benjamin M. Rosen Professor, Immunology and Inflammation Research; Director, Rheumatology Research, Mary Kirkland Center for Lupus Research, Hospital for Special Surgery; and Professor, Departments of Medicine and Immunology, Weill Medical College and Graduate School of Medical Sciences of Cornell University, New York, New York

EDUARDO DAVILA, PhD, Research Fellow in Rheumatology, Department of Medicine and Immunology, Mayo Clinic, Rochester, Minnesota

BETTY DIAMOND, MD, Professor, Division of Rheumatology, Department of Medicine; and Department of Microbiology and Immunology, Albert Einstein College of Medicine, Bronx, New York

CEM GABAY, MD, Associate Professor, Division of Rheumatology, University Hospital of Geneva, Geneva, Switzerland

JÖRG J. GORONZY, MD, Professor and Consultant in Rheumatology, Department of Medicine and Immunology, Mayo Clinic, Rochester, Minnesota

ALISA E. KOCH, MD, Division of Arthritis and Connective Tissue Disease, Department of Medicine, Northwestern University Medical School; and Veterans' Administration Chicago Healthcare System, Lakeside Division, Chicago, Illinois

HONGTAO LIU, MD, PhD, Assistant Professor, Division of Rheumatology, Department of Medicine, Northwestern University, Feinberg School of Medicine, Chicago, Illinios; Veterans' Affairs Medical Center, Chicago, Illinois

HECTOR MOLINA, MD, Associate Professor, Division of Rheumatology, Departments of Medicine, and Pathology and Immunology, Washington University School of Medicine, St. Louis, Missouri

JEANNINE S. NAVRATIL, MS, Research Associate, Division of Rheumatology and Clinical Immunology, University of Pittsburgh School of Medicine–Lupus Center of Excellence, University of Pittsburgh Schools of the Health Sciences, Pittsburgh, Pennsylvania

ELENA PEEVA, MD, Assistant Professor, Division of Rheumatology, Department of Medicine; and Department of Microbiology and Immunology, Albert Einstein College of Medicine, Bronx, New York

RICHARD M. POPE, MD, Professor, Division of Rheumatology, Department of Medicine, Northwestern University, Feinberg School of Medicine, Chicago, Illinois; Veterans' Affairs Medical Center, Chicago, Illinois

CHAIM PUTTERMAN, MD, Associate Professor, Division of Rheumatology, Department of Medicine; and Department of Microbiology and Immunology, Albert Einstein College of Medicine, Bronx, New York

JANICE M. SABATINE, PhD, Research Associate, Division of Rheumatology and Clinical Immunology, University of Pittsburgh School of Medicine–Lupus Center of Excellence, University of Pittsburgh Schools of the Health Sciences, Pittsburgh, Pennsylvania

FRANCES SANTIAGO-SCHWARZ, PhD, Associate Professor, Department of Biology, Farmingdale State University, Farmingdale; and Division of Rheumatology, Department of Medicine, State University of New York, Stony Brook, New York

CHARLES N. SERHAN, MD, The Center for Experimental Therapeutics and Reperfusion Injury, Department of Anesthesiology, Perioperative and Pain Medicine, Brigham and Women's Hospital, Harvard Medical School, Boston, Massachusetts

ZOLTÁN SZEKANECZ, MD, PhD, Associate Professor of Rheumatology, Medicine, and Immunology; and Head, Division of Rheumatology, Third Department of Medicine, University of Debrecen Medical and Health Sciences Center, Debrecen, Hungary

ABBE N. VALLEJO, PhD, Assistant Professor, Department of Medicine and Immunology, Mayo Medical School; and Associate Consultant, Division of Rheumatology, Mayo Clinic, Rochester, Minnesota

ELENA WEINSTEIN, MD, Division of Rheumatology, Department of Medicine, Albert Einstein College of Medicine, Bronx, New York

CORNELIA M. WEYAND, MD, Barbara Woodward Lips Professor of Medicine and Consultant in Rheumatology, Department of Medicine and Immunology, Mayo Clinic, Rochester, Minnesota

ROBERT WINCHESTER, MD, Division of Autoimmune and Molecular Diseases, Departments of Pediatrics and Medicine, Columbia University School of Medicine, New York, New York

CONTENTS

rheumatic diseases. Abnormalities in cytokine production are not the cause of these diseases, but reflect continual production by immune and inflammatory cells. Cytokines are heterogeneous and function in an overlapping and redundant network. An important principle to emerge is that the net biologic response in a diseased organ or tissue reflects a balance between the local levels of proinflammatory and anti-inflammatory cytokines and factors. Thus, a chronic disease may result from the excess production of proinflammatory cytokines or the inadequate production of anti-inflammatory cytokines. This article summarizes the role of cytokines in rheumatic diseases by focusing on each disease and the involved pathways of pathophysiology.

It is well-appreciated that endogenous chemical mediators play key roles in controlling inflammation. Recently, it has become increasingly apparent that novel mediators play a role in resolution. Among them, lipoxins (LXs) and aspirin-triggered LXs evoke actions of interest in a range of physiologic and pathophysiologic processes, and, thus, represent the first class of lipid/chemical mediators that are "switched on" in the resolution phase of an inflammatory reaction. Recently, novel arrays of endogenous local autocoids were identified from dietary polyunsaturated fatty acids that display potent anti-inflammatory and proresolving actions and thus are termed "resolvins." These previously unappreciated "checkpoint controllers" provide new opportunities to design "resolution-targeted" therapies with high degree of precision in controlling inflammatory responses. This article provides an overview and updates of the actions of LXs, their association with human diseases as well as on the actions of recently uncovered resolvins.

Endothelial cells (ECs) are involved in several mechanisms during the immune response, particularly in inflammation. Leukocyte-EC adhesion is regulated by the interactions of receptor-ligand adhesion molecule pairs, as well as by soluble mediators, such as proinflammatory cytokines. ECs are active participants in new vessel formation termed "angiogenesis." There have been several attempts to therapeutically interfere with the cellular and molecular mechanisms described above. Specific targeting of pathologic endothelial function may be useful for the future management of various inflammatory diseases.

expression and interaction of these molecules regulates responses to foreign antigens and avoidance of response to self-antigens. Knowledge of the structure and function of these costimulatory molecules can be used to manipulate immune function and inhibit autoimmunity and inflammation in the setting of disease.

Apoptosis and Immune Responses to Self 193

Jeannine S. Navratil, Janice M. Sabatine, and Joseph M. Ahearn

Most autoantibodies that are produced in patients who have systemic autoimmune diseases target proteins that are normally found inside the cell, and many within the nucleus. Clues to how the immune system becomes primed to recognize these intracellular antigens and whether these autoantibodies contribute to the pathogenesis of autoimmune diseases are being uncovered by studying apoptosis. The intracellular autoantigen targets of many systemic autoimmune diseases become altered during apoptosis in ways that may change how they are perceived by the immune system. Under normal circumstances, apoptotic cells are cleared rapidly by macrophages and dendritic cells, with the result that the apoptosis-altered self-antigens are ignored by the immune system or tolerance to those antigens is maintained actively. Defects in the process whereby apoptotic cells are recognized and cleared may underlie the development of systemic autoimmunity.

The Genetics of Autoimmune-Mediated Rheumatic Diseases: Clinical and Biologic Implications 213

Robert Winchester

This article emphasizes the interpretation of the meaning and significance of the genetic aspects of susceptibility to certain autoimmune-mediated rheumatic diseases. The familial aggregation and identical twin concordance that provides the basis of considering these as genetic diseases are reviewed. Major histocompatibility complex (MHC) genes are taken as the primary examples of candidate genes that regulate the immune response; the potential function of these genes in predisposing to autoimmune diseases is analyzed. Autoimmune diseases are discussed as the consequence of the role of MHC molecules encoded by different alleles that exhibit distinct peptide-binding properties and select a self reactive T-cell repertoire. The low penetrance rates of autoimmune-mediated rheumatic disease is used as an argument that stochastic events in the generation and postthymic maturation of the somatically expressed T-cell repertoire account for the characteristically delayed onset of these diseases. The importance of self-reactivity in the physiologic immune response is used as an argument that the events that are responsible for the development of an autoimmune disease are an untoward exaggeration of normal immune responsiveness, but not a qualitatively distinct biologic event.

ELSEVIER
SAUNDERS

Rheum Dis Clin N Am 30 (2004) ix–x

RHEUMATIC
DISEASE CLINICS
OF NORTH AMERICA

Preface

Immunology for the rheumatologist

Bruce N. Cronstein, MD
Guest Editor

Over the past century, immunologic responses have been investigated in great detail, and our understanding of both innate and adaptive immunity has increased greatly. Our greater understanding of basic immunology has clearly led to an improved understanding of the pathophysiology that occurs in rheumatic disease. Indeed, many of the advances in immunology have come about as a result of investigations into the pathologic mechanisms at work in rheumatic disease. Moreover, in the latter two decades of the twentieth century, the pace of discovery in immunology, as in biology generally, has increased logarithmically.

During the past decade, dramatic leaps in our understanding of the basic pathophysiology of the rheumatic diseases have led to the development of new agents for the treatment of rheumatic disease. Ranging from small molecules to whole antibodies targeted to very specific proteins, rheumatic disease therapy has changed radically. Moreover, because of the effectively targeted nature of newer therapies, consideration of novel toxicities plays a larger role in designing targeted therapies for our patients as well as developing new agents to treat rheumatic diseases. Thus it is more incumbent on the rheumatologist to understand the basics of immunology.

In this issue of the *Rheumatic Disease Clinics of North America*, elements of the innate immune system are covered in several articles devoted to the role of complement, vascular endothelium, phagocytes, and small molecule mediators of inflammation and anti-inflammation in the immune response. Dendritic cells are critical to the transition from innate to adaptive immunity, and their function is covered here as well. Advances in our understanding of the cells of the adaptive immune system—both T cells and B cells—are dissected by experts in the area. The growing understanding of genetics and rheumatic disease, an area that promises to grow by leaps and bounds, is also described.

Clinicians who attempt to design a course of therapy for patients with rheumatic disease must understand the processes that lead to tissue injury in rheumatic disease. In the future, new therapies for rheumatic disease will be developed; an understanding of how these therapies can be added to and complement existing therapies—as well as an understanding of their toxicities—can only be attained by knowledgeable clinicians with an understanding of the underlying pathophysiology. We have designed this issue of *Rheumatic Disease Clinics of North America* to assist clinicians in achieving this understanding.

Bruce N. Cronstein, MD

Professor
Departments of Medicine, Pathology, and Pharmacology

Director
Division of Clinical Pharmacology
Department of Medicine
New York University School of Medicine
550 First Avenue
New York, NY 10016, USA
E-mail address: bruce.cronstein@msnyuhealth.org

ELSEVIER
SAUNDERS

Rheum Dis Clin N Am 30 (2004) 1–18

RHEUMATIC
DISEASE CLINICS
OF NORTH AMERICA

Complement and immunity

Hector Molina, MD

*Division of Rheumatology, Departments of Medicine, and Pathology and Immunology,
Washington University School of Medicine, Box 8045, CSRB 6604, 4940 Parkview Place,
St. Louis, MO 63110, USA*

Our body is programmed to elicit an unconditional attack against alien material. Some of the immune responses are stimulated mainly after exposure to antigen, are highly specific, and improve after subsequent challenges [1]. The adaptive immune responses, however, take longer to fully develop. Therefore, during the first contact with a specific antigen, adaptive immune responses provide minimal protection against an invading pathogen. To defend itself against microbes during the first few days of antigenic encounter, the body uses components of what is known as the "innate immune system" [1]. The innate immune system is prepared to react rapidly against extraneous material and provides the early defense against microbes. One important component of the innate immune response is the complement system. This article explores the different mechanisms of how complement is activated and the consequence of the activation, followed by a description of recent research advances that help us to understand the relationship between complement, inflammation, and autoimmunity that may be of consideration in the planning of therapeutic strategies that are beneficial to clinical endeavors.

Complement activation

A primary innate host defense against invading organisms is provided by a series of more than 30 plasma and cell-bound proteins that are known collectively as the "complement system" [2]. This complex system is involved in the immune response and the inflammatory process by the generation of fragments that promote chemotaxis of inflammatory cells, enhance phagocytosis by neutrophils and macrophages, participate in B-cell and T-cell activation, and expedite the clearance of immune complexes. Abnormalities in cell membrane function are provided by the formation of the membrane attack complex (MAC).

E-mail address: hmolina@imgate.wustl.edu

Complement proteins found in plasma are in a native quiescent state but are activated rapidly under the influence of specific stimuli [2]. Although the complement activation pathways differ in terms of the initial activation stimuli and the unique components involved, they all have as a central objective the proteolytic activation of the third component of complement, C3. Three main pathways induce the coordinated and tightly-regulated activation of C3 (Fig. 1). The classical pathway is initiated by the specific recognition of target-derived molecular motifs by antibodies. Once formed, these antigen-antibody immune complexes cause the binding of complement component 1. C1 is a multimeric protein complex that consists of an antibody binding portion, C1q, and two pairs of enzyme subunits, C1r and C1s. Upon engagement to the Fc portion of an IgM or IgG, C1q suffers a conformational change that leads to the enzymatic activation of C1r, which cleaves and activates C1s. C1s activates C4 in a proteolytic step that generates a major cleavage fragment, C4b, and a smaller fragment, C4a. C4b binds covalently to the target surface in close proximity to C1. C2 attaches to C4b and is cleaved by C1 to generate, C2a, which is part of a potent C4b2a bimolecular enzyme, classical pathway C3 convertase. C4b2a is one of the enzymes that is responsible for the activation of C3 and it is only active when the C2a fragment is attached to the C4b fragment.

The lectin pathway is initiated by plasma proteins, known as mannan-binding lectins (MBL), which recognize specific carbohydrate moieties on the surface of pathogens [2]. Once bound, the lectins interact with serum enzymes that are known as mannan-binding lectin-associated serine esterase. The enzymes participate in the activation of C4 and C2 and the formation of the C3 convertase. Activation of complement through the alternative pathway occurs when a small amount of plasma C3 is hydrolyzed spontaneously in the fluid phase by a process known as "the C3 tickover" [2]. Hydrolyzed plasma C3 suffers a conformational change that permits its binding to another plasma protein, factor B. C3-bound factor B is then recognized by a serum serine esterase, factor D. Factor D cleaves factor B to form a fragment, Bb. Bb attached to hydrolyzed C3b generates a fluid-phase C3Bb bimolecular enzyme known as the "alternative pathway C3 convertase." This enzyme cleaves C3 to generate a major fragment, C3b, and a

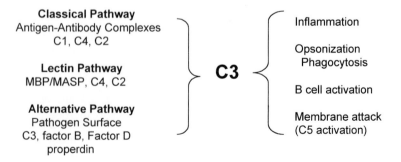

Fig. 1. Complement pathways leading to C3 activation and effector functions. MASP, mannose binding protein-associated serine protease; MBP, mannose binding protein.

smaller fragment, C3a. C3b attaches to target surfaces that are permissive to the subsequent binding of more factor B. These events initiate an amplification cascade in which increasing amounts of alternative pathway C3 convertase and C3b are produced on the target surface. Properdin, another serum protein of the alternative pathway, can attach and stabilize the C3bBb complex. The interaction of properdin with the alternative pathway C3 convertase preferentially occurs on specific targets, such as microbial surfaces, as opposed to host cells.

After the C3 convertase is assembled, binding of C3b to the C4bC2a classical C3 convertase, or binding of a second C3b molecule to the C3bBb alternative pathway convertase, forms a molecular complex that is highly efficient in the cleavage and activation of C5. A C5a proinflammatory peptide is released into solution. The C5b fragment binds to C6. C7 attaches to C5bC6 which allows for the insertion of the trimolecular complex into the cell membrane. C8 and multiple amounts of C9 are added to C5bC6C7 to form what is known as the "membrane attack complex" that is responsible for the abnormalities in cell membrane physiology.

Complement effector functions

Activation of C3 plays a critical role in unleashing the potent effector mechanisms that are associated with complement [3]. Cleavage of C3 generates several biologic, active fragments that are responsible for most of the complement functions (Table 1). The small cationic peptide, C3a, is released into the fluid phase and serves as a potent anaphylatoxin [3,4]. This peptide induces chemotaxis and degranulation of eosinophils and mast cells, which results in the secretion of potent vasoactive and proinflammatory mediators [5,6]. C3a induces potent smooth muscle contraction [6]. In vitro analysis showed that this molecule has

Table 1
General roles of fragments derived from the activation of C3

C3 Component	Receptor	Localization	Function
C3a	C3a receptor	Leukocytes	Chemotaxis
		Endothelium	Anaphylaxis
C3b/iC3b	CR1, CR3, CR4	Leukocytes	Opsonization
			Phagocytosis
			Ag uptake by APCs
			(T-cell priming)
			Adhesion
C3d	CR1, CR2	B and T cells	B-cell activation
		Follicular dendritic cells	Antibody response
			B-cell memory
(C3b)₂Bb or	None	Fluid phase	C5 activation
C4bC2aC3b		Membrane bound	C5a (anaphylaxis/
(C5 convertase)			chemotaxis)
			C5b-9 MAC

Abbreviations: Ag, antigen; APCs, antigen-presenting cells.

an immunosuppressive influence, including inhibition of antibody production by B cells and secretion of anti-inflammatory cytokines by monocytes, in certain cell populations [7]. C3a receptors (C3aR) induce most of these effects. C3aR is a G-protein coupled receptor that is present in a variety of cells, including platelets, mast cells, eosinophils, macrophages, basophils, lymphocytes, and endothelial cells [8]. The wide distribution of C3aR indicates that this anaphylatoxin has a broader spectrum of actions that originally recognized.

C3b is responsible for the activation of the alternative pathway. C3b can be cleaved into smaller fragments by serum enzymes. C3b, and its cleavage fragments, iC3b and C3d, are ligands for complement receptors 1 (CR1, CD35), CR2 (CD21), and the integrins, CR3 (CD11b/CD18) and CD11c/CD18 (CR4) [9,10]. CR1 is a receptor for C3b and also binds to C4b. It is a transmembrane glycoprotein, which is present on red blood cells, macrophages, lymphocytes, and specialized follicular dendritic cells. CR1 also was implicated as a regulator of B-cell proliferation and differentiation [11,12]. Interaction of primate CR1 with C3b/iC3b-containing immune complex on red blood cells facilitated their clearance from the circulation into phagocytic cells in the liver and spleen [9]. On macrophages, CR1 facilitated FcγR-mediated phagocytosis [10,13].

CR2 is a 150 kD membrane protein that binds C3d. It is present mainly on lymphocytes and follicular dendritic cells [9,14]. On B cells, it can form a molecular complex with other proteins, such as CD19 or CR1, which may mediate specific signal transduction events [15,16]. In vitro studies suggested that ligation of CR2 can modulate B-cell activation [14]. As our laboratory and others have demonstrated, in vivo CR2 is important for the interaction of B cells with follicular dendritic cells and for the generation of B-cell memory [17–19]. Deficiencies in CR1 and CR2 decrease the primary antibody response to T-cell dependent and T-cell independent antigens [18,20–22]. CR3 and CR4 are present on a variety of inflammatory and immune accessory cells and are involved in the enhancement of phagocytic function and leukocyte adhesion to endothelium [10,13]. Cross-linking of these receptors activates and increases antigen uptake by antigen-presenting cells (APCs), which results in optimal T-cell activation. C3b also attaches covalently to the target, which is followed by the assembly of the enzyme that is responsible for C5 activation [2].

C5a also interacts with granulocytes and monocytes/macrophages to cause increased chemotaxis, degranulation, adhesion to endothelial cells, and production of reactive oxygen intermediates [23,24]. In mast cells, it shares a comparable function with C3a and induces degranulation, which results in the secretion of potent vasoactive and proinflammatory mediators. C5a also activates endothelial cells to express adhesion and procoagulation molecules. Acute phase reactant production by the liver also is enhanced by this anaphylatoxin. C5aR is another G-protein coupled receptor that is present in several tissues and cells, including granulocytes, monocytes/macrophages, lymphocytes, dendritic cells, platelets, mast cells, liver parenchymal cells, endothelial cells, epithelial cells, and smooth muscle. C5b initiates the nonenzymatic assembly of the MAC [2]. The assembly of C5b–9 causes cell lysis, and recent experimental developments indicated that sublytic generation of terminal complement complexes on nucleated cells initiated multiple signal transduction events, including the activation of membrane phospholipases, G protein activation, activation of mitogen-activated protein kinases, and transcriptional factors [25,26]. The signal transduction pathways may result in C5b–9-induced cell proliferation and antiapoptotic events.

Complement regulation

Activated complement fragments have the capacity to bind to tissues, trigger inflammation, and cause devastating injury. Autologous bystander cells are protected from the deleterious effects of complement by plasma and membrane-bound proteins that regulate complement activation. The complement regulation is performed at different levels in the activation scheme. The enzymatic activities of C1r and C1s are compromised by the plasma protein, C1 inhibitor (C1 INH) [27]. This plasma protein is a serine protease inhibitor that binds irreversibly to C1r/C1s and dissociates them from C1q, which does not allow their interaction with C4 and C2 [28]. C1 INH also is a regulator of other plasma serine proteases, including kallikrein and coagulation factor XII.

An important stage in complement regulation occurs at the level of C3 activation [29]. Inhibition of C3 activation avoids the formation of most of the complement mediators that are involved in humoral immunity, inflammation, and tissue destruction. Two mechanisms are involved in this C3 regulation. The first mechanism prevents the formation of, or accelerates the dissociation of, the C3 convertase by a process known as "decay accelerating activity." The second mechanism consists of the proteolytic inactivation of C3b by a serine esterase, factor I. Optimal factor I enzymatic activity is achieved in the presence of cofactor proteins. Plasma proteins with cofactor properties and decay accelerating activity include factor H and C4-binding protein. Membrane cofactor protein (MCP) is a ubiquitous membrane-bound glycoprotein with cofactor activity [30,31]. Decay accelerating factor (DAF) is another ubiquitous membrane-bound molecule that is responsible for the dissociation of the C3 convertases.

Several proteins that are involved in the regulation of C3 activation belong to a family of proteins called "regulators of complement activity" [29] (Table 2). These molecules are characterized by their capacity to interact with C3 or C4 fragments and by the presence of a common structural motif that consists of repeats of approximately 60 amino acids that are designated complement control protein repeats or short consensus repeats. Factor H is a serum protein whose primary ligand is C3b and is involved in the dissociation of the alternative pathway C3 convertase and serves as a cofactor for factor I–mediated cleavage of C3b. C4-binding protein is a serum protein that binds C4b, is involved in the dissociation of the classical pathway C3 convertase, and serves as a cofactor for factor I–mediated cleavage of C4b. In addition, three membrane-bound proteins regulate the activation of C3 on the surface of most human cells [30,31]. DAF is a ubiquitous 70 kD protein that is bound to the cell membrane by a phosphatidyl-

Table 2
Proteins involved in the regulation of C3 activation

Protein	Localization	Function
Factor I	Plasma	Cleaves C3b and C4b
Factor H	Plasma	Cofactor for factor I in C3b cleavage and decay of C3 convertase
C4-binding protein	Plasma	Cofactor for factor I in C4b cleavage and decay of C3 convertase
Membrane cofactor protein	Membrane-bound ubiquitous (except erythrocytes)	Cofactor for factor I in C3b and C4b cleavage
Decay accelerating factor	Membrane-bound ubiquitous (GPI-anchor)	Decay of the C3 convertase
Complement receptor 1	Membrane-bound: erythrocytes B cells T cells Follicular dendritic cells	Cofactor for factor I in C3b and C4b cleavage Decay of the C3 convertases
Crry	Ubiquitous (rodents)	Cofactor for factor I in C3b and C4b cleavage decay of the C3 convertases

inositol linkage. This molecule is responsible for the dissociation of the C3 convertase. MCP is an approximately 45 to 70 kD membrane-bound glycoprotein that is present on most blood cells (except erythrocytes) and cells of fibroblast, endothelial, and epithelial lineages. MCP serves as a cofactor for factor I cleavage of C4b and C3b. CR1 interacts with C3b and C4b. It can dissociate the alternative and classical pathway C3 convertases and serves as cofactor for factor I cleavage of C3b and C4b.

Rodents also express DAF [32–34]. MCP expression, however, is limited to the testes of mice, rats, and guinea pigs [35]. Alternatively, cells from these animals express an additional molecule that regulates C3 activation [36]. Complement receptor 1–related gene/protein y (Crry) is a ubiquitous murine membrane-bound protein with the ability to serve as a cofactor for factor I–mediated cleavage of mouse C3b and C4b and the capacity to accelerate the dissociation of the C3 convertases [37–40]. Thus, Crry is a functional homolog of human MCP and human DAF.

Finally, regulation of MAC formation is achieved by a glycophosphatidyl-linked protein, CD59 [31]. It is present in many cells and functions by incorporating into C5b–8 which inhibits C9 binding. CD59 blocks MAC formation in the host cell membrane, but some terminal complement complexes may be present in the fluid-phase and insert themselves into neighboring cells. Fluid-phase inhibition of terminal complement complexes is achieved by a plasma protein, protein S, which binds to C5b-7 and prevents its insertion into the cell membrane [1]. Like C1 INH, protein S is involved in the regulation of the coagulation cascade.

Complement deficiencies and autoimmunity

Given that complement unleashes a series of catastrophic events onto the pathogen, it is clear that complement deficiencies predispose the host to bacterial infections [41]. Deficiencies in components of the classical pathway result in a phenotype that is similar to patients who have C3 deficiencies [42]. These patients suffer from recurrent infections with encapsulated bacteria such as *Streptococcus pneumoniae*, *Haemophilus influenzae*, and *Meningococcus*. Deficiencies in components of the alternative pathway and deficiencies in the terminal complement components predispose to *Neisseria meningitidis* infections.

Of more interest is the close association between deficiencies in classical complement components and autoimmune disease [43–45]. Hereditary deficiencies in the complement components of the classical pathway increase the risk of developing lupus and lupus-like disease. Lupus develops in most patients who have complete deficiencies in C1q (93%) and C4 (75%). The relationship between deficiencies in complement components of the classical pathway and the development of lupus indicates that these complement components exert a protective role against the development of this disease. In contrast, C3 deficiency is associated with membranoproliferative glomerulonephritis in 23% of patients, but rarely with the development of autoantibodies that are characteristic of systemic lupus erythematosus (SLE).

The previous theoretical framework related to the protective influence of classical pathway components in the development of lupus relates to the role of complement in the solubilization and adequate clearance of immune complexes from the circulation and from tissues [46,47]. Attachment of complement to immune complex allows for their binding to CR1 on red blood cells and provides a transport mechanism that delivers these complexes to macrophages within the reticuloendothelial system. The absence of complement, then, permits the sustain presence of large immune complexes in the circulation and the potential for target organ deposition. This may cause chronic inflammation with the release of autoantigens and the subsequent development of autoimmunity.

There are several reasons to consider alternate hypothesis [48]. Patients with SLE associated with congenital complement deficiencies do not appear to have excessive immune complex deposition in tissues as compared with SLE patients in general. In addition, one would expect that, besides antinuclear antibodies, there will be the production of tissue specific autoantibodies. It is also very difficult to distinguish if the chronic tissue inflammation precedes the development of autoantibodies in patient with lupus. Finally, most patients with chronic inflammatory disorders do not develop SLE.

Another hypothesis considers the role of complement in the elimination of apoptotic bodies (Fig. 2) [49]. Abnormal clearance of apoptotic cells was suggested to play a major etiologic influence in SLE [50,51]. C1q and C4 were shown to bind these apoptotic cells and assist in their clearance [52,53]. Removal failure, possibly related to abnormalities in the interaction of these apoptotic bodies with classical pathway complement components, may sustain the presence

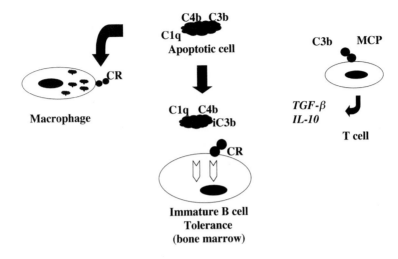

Fig. 2. Hypothesis to explain the increased incidence of autoimmune manifestations in patients who have complement deficiencies in classical components. CR, complement receptor; MCP, membrane cofactor protein.

of this waste substance within tissues and potentially evoke an autoimmune response [54,55]. A provocative model was suggested in which complement binding to apoptotic bodies directs them to complement receptors within the bone marrow [56]. The autoantigen then helps in the education of immature B cells. Engagement of antigen, in concert with the complement/complement receptor interaction, provides tolerogenic signals to the immature B cell that facilitate the clonal deletion of self-reactive cells and the development of clonal anergy. A similar mechanism may apply to peripheral B cells within germinal centers.

Experimental observations also indicate that complement may modify the cytokine milieu from a proinflammatory environment to an anti-inflammatory state that may nurture immunosuppression. In vitro stimulation of human T cells in the presence of anti-MCP antibodies or in the presence of C3b-dimers, induce the generation of immunoregulatory cytokines, such as interleukin 10 and transforming growth factor β2, and the production of regulatory T cells [57]. Interactions between certain APCs and antigen, in the presence of CR3 binding to iC3b, induce the secretion of the same cytokines and a state of antigenic inertia that is dependent on the production of T-regulatory cells [58,59]. This was demonstrated in a mouse model of anterior chamber–associated immune deviation in which inhibition of systemic delay type hypersensitivity reactions was elicited against antigens that were introduced previously in the anterior chamber of the eye [59].

Several genetic polymorphisms in the MBL genes influence the proteins' plasma concentration [60–64]. In a Japanese study, patients who had SLE had a higher frequency of homozygous codon 54 mutations compared with controls. Similar findings were reported in a population of Spanish patients who had SLE.

Patients who have MBL variant alleles may be predisposed to more disease activity and complicating infections that affect the respiratory tract. These studies support the concept that the MBL gene is an SLE disease–modifying gene and that MBL genetic variants may have protective effects on the occurrence and progression of SLE.

Only a small proportion of patients who have SLE suffer from congenital deficiencies in complement components. Acquired deficiencies in complement components, however, are extremely common in this disease. The acquired deficiencies may exacerbate the already abnormal immune response in patients who have lupus. These exciting findings provide a paradigm on which to base further studies to understand lupus etiology and therapeutic implications that may find their way into clinical practice. Particularly alluring is the concept of treating SLE, and other autoimmune diseases, by modifying the developmental program of lymphocytes from a situation in which T-helper 1 effector cells are predominant to conditions in which antigen-specific immunomodulation, through the generation of T-regulatory cells, provides the basis for immunosuppression.

Deficiencies in complement receptors/regulators related to disease

Hereditary angioneurotic edema (HANE) is an autosomal-dominant inherited disease that is caused by deficiency in C1 INH [65]. HANE is characterized by intermittent acute edema formation in the skin and mucosa that produces abdominal pain, vomiting, diarrhea, and potentially life-threatening airway obstruction. The mechanism behind the edema development may be attributed to activation of complement and the production of a C2 fragment with vascular permeability–enhancing activity. Because C1 INH also controls other plasma serine proteases, including kallikrein, it is feasible that the increased vascular permeability is secondary to bradykinin production. Acquired forms of the disease involve the spontaneous production of anti-C1 INH antibodies that prevent the inactivation of the target enzyme or the production of antibodies that activate complement and deplete C1 INH. The latter are related to lymphoproliferative disorders.

Combined deficiencies in DAF and CD59 result in a disease that is characterized by acute bouts of complement-mediated hemolytic anemia [66–68]. The disease, known as paroxysmal nocturnal hemoglobulinuria, is associated with a deficiency in the glycophosphatidylinositol (GPI) anchor that attaches these molecules to the cell surface. It is caused by an acquired somatic mutation in the PIG-A gene in bone marrow precursors [69]. The absence of these complement regulators makes the red blood cell especially susceptible to complement lysis. Other GPI-anchored molecules also are affected. Abnormalities in DAF expression also were found in diseases such as rheumatoid arthritis (RA) and lupus [70,71]. In patients who have RA, reduced expression of DAF on proliferating synovial cells was found. Decreased expression of DAF, Crry, and CD59 was observed in a rat model of inflammatory arthritis [72]. Glomeruli from patients who have lupus also have reduced levels of DAF [71]. The clinical implications of such findings are unclear although one can envision that tissues with reduced expression of this complement regulator may be more susceptible to complement-mediated damage.

The need for these complement inhibitory proteins to control complement-mediated tissue damage also is evident during pregnancy. Throughout gestation , the placenta expresses high levels of complement regulators [73–76]. In addition, up to 20% of miscarriages that occur in the first trimester can be characterized by the onset of hypocomplementemia, and, in some cases, with complement deposition in the placenta [77]. In some cases, hypocomplementemia is associated with reduced DAF expression on the placenta and increased complement consumption at the fetomaternal interface. Complete deficiencies in MCP have not been described; this could be related to lack of clinical manifestation related to the absence of MCP, or more likely, to an essential role of MCP in controlling complement activation in vital tissues. The role of MCP in controlling complement activation is supported by the expression of MCP in sperm which implies an important role in fertilization [73]. Thus, abnormalities in MCP expression may be related to infertility. MCP allelic polymorphism has been related to recurrent human pregnancy loss [78]. An important function of MCP in reproduction also is supported by experiments in mice. Mice expressed a functional homolog of MCP, known as Crry. Mice that were deficient in Crry suffered from embryonic lethality due to excessive complement activation and inflammation in the placenta [79].

Deficiencies in factor H are related to complement consumption through the alternative pathway which causes an acquired deficiency in C3 [80]. It also is associated with glomerulonephritis that is caused by renal deposition of complement fragments [81,82]. Cases of hemolytic uremic syndrome have been associated with abnormalities in factor H expression or function [83,84]. Factor I deficiency also is related to acquired C3 deficiency secondary to increased consumption, increased predisposition to pyogenic infection, and decreased levels of factor H [85]. C3 nephritic factor is an autoantibody that binds to the alternative pathway C3 convertase and protects this enzymatic complex from factor H–mediated dissociation [86]. This results in increased consumption of C3 and the development of glomerulonephritis similar to the phenotype that is presented by patients who are deficient in factor H.

Abnormalities in CR1 and CR2 were described in different autoimmune diseases [87–89]. CR1 expression is reduced on erythrocytes, polymorphonuclear leukocytes, and B lymphocytes from patients who had SLE, autoimmune hemolytic anemia, and Sjögren's syndrome [87]. Expression of CR2 on B cells also is reduced in patients with SLE. The decrease in cell-surface levels of CR1 and CR2 is usually an acquired phenomenon secondary to disease progression, not a primary genetic defect that is responsible for disease development [87]. Recent studies in animal models, however, suggested that genetically-determined decreased expression of these receptors may have a causative role in SLE. For example, in the MRL/Mpj-Fas[lpr] (MRL.lpr) mouse, a model of murine SLE, markedly reduced levels of CR1 and CR2 were found on the surface of B cells before clinical evidence of disease [90]. In addition, Cr2 gene–targeted mice that had a concomitant abnormality in Fas expression developed a progressive, fatal, SLE-like autoimmune disorder that was related to the loss of tolerance induction within the bone marrow [56]. This phenotype is modified by other genetic factors [91]. Recent studies suggested that the gene that encodes for complement receptor 2 (Cr2), located within this region of chromosome 1, is a potential candidate for an SLE-susceptibility gene [92,93]. Thus, decreased expression of complement receptors in patients who have SLE, or susceptible mouse strains, also may be an important factor in the development of this autoimmune disease, or, at least can accelerate disease progression.

Deficiencies in CR3 and CR4 mostly are related to severe recurrent pyogenic infections that are caused by inadequate neutrophil adherence to endothelium at areas of infection that are associated with impaired iC3b-mediated phagocytosis [94]. The condition, leukocyte adhesion deficiency type I, results from a rare mutation in the β chain that is common to the CD11CD18 integrin family.

Complement inhibition as potential treatment for inflammatory disorders

A paradoxical link exists between the complement system and lupus. Hereditary deficiencies in the complement components of the classical pathway increase the risk of developing lupus and lupus-like disease. Immune complex–mediated activation of the classical pathway, however, is believed to be one mechanism by which tissue injury occurs in lupus patients. This observation is supported by experiments that used a blocking anti-C5 antibody. Inhibiting the activation of C5 using this antibody decreased proteinuria and renal disease in NZB/NZW F1 mice, a mouse model of SLE [95]. In addition, the use of a C5aR antagonist attenuated the inflammatory reaction in models of immune complex tissue injury [96,97].

Further proof is provided by Crry-immunoglobulin (Crry-Ig), a recombinant soluble protein that contains the extracytoplasmic domain of the mouse complement regulator Crry followed by the Fc portion of mouse immunoglobulin [98]. This soluble form of Crry retains the complement regulatory functions of the membrane-bound form. Mice that are injected with Crry-Ig are resistant to complement-mediated organ damage in a murine model of antibody-induced glomerulonephritis. Transgenic mice that express a soluble functional form of Crry also have been generated [99]. These recombinant soluble Crry-transgenic mice are resistant to complement-mediated organ damage in the same murine model of antibody-induced glomerulonephritis. Furthermore, transgenic expression of Crry also greatly ameliorates renal disease and promotes survival in a mouse model of lupus [100].

Complement involvement in tissue damage that is associated with lupus is portrayed by studies using a mouse model of the antiphospholipid syndrome, a condition that is associated closely with SLE [101]. The antiphospholipid syndrome is characterized by increased risk of vascular thrombosis involving venous, arterial, and placental circulation [102]. Recurrent miscarriages and pregnancy loss are characteristic of this condition. Antibodies against phospholipid components and associated proteins (β2-glycoprotein I) are involved in the disease pathogenesis. A mouse model was generated in which transfer of these antibodies to pregnant mice increased fetal resorption, the equivalent to human miscarriages. Treatment with Crry-Ig blocked fetal loss and inhibited thrombosis generation in vivo [101]. Mice that were deficient in C3 also were resistant to the fetal injury that was caused by these antibodies. Thus, complement is required in the vascular thrombosis, pregnancy loss, and fetal death that are associated with the antiphospholipid syndrome.

It is difficult to reconcile the dual roles of complement; it may be harmful in some circumstances and protective in others. It is likely that the effect of complement in lupus depends on the specific complement components that are involved, the genetic background of the patient, and the nature and timing of the inflammatory process [103]. Complement may be necessary during the acute inflammatory phase but not during the chronic stages; alternate compensatory pathways of tissue damage or protection may be recruited. Notwithstanding, these studies demonstrate the need for further studies to better define the role of complement in SLE.

Several experimental observations demonstrated a potential seditious role of complement in RA. There is evidence for intra-articular complement activation in the pathogenesis of RA [104–106]. There is deposition of immune complexes in the synovium and articular cartilage and associated elevated levels of activated complement components. Positive correlation exists between the degree of complement activation and disease severity. In animal models of inflammatory arthritis, complement inhibition had a substantial beneficial effect. In collagen-induced arthritis (CIA), inhibition of C5 activity by blocking antibodies prevented the onset of arthritis and ameliorated the clinical findings in established disease [107]. Paw thickness and arthritis index are reduced in anti-C5 treated mice. Levels of proinflammatory cytokines, including tumor necrosis factor (TNF)-α, interleukin (IL)-18, interferon-γ, and IL-1, are reduced [108]. Mice that are deficient in C5 and C3 are resistant to the development of CIA [109,110]. Soluble CR1 also has a demonstrable beneficial effect with delayed development and progression and attenuated inflammation during active disease [111]. Conversely, blocking the function of complement regulators worsens the joint inflammation [72]. Treatment with Crry-Ig has modest effects [108]. This modest effect probably is related to the short period of complete complement inhibition that is associated with in vivo Crry-Ig treatment which suggests that prolonged complement regulation is necessary. Paradoxically, Crry-Ig treatment increases TNF-α mRNA in the joints of affected mice.

In a transgenic mouse model of inflammatory arthritis, K/BxN T-cell receptor–transgenic mice develop a disease that is similar to RA [112]. C3 deficiency and factor B are protective, whereas deficiencies in C1q and C4 are not. Furthermore, mice that are deficient in C5aR are protected but mice that are deficient in C6 are not. These data indicate an important, unexpected role for the alternative pathway of complement in the initiation, and, perhaps, the sustenance of this type of arthritis. In addition, effector mechanisms that are related to the C5a anaphylatoxin are more insidious than terminal complement components. Translated into human clinical experience, it may be equally effective, but less immunosuppressive, to treat patients with selective complement inhibitors of factor B, properdin inhibitors, or inhibitors of C5a function.

Studies on mouse and rat complement regulators are providing significant insight into the roles of the corresponding functionally-related human molecules in vivo that was not appreciated by in vitro analysis or by examination of structural orthologs. Complement also was implicated in the pathogenesis of other inflammatory disorders (eg, sepsis, Alzheimer's disease) and acute and chronic inflammatory conditions [113–118].

The use of complement regulators, such as C1 INH, soluble CR1, C5 blocking reagents, DAF, MCP, and CD59, provides a new potential therapeutic armamentarium to prevent and treat inflammatory tissue destruction in a variety of human diseases [117,118]. Translational research and clinical studies rapidly are opening avenues that will direct these compounds into the clinical arena. The role of complement activation in preventing autoimmune diseases and in controlling infection may compromise the use of some of these reagents. Furthermore, the redundancy that is intrinsic to the inflammatory reaction may dampen the success of reagents that otherwise are highly effective in controlled experimental situations and animal models. More work needs to be done to specifically define the role of these complement regulators in the treatment of human disease.

References

[1] Abbas AK, Lichtman AH, Pober JS. Cellular and molecular immunology. 4th edition. Philadelphia: W.B. Saunders Company; 2000.
[2] Volanakis JE. Overview of the complement system. In: Volanakis JE, Frank MM, editors. The human complement system in health and disease. New York: Marcel Decker; 1998. p. 9–32.
[3] Frank MM, Fries LF. The role of complement in inflammation and phagocytosis. Immunol Today 1991;12:322–6.
[4] Wetsel RA. Structure, function and cellular expression of complement anaphylatoxin receptors. Cur Opin Immunol 1995;7:48–53.
[5] Takafuji S, Tadokoro K, Ito K, et al. Degranulation from human eosinophils stimulated with C3a and C5a. Int Arch Allergy Immunol 1994;104:27–9.
[6] Elsner J, Oppermann M, Czech W, et al. C3a activates reactive oxygen radical species production and intracellular calcium transients in human eosinophils. Eur J Immunol 1994;24: 518–22.
[7] Fischer WH, Hugli TE. Regulation of B cell functions by C3a and C3adesArg: suppression of TNF-α, IL-6, and the polyclonal immune response. J Immunol 1997;159:4279–86.
[8] Ember JA, Jagels MA, Hugli TE. Characterization of complement anaphylatoxins and their biological responses. In: Volanakis JE, Frank MM, editors. The human complement system in health and disease. New York: Marcel Decker; 1998. p. 241–84.
[9] Ahearn JM, Fearon DT. Structure and function of the complement receptors, CR1 (CD35) and CR2 (CD21). Adv Immunol 1989;46:183–219.
[10] Brown EJ. Complement receptors and phagocytosis. Cur Opin Immunol 1991;3:76–82.

[11] Weiss L, Delfraissy JF, Vasquez A, et al. Monoclonal antibodies to the human C3b/C4b receptor (CR1) enhance specific B cell differentiation. J Immunol 1987;138:2988–93.

[12] Hivroz C, Fisher E, Kazatchkine MD, et al. Differential effects of the stimulation of complement receptors CR1 (CD35) and CR2 (CD21) on cell proliferation and intracellular $Ca2^+$ mobilization of chronic lymphocytic leukemia B cells. J Immunol 1991;146:1766–72.

[13] Newman SL, Devery-Pocius JE, Ross G, et al. Phagocytosis by human monocyte-derived macrophages. Independent function of receptors for C3b (CR1) and iC3b (CR3). Complement 1984;1:213–27.

[14] Carroll MC. The role of complement and complement receptors in induction and regulation of immunity. Annu Rev Immunol 1998;16:545–68.

[15] Matsumoto AK, Kopicky-Burd J, Carter RH, et al. Intersection of the complement and immune system: a signal transduction complex of the B lymphocyte-containing complement receptor 2 and CD19. J Exp Med 1991;173:55–64.

[16] Tuveson DA, Ahearn JM, Matsumoto AK, et al. Molecular interactions of complement receptors on B lymphocytes: a CR1/CR2 complex distinct from the CR2/CD19 complex. J Exp Med 1991;173:1083–9.

[17] Molina H, Holers VM, Li B, et al. Markedly impaired humoral immune response in mice deficient in complement receptors 1 and 2. Proc Natl Acad Sci USA 1996;93:3357–61.

[18] Croix D, Ahearn JM, Rosengard AM, et al. Antibody response to T-dependent antigen requires B cell expression of complement receptors. J Exp Med 1996;183:1857–64.

[19] Fang Y, Xu C, Fu Y-X, et al. Expression of complement receptors 1 and 2 on follicular dendritic cells is necessary for the generation of a strong antigen-specific IgG response. J Immunol 1998; 160:5273–9.

[20] Wu X, Jiang N, Fang I, et al. Impaired affinity maturation in $Cr2^{-/-}$ mice is rescued by adjuvants without improvement in germinal center morphology. J Immunol 2000;165:3119–27.

[21] Fischer MB, Goerg S, Shen L, et al. Dependence of germinal center B cells on expression of CD21/CD35 for survival. Science 1998;280:582–5.

[22] Ahearn JM, Fischer M, Croix D, et al. Disruption of the Cr2 locus results in a reduction in B-1a cells and in an impaired B cell response to T-dependent antigen. Immunity 1996;4:251–62.

[23] Gerard C, Gerard NP. C5a anaphylatoxin and its seven transmembrane-segment receptor. Annu Rev Immunol 1994;12:775–808.

[24] Gerard NP, Gerard C. The chemotactic receptor for human C5a anaphylatoxin. Nature 1991; 349:614–7.

[25] Rus HG, Niculescu FI, Shin ML. Role of the C5b-9 complement complex in cell cycle and apoptosis. Immunol Rev 2001;180:49–55.

[26] Niculescu F, Soane L, Badea T, et al. Tyrosine phosphotylation and activation of Janus kinase 1 and STAT3 by sublytic C5b-9 complement complex in aortic endothelial cells. Immunopharmacology 1999;42:187–93.

[27] Tosi M, Duponchel C, Bourgarel P, et al. Molecular cloning of human C1 inhibitor: sequence homologies with 1α-antitrypsin and other members of the serpins superfamily. Gene 1986; 42:265–72.

[28] Sim RB, Reboul A, Arlaud GJ, et al. Interaction of ^{125}I-labelled complement subcomponents C-1r and C1-s with protease inhibitors in plasma. FEBS Lett 1979;97:111–5.

[29] Hourcade D, Holers VM, Atkinson JP. The regulators of complement activation (RCA) gene cluster. Adv Immunol 1989;45:381–416.

[30] Lublin DM, Atkinson JP. Decay-accelerating factor and membrane cofactor protein. Curr Top Microbiol Immunol 1989;153:123–45.

[31] Morgan B, Meri S. Membrane proteins that protect against complement lysis. Springer Sem Immunopath 1994;15:369–96.

[32] Kameyoshi Y, Matsushita M, Okada H. Murine membrane inhibitor of complement which accelerates decay of human C3 convertase. Immunology 1989;68:439–44.

[33] Spicer AP, Seldin MF, Gendler SJ. Molecular cloning and chromosomal localization of the mouse decay-accelerating factor genes. J Immunol 1995;155:3079–91.

[34] Sun X, Funk CD, Deng C, et al. Role of decay-accelerating factor in regulating complement activation on the erythrocyte surface as revealed by gene targeting. Proc Natl Acad Sci USA 1999;96:628–33.

[35] Tsujimura A, Shida K, Kitamura M, et al. Molecular cloning of a murine homologue of membrane cofactor protein (CD46): preferential expression in testicular germ cells. Biochem J 1998;330:163–8.

[36] Holers VM, Kinoshita T, Molina HD. Evolution of mouse and human complement C3 binding proteins: divergence of form but conservation of function. Immunol Today 1992;13:231–6.

[37] Wong W, Fearon DT. P65: a C3b-binding protein on murine cells that shares antigenic determinants with the human C3b receptor (CR1) and is distinct from murine C3b receptor. J Immunol 1985;134:4048–56.

[38] Paul MS, Aegerter M, O'Brien SE, et al. The murine complement receptor gene family I. Analysis of mCRY gene products and their homology to human CR1. J Immunol 1989; 142:582–9.

[39] Molina H, Wong W, Kinoshita T, et al. Distinct receptor and regulatory properties of recombinant mouse complement receptor 1 (CR1) and Crry, the two genetic homologues of human CR1. J Exp Med 1992;175:121–9.

[40] Kim Y-U, Kinoshita T, Molina H, et al. Mouse complement regulatory protein Crry/p65 uses the specific mechanisms of both human decay-accelerating factor and membrane cofactor protein. J Exp Med 1995;181:151–9.

[41] Densen P. Complement deficiencies and infection. In: Volanakis JE, Frank MM, editors. The human complement system in health and disease. New York: Marcel Decker; 1998. p. 409–21.

[42] Singer L, Colten HR, Wetsel RA. Complement C3 deficiency: human, animal, and experimental models. Pathobiology 1994;62:14–28.

[43] Walport MJ, Davies KA, Morley BJ, et al. Complement deficiencies and autoimmunity. Ann N Y Acad Sci 1997;815:267–81.

[44] Morgan BP, Walport MJ. Complement deficiencies and disease. Immunol Today 1994;12:301–6.

[45] Colten HR, Rosen FS. Complement deficiencies. Annu Rev Immunol 1992;10:809–34.

[46] Davies KA. Complement, immune complexes and systemic lupus erythematosus. Br J Rheum 1996;35:5–23.

[47] Walport MJ, Davies KA, Botto M. C1q and systemic lupus erythematosus. Immunobiology 1998;199:265–85.

[48] Navratil JS, Korb LC, Ahearn JM. Systemic lupus erythematosus and complement deficiencies: clues to a novel role for the classical complement pathway in the maintenance of immune tolerance. Immunopharmacology 1999;42:47–52.

[49] Mevorach D, Mascarenhas JO, Gershov D, et al. Complement-dependent clearance of apoptotic cells by human macrophages. J Exp Med 1998;188:2313–20.

[50] Casciola-Rosen LA, Anhalt G, Rosen A. Autoantigens targeted in systemic lupus erythematosus are clustered in two populations of surface structures on apoptotic keratinocytes. J Exp Med 1994;179:1317–30.

[51] Casciola-Rosen L, Rosen A, Petri M, et al. Surface blebs of apoptotic cells are sites of enhanced procoagulant activity: implications for coagulation events and antigenic spread in systemic lupus erythematosus. Proc Natl Acad Sci USA 1996;93:1624–9.

[52] Korb LC, Ahearn JM. C1q binds directly and specifically to surface blebs of apoptotic human keratinocytes; complement deficiencies and systemic lupus erythematosus revisited. J Immunol 1997;158:4525–8.

[53] Taylor PR, Carugati A, Fadok VA, et al. A hierarchical role for the classical pathway complement proteins in the clearance of apoptotic cells in vivo. J Exp Med 2000;192:359–66.

[54] Botto M, Dell'Agnola C, Bygrave AE, et al. Homozygous C1q deficiency causes glomerulonephritis associated with multiple apoptotic bodies. Nat Genet 1998;19:56–9.

[55] Botto M. Links between complement deficiency and apoptosis. Arthritis Res 2001;3:207–10.

[56] Prodeus AP, Georg S, Shen L-M, et al. A critical role for complement in maintenance of self tolerance. Immunity 1998;8:721–31.

[57] Kemper C, Chan A, Green JM, et al. Activation of human CD4$^+$ cells with CD3 and CD46 induces a T-regulatory cell 1 phenotype. Nature 2003;421:388–92.

[58] Karp CL, Wysocka M, Wahl LM, et al. Mechanism of suppression of cell-mediated immunity by measles virus. Science 1996;273:228–31.

[59] Sohn J-H, Bora PS, Suk H-J, et al. Tolerance is dependent on complement C3 fragment iC3b binding to antigen-presenting cells. Nat Med 2003;9:206–12.

[60] Davies EJ, Snowden N, Hillarby MC, et al. Mannose binding protein gene polymorphism in systemic lupus erythematosus. Arthritis Rheum 1995;38:110–4.

[61] Ip WK, Chan SY, Lau CS, et al. Association of systemic lupus erythematosus with promoter polymorphisms of the mannose-binding lectin gene. Arthritis Rheum 1998;41:1663–8.

[62] Tsutsumi A, Sasaki K, Wakamiya N, et al. Mannose-binding lectin gene: polymorphisms in Japanese patients with systemic lupus erythematosus, rheumatoid arthritis and Sjögren's syndrome. Genes Immun 2001;2:99–104.

[63] Villareal J, Crosdale D, Ollier W, et al. Mannose binding lectin and FcgammaRIIa (CD32) polymorphism in Spanish systemic lupus erythematosus patients. Rheumatol 2001;40:1009–12.

[64] Garred P, Voss A, Madsen HO, et al. Association of mannose-binding lectin gene variation with disease severity and infections in a population-based cohort of systemic lupus erythematosus patients. Genes Immun 2001;2:442–50.

[65] Davis III AE. C1 inhibitor and hereditary angioneurotic edema. Annu Rev Immunol 1988;6:595–628.

[66] Pangburn MK, Schreiber RD, Muller-Eberhard H. Deficiency of an erythrocyte membrane protein with complement regulatory activity in paroxysmal nocturnal hemoglobinuria. Proc Natl Acad Sci USA 1983;80:5430–4.

[67] Kinoshita T, Medof ME, Silber R, et al. Distribution of decay-accelerating factor in the peripheral blood of normal individuals and patients with paroxysmal nocturnal hemoglobinuria. J Exp Med 1985;162:75–92.

[68] Nicholson-Weller A, March JP, Rosenfeld SI, et al. Affected erythrocytes of patients with paroxysmal nocturnal hemoglobinuria are deficient in the complement regulatory protein, decay accelerating factor. Proc Natl Acad Sci USA 1983;80:5066–70.

[69] Takeda J, Miyata T, Kawagoe K, et al. Deficiency of the GPI anchor caused by a somatic mutation of the PIG-A gene in paroxysmal nocturnal hemoglobinuria. Cell 1993;73:703–11.

[70] Itoh J, Nose M, Fujita T, et al. Expression of decay-accelerating factor is reduced on hyperplastic synovial lining cells in rheumatoid synovitis. Clin Exp Immunol 1991;83:364–8.

[71] Cosio FG, Sedmak DD, Mahan JD, et al. Localization of decay accelerating factor in normal and diseased kidneys. Kidney Int 1989;36:100–7.

[72] Mizuno M, Nishikawa K, Spiller OB, et al. Membrane complement regulators protect against the development of type II collagen-induced arthritis in rats. Arthritis Rheum 2001;44:2425–34.

[73] Rooney IA, Oglesby TJ, Atkinson JP. Complement in human reproduction: activation and control. Immunol Res 1993;12:276–94.

[74] Holmes CH, Simpson KL. Complement and pregnancy: new insights into the immunobiology of the fetomaternal relationship. Baillieres Clin Obstet Gynaecol 1992;6:439–60.

[75] Hsi BL, Hunt JS, Atkinson J. Differential expression of complement regulatory proteins on subpopulations of human trophoblast cells. J Reprod Immunol 1991;19:209–23.

[76] Holmes CH, Simpson KL, Okada H, et al. Complement regulatory proteins at the fetomaternal interface during human placental development: distribution of CD59 by comparison with membrane cofactor protein (CD46) and decay accelerating factor (CD55). Eur J Immunol 1992;22:1579–85.

[77] Cunningnham DS, Tichenor Jr JR. Decay-accelerating factor protects human trophoblast from complement-mediated attack. Clin Immunol Immunopath 1995;74:156–61.

[78] Risk JM, Flanagan BF, Johnson PM. Polymorphism of the human CD46 gene in normal individuals and in recurrent spontaneous abortion. Hum Immunol 1991;30:162–7.

[79] Xu C, Mao D, Holers VM, et al. A critical role for the murine complement regulator Crry in fetomaternal tolerance. Science 2000;287:498–501.

[80] Zipfel PF, Hellwage J, Friese MA, et al. Factor H and disease: a complement regulator affects vital body functions. Mol Immunol 1999;36:241–8.

[81] Levy M, Halbwachs-Mecarelli L, Gubler MC, et al. H deficiency in two brothers with atypical dense intramembranous deposit disease. Kidney Int 1986;30:949–56.

[82] Hogasen K, Jansen JH, Mollnes TE, et al. Hereditary porcine membranoproliferative glomerulonephritis type II is caused by factor H deficiency. J Clin Invest 1995;95:1054–61.

[83] Pichette V, Querin S, Schurch W, et al. Familial hemolytic-uremic syndrome and homozygous factor H deficiency. Am J Kidney Dis 1994;24:936–41.

[84] Ying L, Katz Y, Schlesinger M, et al. Complement factor H mutation associated with autosomal recessive atypical hemolytic syndrome. Am J Hum Genet 1999;65:1538–46.

[85] Amadei N, Baracho GV, Nudelman V. Inherited complement factor I deficiency associated with systemic lupus erythematosus, higher susceptibility to infection and low levels of factor H. Scand J Immunol 2001;53:615–21.

[86] Williams DG. C3 nephritic factor and mesangiocapillary glomerulonephritis. Pediatr Nephrol 1997;11:96–8.

[87] Walport MJ, Lachmann PJ. Erythrocyte complement receptor type 1, immune complexes, and the rheumatic diseases. Arthritis Rheum 1988;31:153–8.

[88] Wilson JG, Ratnoff WD, Schur PH, et al. Decreased expression of the C3b/C4b receptor (CR1) and the C3d receptor (CR2) on B lymphocytes and of CR1 on neutrophils of patients with systemic lupus erythematosus. Arthritis Rheum 1986;29:739–47.

[89] Fyfe A, Holme ER, Zoma A, et al. C3b receptor (CR1) expression on the polymorphonuclear leukocytes from patients with systemic lupus erythematosus. Clin Exp Immunol 1987;67:300–8.

[90] Takahashi K, Kozono Y, Waldschmidt TJ, et al. Mouse complement receptors type 1 (CR1; CD35) and type 2 (CR2;CD21): expression on normal B cell subpopulations and decreased levels during the development of autoimmunity in MRL/lpr mice. J Immunol 1997;159: 1557–69.

[91] Wu X, Jiang N, Deppong C, et al. A role for the Cr2 gene in modifying autoantibody production in systemic lupus erythematosus. J Immunol 2002;169:1587–92.

[92] Boackle SA, Holers VM, Chen X, et al. Cr2, a candidate gene in the murine Sle1c lupus susceptibility locus, encodes a dysfunctional protein. Immunity 2001;15:775–85.

[93] Morel L, Blenman KR, Croker BP, et al. The major murine systemic lupus erythematosus susceptibility locus, Sle1, is a cluster of functionally related genes. Proc Natl Acad Sci USA 2001;98:1787–92.

[94] Bunting M, Harris ES, McIntyre TM, et al. Leukocyte adhesion deficiency syndromes: adhesion and tethering defects involving beta 2 integrins and selecting ligands. Curr Opin Hematol 2002;9:30–5.

[95] Wang Y, Hu Q, Madri JA, et al. Amelioration of lupus-like autoimmune disease in NZB/W F1 nice after treatment with a blocking monoclonal antibody specific for complement component C5. Proc Natl Acad Sci USA 1996;93:8563–8.

[96] Pellas TC, Boyar W, Oostrum JV, et al. Novel C5a receptor antagonist regulates neutrophil functions in vitro and in vivo. J Immunol 1998;160:5616–21.

[97] Heller T, Hennecke M, Baumann U, et al. selection of C5a receptor antagonist from phage libraries attenuating the inflammatory response in immune complex disease and ischemia/ reperfusion injury. J Immunol 1999;163:985–94.

[98] Quigg RJ, Kozono Y, Berthiaume D, et al. Blockade of antibody-induced glomerulonephritis with Crry-Ig, a soluble murine complement inhibitor. J Immunol 1998;160:4553–60.

[99] Quigg RJ, He C, Lim A, et al. Transgenice mice overexpressing the complement inhibitor Crry as a soluble protein are protected from antibody-induced glomerular injury. J Exp Med 1998; 188:1321–31.

[100] Bao L, Hass M, Boackle SA, et al. Transgenic expression of a soluble complement inhibitor protects against renal disease and promotes survival in MRL/lpr mice. J Immunol 2002; 168:3601–7.

[101] Holers VM, Girardi G, Mo L, et al. Complement C3 activation is required for the antiphospholipid antibody-induced fetal loss. J Exp Med 2002;195:211–20.

[102] Lockshin MD. Antiphospholipid antibody syndrome. In: Ruddy S, Harris Jr ED, Sledge CB, editors. Kelley's textbook of rheumatology. Philadelphia: W.B. Saunders Company; 2001.

[103] Molina H. Update on complement in the pathogenesis of systemic lupus erythematosus. Curr Opin Rheumatol 2002;14:492–7.

[104] Konttinen YT, Ceponis A, Meri S, et al. Complement in acute and chronic arthitides: assessment of C3c, C9, and protectin (CD59) in synovial membrane. Ann Rheum Dis 1996;55:888–94.

[105] Jose PJ, Moss IK, Maini RN, et al. Measurement of the chemotactic complement fragment C5a in rheumatoid synovial fluids by radioimmunoassay: role of C5a in the acute inflammatory phase. Ann Rheum Dis 1990;49:747–52.

[106] Neumman E, Barnum SR, Tarner IH, et al. Local production of complement proteins in rheumatoid arthritis synovium. Arthritis Rheum 2002;46:934–45.

[107] Wang Y, Rollins SA, Madri JA. Anti-C5 monoclonal antibody therapy prevents collagen-induced arthritis and ameliorates established disease. Proc Natl Acad Sci USA 1995;92: 8955–9.

[108] Banda NK, Kraus D, Vondracek A, et al. Mechanisms of effects of complement inhibition in murine collagen-induced arthritis. Arthritis Rheum 2002;46:3065–75.

[109] Hietala MA, Jonsson I, Tarkowski A, et al. Complement deficiency ameliorates-collagen induced arthritis in mice. J Immunol 2002;169:454–9.

[110] Watson WC, Townes AS. Genetic susceptibility to murine collagen-induced arthritis: proposed relationship to the IgG2 autoantibody subclass response, complement C3, major histocompatibility complex (MHC) and non-MHC loci. J Exp Med 1985;162:1878–91.

[111] Goodfellow RM, Williams AS, Levin JL, et al. Soluble complement receptor 1 (sCR1) inhibits the development and progression of rat collagen-induced arthritis. Clin Exp Immunol 2000; 119:210–6.

[112] Ji J, Ohmura K, Mahmood U, et al. Arthritis critically dependent on innate immune system players. Immunity 2002;16:157–68.

[113] Mizuno M, Nishikawa K, Okada N, et al. Inhibition of a membrane complement regulatory protein by a monoclonal antibody induces acute lethal shock in rats primed with lipopolysaccharide. J Immunol 1999;162:5477–82.

[114] Gerard C. Complement C5a in the sepsis syndrome-too much of a good thing? N Engl J Med 2003;348:167–9.

[115] McGeer PL, McGeer EG. Inflammation of the brain in Alzheimer's disease: implications for therapy. J Leukoc Biol 1999;65:409–15.

[116] Yeh CG, Marsh Jr HC, Carson GR, et al. Recombinant soluble human complement receptor type 1 inhibits inflammation in the reversed passive arthus reaction in rats. J Immunol 1991; 146:250–6.

[117] Makrides SC. Therapeutic inhibition of the complement system. Pharmacol Rev 1998;50:59–87.

[118] Kirschfink M. Targeting complement in therapy. Immunol Rev 2001;180:177–89.

ELSEVIER
SAUNDERS

RHEUMATIC
DISEASE CLINICS
OF NORTH AMERICA

Rheum Dis Clin N Am 30 (2004) 19–39

Phagocytes: mechanisms of inflammation and tissue destruction

Hongtao Liu, MD, PhD[a,b], Richard M. Pope, MD[a,b],*

[a]Division of Rheumatology, Department of Medicine, Northwestern University, Feinberg School of
Medicine, 303 East Chicago Avenue, Ward 3-315, Chicago, IL 60611, USA
[b]The Veterans' Affairs Medical Center, Chicago, IL, USA

Macrophages and neutrophils are the professional phagocytes of the innate immune system. Neutrophils are best known for their contribution to the acute inflammatory response (eg, fighting a bacterial infection). Even in the absence of an apparent infection, neutrophils may be the critical inflammatory cell in a variety of conditions, including certain forms of vasculitis (eg, leukocytoclastic vasculitis) and in crystal- induced arthritis (eg, gout). Macrophages are a major component of the chronic inflammatory response that is observed in chronic infections, such as tuberculosis. In many forms of chronic synovitis, best exemplified by rheumatoid arthritis (RA), both cell types are present, neutrophils primarily in the synovial fluid and macrophages in the synovial tissue; each contributes to the pathogenesis of the disease. Neutrophils and macrophages also may simultaneously contribute to certain forms of vasculitis, such as Wegener's granulomatosis and microscopic polyarteritis.

Neutrophils and macrophages belong to the mononuclear phagocyte system, a population of cells that is derived from common progenitor cells in the bone marrow, called the granulocyte-macrophage colony-forming unit. With the appropriate stimuli, the progenitor cells differentiate into circulating monocytes and neutrophils. When inflammation is induced, chemotactic signals are sent out that attract neutrophils and then mononuclear cells, including monocytes, to the site. These cells begin the process of migration toward the offending stimulus by rolling on endothelial cells, firmly attaching, then migrating through the endothelial cell barrier to the site of the stimulus. The process of monocyte differentiation into an inflammatory macrophage may begin during migration. During differentiation, monocytes upregulate the expression of the antiapoptotic molecules, including FLICE inhibitory protein (FLIP) and Bcl-x$_L$, which promote

* Corresponding author. Division of Rheumatology, Department of Medicine, Northwestern University, Feinberg School of Medicine, 303 East Chicago Avenue, Ward 3-315, Chicago, IL 60611.
   E-mail address: rmp158@nwu.edu (R.M. Pope).

0889-857X/04/$ – see front matter © 2004 Elsevier Inc. All rights reserved.
doi:10.1016/S0889-857X(03)00107-8

longevity within the tissue, in contrast to circulating monocytes which have a short half-life. Like monocytes, the half-life of circulating neutrophils is short, less than 12 hours, although the lifespan of neutrophils is prolonged within an inflammatory lesion, such as the rheumatoid joint. Once in the inflammatory joint or the vasculitic lesion, macrophages and neutrophils contribute to the pathology observed. This article examines the mechanisms by which phagocytes contribute to the pathogenesis of inflammatory joint disease and vasculitic lesion, such as RA and Wegener's granulomatosis.

Mechanism of migration

The recruitment of neutrophils and monocytes from blood to the site of inflammation proceeds through an orderly process, that is orchestrated by a variety of adhesion molecules, that includes: tethering or capture, rolling, activation and firm adhesion, and migration across the endothelium (diapedesis) (Table 1) (reviewed in [1–3]).

Tethering and rolling

The process begins with the selectin-mediated tethering, or initial weak engagement, to the activated endothelial cells. As the leukocyte motion slows

Table 1
Mechanisms of phagocyte migration

Stage	Phagocyte molecule	Endothelial cell molecule	Other
Capture or tethering	L-selectin PSGL-1 PSGL-1	GlyCAM-1 E-selectin P-selectin	P-selectin is released from platelets, E-selectin induced on endothelial cells by TNF-α and IFN-γ
Rolling	L-selectin PSGL-1	GlyCAM-1 E, P-selectin	
Activation	Increased avidity of integrins (ie, CD11b/CD18)		L-selectin shed Induced by chemokines (eg, IL-8, MCP-1)
Firm adhesion	CD11a/CD18 (LFA-1) CD11b/CD18 (Mac-1) αvβ1(VLA-4)	ICAM-1, 2 VCAM-1	—
Diapedesis	VE-cadherin αvβ3 PECAM-1	VE-cadherin PECAM-1 PECAM-1	

Abbreviations: E, endothelial; GlyCAM-1, glycosylation-dependent cell adhesion molecule 1; ICAM-1, intercellular adhesion molecule 1; L, leukocyte; MCP, monocyte chemoattractant protein; P, platelet; PECAM-1, platelet/endothelial cell adhesion molecule 1; PSGL-1, P-selectin glycoprotein ligand 1; VCAM-1, vascular cell adhesion molecule 1.

as a result of these interactions they begin to roll. Selectins are type-1 membrane glycoprotein adhesion molecules, which include leukocyte (L)-selectin, platelet (P)-selectin, and endothelial (E)-selectin. L-selectin is expressed on most leukocytes, including neutrophils and monocytes, whereas E- and P-selectin are expressed mainly on the surface of cytokine-activated endothelial cells. The P-selectin that is expressed is not synthesized by endothelial cells, but is derived from platelets. The selectins bind to a variety of glycans or mucins that possess the Sialyl Lewis^X moity. For example, L-selectin binds to a group of mucins on the activated endothelial cells, including glycosylation-dependent cell adhesion molecule 1 [3]. The ligand for P-selectin, P-selectin glycoprotein ligand 1 (PSGL-1), which also contains Sialyl Lewis^X, is found on leukocytes and endothelial cells. PSGL-1, which is expressed constitutively on neutrophils and monocytes, serves as the dominant ligand for P- and E-selectin on endolethial cells [4–6]. Further, the engagement of PSGL-1 enhances tether strength and stabilizes cell rolling of neutrophils and monocytes on endothelial cells under blood shear flow conditions [7,8]. In addition to its function in tethering and rolling, engagement of PSGL-1 also may regulate gene expression posttranscriptionally in monocytes [9,10]. Because of the importance of PSGL-1 signaling, inhibition of PSGL-1/selectin interactions may be an effective tool to curb inflammation [11–13].

Activation and firm adherence

To migrate outside of blood vessels, neutrophils and monocytes must adhere firmly to endothelial cells. Firm adherence is mediated by integrin molecules, including lymphocyte function-associated antigen 1 (LFA-1; $\alpha_L\beta2$ or CD11a/CD18) and macrophage 1 antigen (Mac-1; $\alpha_M\beta2$ or CD11b/CD18) on the surface of the both cell types, and very late activation antigen-4 (VLA-4; $\alpha4\beta1$) on monocytes. These integrins interact with their ligands on the endothelial cells (ICAM-1 and -2 and VCAM-1). The integrin-dependent adhesion is trigged by chemokine activation of neutrophils and monocytes, which also induces the shedding of L-selectin. Leukocyte activation results in increased adhesion, which is mediated either by enhanced integrin affinity that is induced through conformational changes or by an increased integrin avidity that results from integrin clustering (reviewed in [14,15]). Chemokines, such as monocyte chemoattractant protein 1 (MCP-1), macrophage inflammatory protein 1 α (MIP-1α), and interleukin (IL)-8, that are produced in the rheumatoid joint, are capable of inducing these changes [14,16]. Interaction of integrins with their ligands contributes to the adhesion and migration of neutrophils and monocytes and promotes further activation. During adhesion, ligation of β2 integrins or stimulation by IL-8 induces degranulation and oxygen radical production by neutrophils [16,17]. Integrin engagement also may result in increased transcription and expression of cytokines in monocytes, including IL-1β, tumor necrosis factor-α (TNF-α), and IL-8 [18], which may contribute further to the persistence of inflammation.

Diapedesis

Diapedesis, or passage of neutrophils and monocytes across the endothelial lining into the site of inflammation, plays a key role in the pathogenesis of many inflammatory and autoimmune diseases. Evidence demonstrates that homophilic binding of vascular endolethial (VE)-cadherin (VE-cadherin–VE-cadherin) or platelet/endothelial cell adhesion molecule-1 (PECAM) (PECAM-PECAM), that are present at the adherence junctions between the endothelial cells and on the leukocytes, is critical for diapedesis [2]. In addition to homophilic binding, PECAM also may serve as a ligand of $\alpha v\beta 3$ [19,20]. Inhibition of PECAM blocks leukocyte transmigration through endothelial cells [21,22].

Phagocytes during transition from acute to chronic inflammation

After neutrophils migrate into the inflammatory milieu, phagocytosis, the production of reactive oxygen species (ROS), and the release of antimicrobial peptides and proteases promote the elimination of the inciting agent. Under normal circumstances, the neutrophils undergo apoptosis which results in resolution of the acute inflammatory response. If the inciting agent is not eliminated, however, chronic inflammation may result. In this case, mononuclear cells, including blood monocytes, will migrate into the area and differentiate into inflammatory macrophages. Interaction with the extracellular matrix (ECM)-rich extravascular environment, particularly through the integrins on the surface of monocytes with ECM proteins, such as vitronectin (binds the $\alpha v\beta 3$ integrin) or fibrinogen (binds Mac-1), may be critical in differentiation and activation. In the presence of growth factors that are present in the serum, integrin/ECM interactions are capable of activation of proinflammatory cytokine genes, including IL-1β, IL-8, and TNF-α [23]. Engagement with ECM also may upregulate other genes, such as cell surface CD40 and CD44, which may promote further activation by cell-cell interactions (reviewed in [24]). In acute inflammation, the initial leukocytes that are infiltrated are mainly neutrophils. After 24 to 48 hours, monocytes and lymphocytes accumulate and predominate, whereas neutrophils die in situ by apoptosis, which may be mediated through upregulation of cell death genes that are induced by phagocytosis of bacteria [25]. The apoptotic neutrophils are cleaned by macrophage phagocytosis.

Recent studies identified an important role for IL-6 in the transition to chronic inflammation. Using IL-6–deficient mice, only neutrophils accumulated in the inflammatory infiltrate; injection of exogenous IL-6 plus soluble IL-6 receptor (sIL-6Rα) restored monocyte influx, which suggested that IL-6 production is vital for the switch of neutrophils to macrophages in inflammatory tissue [26]. Consistent with these findings, IL-6–deficient mice were resistant to antigen- and collagen-induced arthritis, models in which macrophage-derived mediators are important [27–30]. Therefore, it is possible that the high levels of IL-6 that is present in the joints of patients with RA may contribute to the accumulation of monocytes and the persistence of macrophages. Further, these observations suggest that inhibition of monocyte and lymphocyte migration into the joint through inhibition of IL-6 production may be an effective therapeutic strategy [31,32].

Mechanisms of phagocytosis

Phagocytosis, which is the characteristic function of neutrophils and macrophages, is the act of engulfing, with the intent of destroying, an object, such as a microorganism. Phagocytosis may occur in the absence of an apparent receptor-mediated mechanism (eg, splinter or particulate titanium or methylmethacrolate used in a total joint arthroplasty). More often, however, it is mediated by specific receptors that may or may not require opsonization, or coating. For example, lectin receptors, such as the mannose receptor that binds directly with mannose residues on bacteria, or the scavenger receptors A and B that are important in the clearance of apoptotic cells, do not require opsonization. Binding to other receptors, such as the Fcγ and complement receptors, requires opsonization to allow specific recognition. Although a major role of phagocytosis is the protection of the host against foreign invaders, particularly microbes, it recently became clear that phagocytosis of the host's apoptotic cells is essential for normal homeostasis. Further, the dysregulation of the phagocytosis may be critical to the pathogenesis of a variety of autoimmune diseases, including RA and systemic lupus erythematosus (SLE).

Receptors involved in phagocytosis and their role in disease pathogenesis

Immune complexes composed of IgG antibodies, that are directed against microorganisms or to autoantigens, may bind directly through the Fcγ receptors promoting phagocytosis, antibody-dependent cell-mediated cytotoxicity, the generation of ROS or reactive nitrogen species (RNS), and the activation of the

Table 2
IgG Fc receptors on phagocytes

Receptor	Phagocyte	Role	Other
FcγRI (CD64)	Macrophage, neutrophil	Activation, phagocytosis	High affinity ITAM
FcγRIIA (CD32)	Macrophage, neutrophil	Activation, phagocytosis	Low affinity polymorphism associated with SLE ITAM
FcγRIIB (CD32)	Macrophage also on B cells	Inhibits FcγRI & IIA	IL-4 increases expression, ITIM
FcγRIIIA (CD 16)	Macrophage also NK cells	Activation, phagocytosis	Low affinity polymorphism associated with SLE and RA ITAM
FcγRIIIB (CD 16)	Neutrophil	Decoy	Following TNF treatment, soluble immune complexes activate linked GPI

mitogen-activated protein (MAP) kinase pathway (Table 2). FcγRI, IIA, and IIIA activation signals are mediated through immunoreceptor tyrosine-based activation motifs (ITAMs), whereas suppression is induced by FcγIIB ligation which is mediated by an immunoreceptor tyrosine-based inhibitory motif (ITIM). FcγRIIIB is linked to the plasma membrane by a glycosyl phosphtidylinositiol (GPI) anchor. Although FcγRIIIB does not possess a signal transducing component, under certain conditions, activation may be mediated by interaction with complement receptor-3 (CR3) or Mac-1 [42]. IgG-containing immune complexes also may activate complement resulting in the soluble phase (C5a) or complement components bound to an immune complex, such as iC3b, which also may promote phagocytosis and activation (Table 3). Recent studies demonstrated the potential clinical relevance of the receptors that bind these complexes. Immune complexes and the products of complement activation are detected readily in the joints of patients who have RA. Mice that are deficient in CR3 or CR5 fail to develop arthritis in an antibody-mediated model of RA [33]. Additionally, patients who have FcγRIIA or IIIA polymorphisms are more prone to develop SLE, whereas FcγRIIIA polymorphisms are associated with RA as well [34,35]. These disease-associated polymorphisms may result in the reduced clearance of immune complexes which promotes inflammation that is mediated by more prolonged circulation, with the subsequent deposition of pathogenic immune complexes into the tissues, such as the joint. Further supporting the role of abnormalities of phagocytosis in disease pathogenesis, individuals who are deficient in C1q possess defects in the clearance of apoptotic cells and develop

Table 3
Complement receptors on phagocytes

Receptor	Ligand	Role	Selected other cells	Other associations
CR1 (CD35)	C3b, C4b	Phagocytosis, activation, IL-1, PGE secretion	Also found on B cells and RBCs	Shuttles IC to RE system Reduced in SLE
CR2 (CD21)	C3d	B-cell activation	B cells, FDC, not neutrophils or macrophages	Reduced in SLE A susceptibility gene in murine lupus
CR3 (Mac-1)	iC3b ICAM-1	Phagocytosis, activation migration	FDC, eosinophils	Cooperates with CD16/FcγRIIIB
C1qR	C1q	Phagocytosis	Endothelial cells	Defect results in autoimmunity
C5aR (CD88)	C5a	Neutrophil chemotaxis	Many including eosinophils, mast cells, endothelial cells	Deficiency suppresses inflammation

Abbreviations: FDC, follicular dendritic cell; IC, immune complex; RBC, red blood cell count; RE, reticuloendothelial.

autoimmune disease. Therefore, although of great importance in defending the host against foreign invaders, deficiencies of phagocytic mechanisms also may contribute to the pathogenesis of RA, SLE, and some forms of vasculitis.

Clearance of apoptotic cells

In addition to killing microorganisms, the phagocytic function of macrophages (and dendritic cells, which will be discussed elsewhere in this issue) has other critical roles, including the processing of antigens for priming of the adaptive immune system, which promotes the generation of specific T-cell and B-cell responses. Another critical phagocytic function of macrophages is the clearance of apoptotic cells, which is essential for normal homeostasis and the prevention of autoimmunity. The phagocytosis of apoptotic cells is particularly relevant to the regulation of inflammation. Neutrophils have a short life span, measured in hours; death by apoptosis is important in the resolution of an acute inflammatory response after the inciting agent has been eliminated. Macrophages are critical for the clearance of apoptotic cells. A characteristic feature of apoptosis is the flipping of phosphatidylserine (PtdSer) from facing intracellularly to the outside of the cell. The exposed PtdSer is a critical sign for the macrophage, which uses the PtdSer receptor, the $\beta2$-glycoprotein 1 receptor, and the vitronectin receptor ($\alpha v\beta3$) to recognize the apoptotic cell [36]. Other receptors that are important in this process include the class B- (CD36) and class A-scavenger receptors and the oxidized low-density lipoprotein receptor-1 [36]. Phagocytosis of apoptotic cells removes the dead cell and controls inflammation by the suppression of proinflammatory cytokines, such as TNF-α that may be expressed by activated macrophages. Suppression is mediated by the production of transforming growth factor β (TGF-β), and, in some circumstances, prostaglandins E (PGE$_2$) and IL-10. This may be a critical component to the suppression of acute inflammation. Injection of apoptotic cells into the joints of experimental animals suppressed the acute arthritis that was induced by the injection of immune complexes [37]. An essential element of apoptosis is cleavage of DNA, which results in nucleosome fragments that may be a principle immunogen in SLE. Normally, however, apoptotic cells that still contain the fragmented DNA are taken up by macrophages and autoimmunity does not result. Overloading the system with apoptotic cells may permit some of them to undergo secondary necrosis with fragmentation and release of the nucleosome fragments, which may be inflammatory and immunogenic [36,38]. Supporting the relevance of this observation, in most individuals who are C1q deficient, defects in the clearance of apoptotic cells is associated with a lupus-like autoimmunity [39]. Of further interest, antiphospholipid antibodies may bind to the PtdSer that is exposed on the surface of apoptotic cells, which may further affect their clearance and possibly promote activation and inflammation by binding to Fcγ receptors on macrophages or neutrophils. Therefore, the clearance of apoptotic cells by macrophages is critical to homeostasis of the immune system and suppression of inflammation.

Mediators of function produced by phagocytes

Many of the mediators that are generated by neutrophils and monocytes or macrophages are shared; some are unique to a given cell type. Some of the mediators are preformed (eg, mediators found in neutrophil-specific granules) and some are formed after activation (eg, ROS).

Granules and lysozomes

Once bound to the particle or immune complex, the phagocyte engulfs it and takes it up into a phagosome, which is a plasma membrane–derived intracellular vacuole [40]. In the neutrophils, this process induces a respiratory burst, which results in ROS being emptied into the phagosome. Within the neutrophils, preformed azurophilic or primary granules that contain antimicrobial peptides (eg, defensins) and antimicrobial enzymes (eg, myeloperoxidase, proteinase 3, elastase, and cathepsins) also are emptied into the phagosomes, which further promotes destruction of the microorganism. The neutrophil also possesses specific

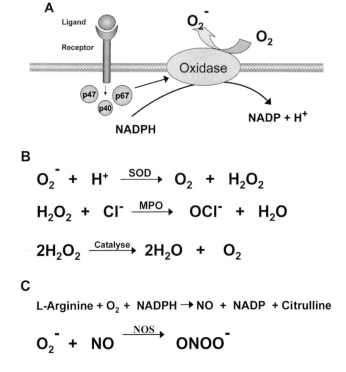

Fig. 1. Pathways for the generation of ROS and RNS. (*A*) The generation of reactive oxygen (O_2^-) following receptor-mediated activation. (*B*) The downstream reactions the follow the generation of O_2^-. (*C*) The reactions that lead to NO and $ONOO^-$. MPD, myeloperoxidase; NOS, nitric oxide synthase; SOD, superoxide dismutase.

or secondary granules that contain anti-microbial enzymes (eg, collagenase and lysozyme). The azurophilic and the specific granules possess membrane-associated molecules, such as FcγRs, TNF receptor (TNFR), and CD11b/CD18 (CR3) that may promote further activation and phagocytosis. For example, activation of neutrophils with TNF-α, as found in the joints of patients who have RA, results in the upregulation of FcγRIIIB which may promote further activation of neutrophils by soluble immune complexes [41]. Phagocytosis by monocytes and macrophages also is important in controlling certain infections, particularly chronic infections, such as tuberculosis. Monocytes and macrophages do not possess preformed granules but do possess lysozymes, which possess acid hydrolases, lysozyme, and proteases, such as collagenase, which may be preformed or synthesized following phagocytosis or activation.

Reactive oxygen and nitrogen species

Phagocytosis, or activation, for example by lipolysacchride (LPS) in the absence of phagocytosis, is capable of generating ROS and RNS. A scheme for the generation of the ROS and RNS is presented in Fig. 1. Following the appropriate stimulus, phox cytoplasmic proteins are recruited to the membrane-bound oxidase, which results in the reduction of nicotinamide adenine dinucleotide phosphate (NADPH) and the generation of reactive oxygen (O_2^-) (see Fig. 1; reviewed in [43]). The O_2^- generated is toxic but short lived and either spontaneously or under the control of superoxide dismutase, results in the production of hydrogen peroxide (H_2O_2), which is more long lasting (see Fig. 1). H_2O_2 may be catalyzed by myeloperoxidase to hypochlorous acid (OCl^-) or to water and O_2 by catalase (see Fig. 1). Nitric oxide (NO) maybe generated from L-arginine and NADPH under the control of nitric oxide synthase (NOS) and may combine with O_2^- to generate peroxynitrite ($ONOO^-$), which is capable of inducing tyrosine nitration. When generated within the phagosome, the ROS and RNS are antimicrobial. The inability to generate functional NADPH oxidase activity results in chronic granulomatous disease, which is associated with recurring infections. ROS and RNS have other physiologic and pathophysiologic functions when generated within the cell or when released from the cell (Box 1). Although the mechanisms have not been elucidated fully, within the cell these mediators seem to be important in the signal transduction that results in the expression of many proinflammatory genes [44]. When released from the cell, ROS and RNS may contribute to several pathologic conditions, including atherosclerosis, DNA mutation, and malignancy, as well as apoptosis and necrosis [43]. Of potential significance to the nonphagocytic effects of ROS, O_2^- also may be generated from the mitochondria in the absence of phagocytosis [44].

Proinflammatory mediators

Although neutrophils may contribute, macrophages serve as a major source for the proinflammatory cytokines, chemokines, and growth factors that promote

---

Box 1. Cause and effects of ROS and RNS that are produced by macrophages and neutrophils

Induction

Phagocytosis
Cytokine activation
Toll-like receptor activation
UV irradiation

Physiologic effects (short oxidative bursts that last less than 30 minutes)

Within phagosomes, antimicrobial
Promote signaling - contribute to activation of transcription factors

Pathophysiologic effects (persistent or prolonged, possibly lasting longer than 1 hour)

Oxidation of lipids (eg, oxidized LDL in atherosclerosis)
DNA damage (eg, loss of function mutations in p53 in RA and various malignancies)
Apoptosis or necrosis

Table 4
Inflammatory mediators generated by macrophages

Family	Members
Proinflammatory	TNF-α, IL-1α, IL-1β, IL-6, LIF
Anti-inflammatory	IL-10, TGF-β, IL-1Rα, sTNFR-I/II, IL-1RII
Immunoregulation	IL-12, IL-15, IL-18, IL-13
Chemokines	IL-8, MCP-1, MIP-1α/1β, RANTES
Metalloproteinases	MMP-1, MMP-3, MMP-8, TIMP-1
Growth factors	GM-CSF, PDGF, FGF-1, VEGF, M-CSF
Lipid mediators	
Proinflammatory	PGE$_2$, PGI$_2$, LTB$_4$, LTC$_4$
Anti-inflammatory	PGJ$_2$, PGA$_{1/2}$, lipoxins

Abbreviations: FGF, fibroblast growth factor; GM-CSF, granulocyte–macrophage colony–stimulating factor; LIF, leukemia inhibitory factor; LTB, leukotriene B; LTC, leukotriene C; MCSF, macrophage colony–stimulating factor; PDGF, platelet derived growth factor; PGA, prostaglandin A; PGJ, prostaglandin J; RANTES, regulated upon activation in normal T cells, expressed, and secreted; TIMP, tissue inhibitor of metalloproteinases; VEGF, vascular endolethial cell growth factor.

chronic inflammation (Table 4). Neutrophils and macrophages also are capable of producing a variety of proteolytic enzymes, such as elastase and matrix metalloproteinases (MMP), which may induce damage to structures, such as blood vessels and joints. Macrophages also are capable of secreting molecules that suppress inflammation and promote healing (see macrophage activation section). Phagocytes also serve as a major source of metabolites of arachidonic acid, including prostaglandins (PGs), thromboxanes, and leukotrienes, which play important roles in normal physiology and inflammation. PGs, such as PGE_2 and prostaglandin I (PGI_2), are generated by inducible cyclooxygenase (COX)-2, and contribute to the symptoms of inflammation that are characterized by pain, swelling, and local vasodilatation. Although COX-1 is expressed at a constant level and is important in a variety of normal physiologic functions, such as platelet adhesiveness, COX-2 is undetectable in most resting tissues and can be induced rapidly in macrophages and other cells by growth factors, cytokines, and bacterial LPS. Recent observations that used COX-deficient mice suggested that both COX-1 and COX-2 may contribute to the inflammatory response (reviewed in [45,46]).

Role of phagocytic dysregulation in disease

Although the antimicrobial mediators that are present in phagocytes are critical for protection of the host, when released extracellularly from either neutrophils or macrophages, proteolytic enzymes, ROS, and RNS contribute to tissue destruction and inflammation of the joints or blood vessels [47,48]. Additionally, the humoral immune response directed against myeloperoxidase (in microscopic polyarteritis and idiopathic cresenteric glomerulonephritis) and proteinase 3 (in Wegener's granulomatosis) that is released from neutrophils may contribute directly to the pathophysiology of these diseases [49]. Following priming by locally-released cytokines, myeloperoxidase and proteinase 3 may be expressed on the surface of TNF-α–primed neutrophils or monocytes. IgG antibodies to these antigens may promote activation of complement, adherence, migration, and further activation with release of proteolytic enzymes and ROS [50,51]. Within the vasculitic lesions, antibodies that bind released myeloperoxidase or proteinase 3 may also contribute to the release of cytokines and chemokines, such as MCP-1 and IL-8, which perpetuate the process.

In addition to their role in these forms of vasculitis, ROS and RNS, which may be released from neutrophils or macrophages, may be important in the perpetuation of RA. Within the rheumatoid joint, the increased content of carbonyl groups indicates previous damage by ROS, whereas the nitration of proteins suggests the combined effects of ROS and RNS (see Table 4) (reviewed in [43]). Additionally, the presence of different p53 missense transition mutations in various regions within rheumatoid synovial tissue is consistent with oxidative DNA damage [52]. The oxidative damage to p53 may contribute to the pathogenesis of RA because the mutated p53 may function as a dominant negative of the normal or wild type p53, thereby suppressing the function of the wild type p53 resulting in the the enhanced expression of IL-6 and protects against apoptosis.

Neutrophil activation

Neutrophil activation occurs primarily following ligation of Fcγ or complement receptors, which results in phagocytosis, degranulation, and the production of ROS. Priming with TNF-α, IL-8, or IL-18 may enhance neutrophil activation. Further, the MAP kinase pathway may be activated by ligation with L-selectin, which is associated with an increased oxidative burst, whereas engagement with β2 integrins, such as LFA-1 or Mac-1, may trigger degranulation and ROS production [16]. Recent observations suggest a link between primed neutrophils and the adaptive immune system. For example, in a model of delayed type hypersensitivity, primed neutrophils secreted MCP-1, which was critical for the recruitment of monocytes and lymphocytes [53]. Additionally, neutrophils from patients who were treated with granulocyte colony–stimulating factor (G-CSF) secreted significantly increased concentrations of B-lymphocyte stimulator, a member of the TNF superfamily that is important in B-cell maturation and survival [54].

Macrophage activation

The definition of an "activated macrophage" as one that produces cytokines, such as TNF-α, ROS, and RNS, has evolved over the past several years. Macrophage functional status may be viewed in terms of the classic and alternative forms of activation and of deactivation (reviewed in [55,56]). Classic activation, which results in a proinflammatory response, may be induced through receptor ligation by cytokines, such as interferon (IFN)-γ and TNF-α; by activation that is mediated through pattern recognition receptors, primarily the toll-like receptors (TLRs); and by humoral activation that is mediated through the Fcγ and complement receptors (Table 5). Alternate activation is mediated by IL-4, IL-13, or the phagocytosis of apoptotic cells. Alternatively activated macrophages may produce IL-10, TGF-β, and IL-1Ra, which, in turn, promote macrophage deactivation. Macrophage deactivation also may be mediated through ligation of the glucocorticoid receptor (GCR).

Classic activation

The different pathways that are involved in classic activation may work coordinately to enhance the inflammatory response. The activation of macrophages mediated by the helper T-lymphocyte (Th-1) lymphokine, IFN-γ, results in the upregulation of costimulatory molecules, such as B7 and major histocompatibility complex (MHC) class II molecules, that are important in antigen presentation (reviewed in [55]). IFN-γ also promotes phagocytosis and upregulates microbial killing by promoting the induction of IgG to opsonize bacteria, the expression of

Table 5
Macrophage activation

Activation type	Macrophage receptor	Stimulus	Macrophage product	Effect
Classic activation				
Cytokine receptors	IFN-γR, TNFR	IFN-γ TNFα	ROS, RNS, enhances TNF-α, IL-1, IL-6, IL-12	Proinflammatory, DTH
Humoral	FcγRs CRs	Immune complexes	ROS, RNS,	Phagocytosis, proinflammatory
Innate	TLRs	Microbial organisms, HSP, fibronectin	TNF-α, IL-1, IL-6, IL-12, ROS, RNS	Proinflammatory, antimicrobial
Alternate activation	IL-4R, IL-13R, receptors for apoptotic cells	IL-4, IL-13, apoptotic cells	Increased mannose R, IL-1Rα, IL-10, TGF-β	Results antagonize classic macrophage activation
Deactivation	IL-10R, TGF-βR, GCR	IL-10, TGF-β, GC	Decreased proinflammatory cytokines, (eg, inhibit TNF-α, IL-1)	Results suppress macrophage activation

Abbreviations: DTH, delayed-type hypersensitivity; HSP, heat shock proteins.

FcγRI receptors, and by enhancing production of ROS and RNS (reviewed in [57]). IFN-γ–primed cells produce an enhanced response to a proinflammatory cytokine, such as TNF-α, which may further enhance macrophage activation. IFN-γ–activated cells also demonstrate an enhanced response to bacterial products, such as LPS, mediated though TLR4, or through interaction with CD40L on the surface of activated T cells [58]. Full activation that is initiated through the classic pathway may result in the expression of proinflammatory cytokines, including TNF-α, IL-1, IL-6, and IL-12. IL-12 is particularly important for the generation of Th-1 T cells, which may promote further production of IFN-γ and leads to further macrophage activation.

TLRs, a component of the innate immune system, are a family of pattern recognition receptors (PRRs) that is critical to the recognition of microbes (reviewed in [59]). TLRs are type-1 transmembrane receptors with extracellular leucine-rich domains that recognize pathogen-associated molecular patterns, which are invariant within classes of microorganisms and are essential for their survival. TLR-2 is critical for the recognition of peptidoglycan from gram-positive organisms, whereas TLR-4 and CD14 recognize LPS from gram-negative organisms. TLR-2 and TLR-4 are expressed strongly on monocytes and macrophages, but are expressed weakly on neutrophils [60]. Mannose receptors and CD14 are other PRRs that are found on macrophages. The cytoplasmic tails of the TLRs possess common toll/IL-1 receptor (TIR) domains, that also are shared with type 1 IL-1R. Following ligation of a TLR, myeloid differentiation factor 88 (MyD88) is recruited through its TIR domain (Fig. 2). Bound MyD88 recruits IL-1

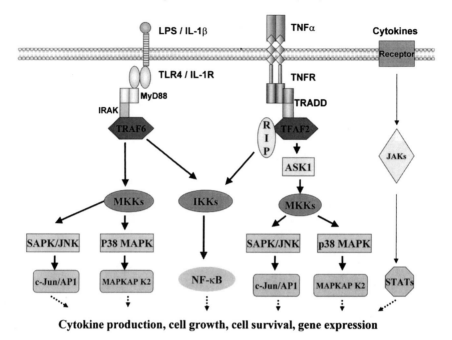

Fig. 2. The major signal pathways that are involved in inflammation. ASK1, apoptosis signal regulating kinase 1; IKK, IκB kinase; JAK, Janus kinase; JNK, c-Jun N-terminal kinase; MAPK, mitogen-activated protein kinase; MAPKAP K2, MAP kinase activated protein kinase 2; MKK, MAPK kinase; RIP, receptor interacting protein; SAPK, stress-activated protein kinase; STAT, signal transducer and activator of transcription; TRADD, TNF-α receptor-associated death domain.

receptor-associated kinase (IRAK) and TNF-α receptor associated factor (TRAF)-6 which results in nuclear factor (NF)-κB activation. The MAP kinase pathways, including c-Jun N-terminal kinase (JNK) and p38, also may be activated through TLR ligation.

Macrophages also may be activated by immune complexes bound to through FcγRs and complement receptors (CRs), which induce proinflammatory ROS and RNS (see Tables 2 and 3). Although included under the classic pathway of activation because of these proinflammatory responses, the effects of FcγR and CR ligation on macrophage function are more complex. Ligation of FcγRI markedly suppresses the expression of IL-12 (characteristic of classical activation) that is induced by TLR4 ligation and induces the expression of IL-10 (characteristic of alternative activation), whereas the expression of IL-1 and TNF-α (characteristic of classic activation) are not suppressed [61]. Similar effects of FcγRI ligation were observed when IFN-γ–primed macrophages were activated by CD40 ligation. Additionally, the phagocytosis of apoptotic cells, which is mediated in part through C1qR, results in alternative activation. Therefore, ligation of the FcγRs or CRs may be proinflammatory or it may induce, at least in part, a shift from a proinflammatory response to one that is anti-inflammatory.

Alternative activation

The Th-2 cytokines, IL-4 and IL-13, promote the alternative activation of macrophages [55]. IL-4 is also capable of polarizing T cells to a Th-2–type response. IL-4 and IL-13 may antagonize the effects of IFN-γ, including its ability to enhance mannose receptor expression and the synthesis of TNF-α, IL-1, and IL-6. Alternate activation is also promoted by the phagocytes of apoptotic cells (reviewed earlier). The principal cytokines that are secreted by alternatively activated macrophages are anti-inflammatory molecules, including IL-10, IL-1Ra, and TGF-β. Therefore, this mode of macrophage activation provides inhibitory signals to deactivate macrophages, which curbs the inflammatory reaction and protects the host from further damage. IL-10 is an important anti-inflammatory cytokine that inhibits production of proinflammatory cytokines, such as TNF-α and IL-1, and suppresses the release of NO that is induced by LPS in macrophages. IL-10 also downregulates the expression of MHC class II molecules and mannose receptors [62] and cell surface of TNFRs, while inducing the release of soluble TNFRs, which inhibit activation by TNF-α [63]. The importance of IL-10 has been documented since IL-10 deficient mice developed widespread inflammatory cell infiltrates in multiple organs [64]. TGF-β1 inhibits the LPS-induced oxidative burst and TNF-α production [65]. IL-1Ra binds to IL-1R, which inhibits the activation that is mediated by IL-1. In summary, alternatively activated macrophages generate mediators that promote macrophage deactivation.

Alternatively activated macrophages also promote wound healing and fibrosis. They produce more fibronectin and other matrix proteins that may contribute to ECM deposition and wound healing [66]. Data from mice that are deficient in TGF-β1, or its receptor signaling molecule, Smad-3, confirm that macrophage-derived TGF-β is essential for matrix deposition in the normal healing process [67,68]. Additionally, IL-4 and IL-13 induced arginase-1 also may contribute to ECM deposition by metabolizing arginine to proline, which is essential for collagen production, and may account for the fibrosis that is observed in Th-2–type responses [55]. In summary, if macrophages are activated through the classic pathway, stimulation with IL-4 and IL-13 will counteract the effects through the induction of the anti-inflammatory molecules, TGF-β, IL-1Ra, and IL-10, which promote macrophage deactivation. These alternatively activated macrophages also promote wound healing and fibrosis.

Deactivation

Macrophage deactivation occurs in response to TGF-β, IL-10, and PGE$_2$, or following the ligation of the GCR. GCR ligation and IL-10 suppress the expression of proinflammatory mediators, such as TNF-α, IL-12, and IL-1, by inhibition of the transcriptional function of activated NF-κB and activator protein-1 (AP-1). Although the potential mechanisms for suppression have not been elucidated fully, GCR ligation by dexamethasone or IL-10 resulted in the induction of the glucocorticoid-induced leucine zipper protein (GILZ) [69]. GILZ suppressed transcriptional activation by NF-κB and AP-1. Although GILZ was detected in macrophages in noninflamed tissues, it was downregulated in the macrophages that were present in delayed-type hypersensitivity reactions [69]. The importance of macrophage deactivation in RA is clear because inhibition of macrophage products, TNF-α and IL-1, have an ameliorative effect on inflammation and joint destruction. Further, although IL-10 is detected readily in the rheumatoid joint, antibodies to IL-10 enhance, and additional IL-10 suppresses, the activation of macrophages that were isolated from the joints of patients who had RA; this suggests that these cells are appropriately responsive to further deactivation by this cytokine [70].

Regulation of inflammatory mediators

Over the past several years, an increased understanding of the mechanisms that regulate the expression of cytokine, chemokine, and MMP gene expression has provided insights into potential new therapeutic targets for patients who suffer from chronic inflammatory conditions. A better understanding of how the expression of these genes is regulated at the transcriptional and posttranscriptional level will provide a basis to develop new, potentially more effective options.

Transcriptional regulation

Among the pathways characterized, the NF-κB, MAP kinase, and Janus kinase (JAK)/STAT pathways may be the most relevant. The MAP kinase pathway includes extracellular signal-regulated kinases (ERKs), JNKs, and p38 MAP kinases. Activation of NF-κB and the ERK, JNK, and p38 MAP kinase pathways have been observed in RA synovial tissue (reviewed in [71]). These pathways (see Fig. 2) contribute to the regulation of the expression of many of the inflammatory mediators that are observed in macrophages and other cell types within the rheumatoid joint. NF-κB activation is critical for the expression of TNF-α, IL-1, IL-6 and IL-8, whereas the MAP kinases, especially JNK, are important in the expression of the MMPs. In turn, TNF-α and IL-1 may activate the NF-κB and MAP kinase pathways, whereas IL-6 activates through the JAK/STAT pathway. Ligation of the TLR pathway also results in the activation of the NF-κB and MAP kinase pathways. Inhibition of NF-κB activation by overexpression of super-repressor IκBα in RA synovial tissue suppressed the expression of TNF-α and other proinflammatory cytokines and the synthesis of MMP-1 and -3. In contrast, the production of anti-inflammatory cytokines IL-10, IL-1Rα, and tissue inhibitor of metalloproteinases-1 (TIMP-1) was maintained [72].

Posttranscriptional regulation

Following the transcription of the mRNA for a given gene, the expression of the protein is regulated posttranscriptionally. This may be achieved by controlling the stability of mRNA or its translation. For many proinflammatory molecules this is accomplished by the binding of regulatory proteins to the 3' untranslated regions (UTRs) of the mature mRNA. Recent work has focused on the regulation of TNF-α by adenosine/uridine-rich elements (AREs) in 3' UTRs. Besides TNF-α, AREs, which are characterized by the repeats of AUUUA sequence, also exist in the 3' UTRs of COX2, IL-1α, IL-1β, IL-6, IL-8, IFN-γ, and granulocyte–macrophage colony–stimulating factor (GM-CSF), all of which promote inflammation (reviewed in [73,74]). Interaction of regulatory proteins with the AREs may increase or decrease the expression of a gene at the protein level. For example, tristetraprolin (TTP) is one of the factors that interacts with TNF-α AREs. The binding of TTP to TNF-α AREs provides inhibitory signaling by promoting mRNA degradation. In TTP-deficient mice, the increase of the stability of TNF-α mRNA contributes to over-expression of TNF-α (reviewed in [73]). The deletion of the AREs from TNF-α mRNA sustained LPS-induced TNF-α mRNA, which further supports the role of AREs in regulating TNF-α production [73]. Further, p38 MAP kinase was shown to regulate the production of TNF-α translation. The translation of TNF-α gene is suppressed by inhibition of the activation of p38. Recent studies demonstrated that p38 phosphorylates and activates mitogen-activated protein kinase-activated protein kinase 2 (MAPKAP 2), which is responsible for the enhanced TNF-α mRNA translation [73]. In contrast, other ARE containing genes, such as IL-6, GM-CSF, and COX-2, are regulated by p38 and MAPKAP 2 by effects on mRNA stability [73]. Glucocorticoids and anti-inflammatory cytokine IL-10 also may inhibit LPS-induced TNF-α and COX-2 production, in part, through effects mediated by the AREs, which result in reduced translation that is due to enhanced mRNA degradation [73]. The understanding of the transcriptional and posttranscriptional regulation of pro-inflammatory cytokines may provide new therapeutic targets for conditions such as RA.

References

[1] Worthylake RA, Burridge K. Leukocyte transendothelial migration: orchestrating the underlying molecular machinery. Curr Opin Cell Biol 2001;13:569–77.

[2] Johnson-Leger C, Aurrand-Lions M, Imhof BA. The parting of the endothelium: miracle, or simply a junctional affair? J Cell Sci 2000;113(Pt 6):921–33.

[3] McEver RP. Selectins: lectins that initiate cell adhesion under flow. Curr Opin Cell Biol 2002;14: 581–6.

[4] Moore KL, Patel KD, Bruehl RE, Li F, Johnson DA, Lichenstein HS, et al. P-selectin glycoprotein ligand-1 mediates rolling of human neutrophils on P-selectin. J Cell Biol 1995;128:661–71.

[5] McEver RP, Cummings RD. Role of PSGL-1 binding to selectins in leukocyte recruitment. J Clin Invest 1997;100:S97–103.

[6] Xia L, Sperandio M, Yago T, McDaniel JM, Cummings RD, Pearson-White S, et al. P-selectin

glycoprotein ligand-1-deficient mice have impaired leukocyte tethering to E-selectin under flow. J Clin Invest 2002;109:939–50.

[7] Ramachandran V, Yago T, Epperson TK, Kobzdej MM, Nollert MU, Cummings RD, et al. Dimerization of a selectin and its ligand stabilizes cell rolling and enhances tether strength in shear flow. Proc Natl Acad Sci USA 2001;98:10166–71.

[8] Zimmerman GA. Two by two: the pairings of P-selectin and P-selectin glycoprotein ligand 1. Proc Natl Acad Sci USA 2001;98:10023–4.

[9] Lindemann S, Tolley ND, Eyre JR, Kraiss LW, Mahoney TM, Weyrich AS. Integrins regulate the intracellular distribution of eukaryotic initiation factor 4E in platelets. A checkpoint for translational control. J Biol Chem 2001;276:33947–51.

[10] Mahoney TS, Weyrich AS, Dixon DA, McIntyre T, Prescott SM, Zimmerman GA. Cell adhesion regulates gene expression at translational checkpoints in human myeloid leukocytes. Proc Natl Acad Sci USA 2001;98:10284–9.

[11] Zhou Z, Penn MS, Forudi F, Zhou X, Tarakji K, Topol EJ, et al. Administration of recombinant P-selectin glycoprotein ligand Fc fusion protein suppresses inflammation and neointimal formation in Zucker diabetic rat model. Arterioscler Thromb Vasc Biol 2002;22:1598–603.

[12] Hicks AE, Leppanen A, Cummings RD, McEver RP, Hellewell PG, Norman KE. Glycosulfopeptides modeled on P-selectin glycoprotein ligand 1 inhibit P-selectin-dependent leukocyte rolling in vivo. FASEB J 2002;16:1461–2.

[13] Molenaar TJ, Appeldoorn CC, de Haas SA, Michon IN, Bonnefoy A, Hoylaerts MF, et al. Specific inhibition of P-selectin-mediated cell adhesion by phage display-derived peptide antagonists. Blood 2002;100:3570–7.

[14] Laudanna C, Kim JY, Constantin G, Butcher E. Rapid leukocyte integrin activation by chemokines. Immunol Rev 2002;186:37–46.

[15] Johnston B, Butcher EC. Chemokines in rapid leukocyte adhesion triggering and migration. Semin Immunol 2002;14:83–92.

[16] Ley K. Integration of inflammatory signals by rolling neutrophils. Immunol Rev 2002;186:8–18.

[17] Zhou M, Brown EJ. Leukocyte response integrin and integrin-associated protein act as a signal transduction unit in generation of a phagocyte respiratory burst. J Exp Med 1993;178:1165–74.

[18] Rossetti G, Collinge M, Bender JR, Molteni R, Pardi R. Integrin-dependent regulation of gene expression in leukocytes. Immunol Rev 2002;186:189–207.

[19] Piali L, Hammel P, Uherek C, Bachmann F, Gisler RH, Dunon D, et al. CD31/PECAM-1 is a ligand for alpha v beta 3 integrin involved in adhesion of leukocytes to endothelium. J Cell Biol 1995;130:451–60.

[20] Buckley CD, Doyonnas R, Newton JP, Blystone SD, Brown EJ, Watt SM, et al. Identification of alpha v beta 3 as a heterotypic ligand for CD31/PECAM-1. J Cell Sci 1996;109(Pt 2):437–45.

[21] Muller WA, Weigl SA, Deng X, Phillips DM. PECAM-1 is required for transendothelial migration of leukocytes. J Exp Med 1993;178:449–60.

[22] Martin-Padura I, Lostaglio S, Schneemann M, Williams L, Romano M, Fruscella P, et al. Junctional adhesion molecule, a novel member of the immunoglobulin superfamily that distributes at intercellular junctions and modulates monocyte transmigration. J Cell Biol 1998;142:117–27.

[23] de Fougerolles AR, Chi-Rosso G, Bajardi A, Gotwals P, Green CD, Koteliansky VE. Global expression analysis of extracellular matrix-integrin interactions in monocytes. Immunity 2000; 13:749–58.

[24] de Fougerolles AR, Koteliansky VE. Regulation of monocyte gene expression by the extracellular matrix and its functional implications. Immunol Rev 2002;186:208–20.

[25] Kobayashi SD, Voyich JM, Buhl CL, Stahl RM, DeLeo FR. Global changes in gene expression by human polymorphonuclear leukocytes during receptor-mediated phagocytosis: cell fate is regulated at the level of gene expression. Proc Natl Acad Sci USA 2002;99:6901–6.

[26] Hurst SM, Wilkinson TS, McLoughlin RM, Jones S, Horiuchi S, Yamamoto N, et al. Il-6 and its soluble receptor orchestrate a temporal switch in the pattern of leukocyte recruitment seen during acute inflammation. Immunity 2001;14:705–14.

[27] Kobayashi H, Ohshima S, Nishioka K, Yamaguchi N, Umeshita-Sasai M, Ishii T, et al. Antigen

induced arthritis (AIA) can be transferred by bone marrow transplantation: evidence that interleukin 6 is essential for induction of AIA. J Rheumatol 2002;29:1176–82.

[28] Boe A, Baiocchi M, Carbonatto M, Papoian R, Serlupi-Crescenzi O. Interleukin 6 knock-out
mice are resistant to antigen-induced experimental arthritis. Cytokine 1999;11:1057–64.

[29] Alonzi T, Fattori E, Lazzaro D, Costa P, Probert L, Kollias G, et al. Interleukin 6 is required for
the development of collagen-induced arthritis. J Exp Med 1998;187:461–8.

[30] Ohshima S, Saeki Y, Mima T, Sasai M, Nishioka K, Nomura S, et al. Interleukin 6 plays a key
role in the development of antigen-induced arthritis. Proc Natl Acad Sci USA 1998;95:8222–6.

[31] Choy EH, Isenberg DA, Garrood T, Farrow S, Ioannou Y, Bird H, et al. Therapeutic benefit of
blocking interleukin-6 activity with an anti-interleukin-6 receptor monoclonal antibody in rheumatoid arthritis: a randomized, double-blind, placebo-controlled, dose-escalation trial. Arthritis
Rheum 2002;46:3143–50.

[32] Nishimoto N, Yoshizaki K, Maeda K, Kuritani T, Deguchi H, Sato B, et al. Toxicity, pharmacokinetics, and dose-finding study of repetitive treatment with the humanized anti-interleukin 6
receptor antibody MRA in rheumatoid arthritis Phase I/II clinical study. J Rheumatol 2003;30(7):
1426–35.

[33] Ji H, Ohmura K, Mahmood U, Lee DM, Hofhuis FM, Boackle SA, et al. Arthritis critically
dependent on innate immune system players. Immunity 2002;16:157–68.

[34] Nieto A, Caliz R, Pascual M, Mataran L, Garcia S, Martin J. Involvement of Fcgamma receptor
IIIA genotypes in susceptibility to rheumatoid arthritis. Arthritis Rheum 2000;43:735–9.

[35] Kimberly RP, Wu J, Gibson AW, Su K, Qin H, Li X, et al. Diversity and duplicity: human
FCgamma receptors in host defense and autoimmunity. Immunol Res 2002;26:177–89.

[36] Savill J, Dransfield I, Gregory C, Haslett C. A blast from the past: clearance of apoptotic cells
regulates immune responses. Nat Rev Immunol 2002;2:965–75.

[37] van Lent PI., Licht R, Dijkman H, Holthuysen AE, Berden JH, van den Berg WB. Uptake of
apoptotic leukocytes by synovial lining macrophages inhibits immune complex-mediated arthritis. J Leukoc Biol 2001;70:708–14.

[38] Harper L, Ren Y, Savill J, Adu D, Savage CO. Antineutrophil cytoplasmic antibodies induce
reactive oxygen-dependent dysregulation of primed neutrophil apoptosis and clearance by macrophages. Am J Pathol 2000;157:211–20.

[39] Taylor PR, Carugati A, Fadok VA, Cook HT, Andrews M, Carroll MC, et al. A hierarchical role
for classical pathway complement proteins in the clearance of apoptotic cells in vivo. J Exp Med
2000;192:359–66.

[40] Vieira OV, Botelho RJ, Grinstein S. Phagosome maturation: aging gracefully. Biochem J 2002;
366:689–704.

[41] Fossati G, Moots RJ, Bucknall RC, Edwards SW. Differential role of neutrophil Fcgamma
receptor IIIB (CD16) in phagocytosis, bacterial killing, and responses to immune complexes.
Arthritis Rheum 2002;46:1351–61.

[42] Lei B, DeLeo FR, Hoe NP, Graham MR, Mackic SM, Cole RL, et al. Evasion of human innate
and acquired immunity by a bacterial homolog of CD11b that inhibits opsonophagocytosis. Nat
Med 2001;7:1298–305.

[43] Babior BM. Phagocytes and oxidative stress. Am J Med 2000;109:33–44.

[44] Bogdan C, Rollinghoff M, Diefenbach A. Reactive oxygen and reactive nitrogen intermediates in
innate and specific immunity. Curr Opin Immunol 2000;12:64–76.

[45] Parente L, Perretti M. Advances in the pathophysiology of constitutive and inducible cyclooxygenases: two enzymes in the spotlight. Biochem Pharmacol 2003;65:153–9.

[46] Lawrence T, Willoughby DA, Gilroy DW. Anti-inflammatory lipid mediators and insights into
the resolution of inflammation. Nat Rev Immunol 2002;2:787–95.

[47] Pope RM, Perlman H. Rheumatoid Arthritis. In: Tsokas GC, editor. Principles of molecular
rheumatology. Totowa (NJ): Humana Press; 2000. p. 325–61.

[48] Martel-Pelletier J, Welsch DJ, Pelletier JP. Metalloproteases and inhibitors in arthritic diseases.
Best Pract Res Clin Rheumatol 2001;15:805–29.

[49] Muller Kobold AC, van der Geld YM, Limburg PC, Tervaert JW, Kallenberg CG. Pathophysiology of ANCA-associated glomerulonephritis. Nephrol Dial Transplant 1999;14:1366–75.

[50] Weidner S, Neupert W, Goppelt-Struebe M, Rupprecht HD. Antineutrophil cytoplasmic antibodies induce human monocytes to produce oxygen radicals in vitro. Arthritis Rheum 2001; 44:1698–706.

[51] Harper L, Radford D, Plant T, Drayson M, Adu D, Savage CO. IgG from myeloperoxidase-antineutrophil cytoplasmic antibody-positive patients stimulates greater activation of primed neutrophils than IgG from proteinase 3-antineutrophil cytosplasmic antibody-positive patients. Arthritis Rheum 2001;44:921–30.

[52] Yamanishi Y, Boyle DL, Rosengren S, Green DR, Zvaifler NJ, Firestein GS. Regional analysis of p53 mutations in rheumatoid arthritis synovium. Proc Natl Acad Sci USA 2002;99: 10025–30.

[53] Yamashiro S, Kamohara H, Wang JM, Yang D, Gong WH, Yoshimura T. Phenotypic and functional change of cytokine-activated neutrophils: inflammatory neutrophils are heterogeneous and enhance adaptive immune responses. J Leukoc Biol 2001;69:698–704.

[54] Scapini P, Nardelli B, Nadali G, Calzetti F, Pizzolo G, Montecucco C, et al. G-CSF-stimulated neutrophils are a prominent source of functional BLyS. J Exp Med 2003;197:297–302.

[55] Gordon S. Alternative activation of macrophages. Nat Rev Immunol 2003;3:23–35.

[56] Mosser DM. The many faces of macrophage activation. J Leukoc Biol 2003;73:209–12.

[57] Boehm U, Klamp T, Groot M, Howard JC. Cellular responses to interferon-gamma. Annu Rev Immunol 1997;15:749–95.

[58] Bosisio D, Polentarutti N, Sironi M, Bernasconi S, Miyake K, Webb GR, et al. Stimulation of toll-like receptor 4 expression in human mononuclear phagocytes by interferon-gamma: a molecular basis for priming and synergism with bacterial lipopolysaccharide. Blood 2002;99:3427–31.

[59] Medzhitov R. Toll-like receptors and innate immunity. Nat Rev Immunol 2001;1:135–45.

[60] Andonegui G, Goyert SM, Kubes P. Lipopolysaccharide-induced leukocyte-endothelial cell interactions: a role for CD14 versus toll-like receptor 4 within microvessels. J Immunol 2002; 169:2111–9.

[61] Gerber JS, Mosser DM. Reversing lipopolysaccharide toxicity by ligating the macrophage Fc gamma receptors. J Immunol 2001;166:6861–8.

[62] Donnelly RP, Dickensheets H, Finbloom DS. The interleukin-10 signal transduction pathway and regulation of gene expression in mononuclear phagocytes. J Interferon Cytokine Res 1999; 19:563–73.

[63] Joyce DA, Gibbons DP, Green P, Steer JH, Feldmann M, Brennan FM. Two inhibitors of pro-inflammatory cytokine release, interleukin-10 and interleukin-4, have contrasting effects on release of soluble p75 tumor necrosis factor receptor by cultured monocytes. Eur J Immunol 1994;24:2699–705.

[64] Lang R, Rutschman RL, Greaves DR, Murray PJ. Autocrine deactivation of macrophages in transgenic mice constitutively overexpressing IL-10 under control of the human CD68 promoter. J Immunol 2002;168:3402–11.

[65] Pilette C, Ouadrhiri Y, Van Snick J, Renauld JC, Staquet P, Vaerman JP, et al. IL-9 inhibits oxidative burst and TNF-alpha release in lipopolysaccharide-stimulated human monocytes through TGF-beta. J Immunol 2002;168:4103–11.

[66] Gratchev A, Guillot P, Hakiy N, Politz O, Orfanos CE, Schledzewski K, et al. Alternatively activated macrophages differentially express fibronectin and its splice variants and the extracellular matrix protein betaIG-H3. Scand J Immunol 2001;53:386–92.

[67] Koch RM, Roche NS, Parks WT, Ashcroft GS, Letterio JJ, Roberts AB. Incisional wound healing in transforming growth factor-beta1 null mice. Wound Repair Regen 2000;8:179–91.

[68] Glick A, Popescu N, Alexander V, Ueno H, Bottinger E, Yuspa SH. Defects in transforming growth factor-beta signaling cooperate with a Ras oncogene to cause rapid aneuploidy and malignant transformation of mouse keratinocytes. Proc Natl Acad Sci USA 1999;96:14949–54.

[69] Berrebi D, Bruscoli S, Cohen N, Foussat A, Migliorati G, Bouchet-Delbos L, et al. Synthesis of

glucocorticoid-induced leucine zipper (GILZ) by macrophages: an anti-inflammatory and immunosuppressive mechanism shared by glucocorticoids and IL-10. Blood 2003;101:729–38.

[70] Katsikis PD, Chu CQ, Brennan FM, Maini RN, Feldmann M. Immunoregulatory role of interleukin 10 in rheumatoid arthritis. J Exp Med 1994;179:1517–27.

[71] Firestein GS, Manning AM. Signal transduction and transcription factors in rheumatic disease. Arthritis Rheum 1999;42:609–21.

[72] Bondeson J, Foxwell B, Brennan F, Feldmann M. Defining therapeutic targets by using adenovirus: blocking NF-kappaB inhibits both inflammatory and destructive mechanisms in rheumatoid synovium but spares anti-inflammatory mediators. Proc Natl Acad Sci USA 1999;96:5668–73.

[73] Clark A. Post-transcriptional regulation of pro-inflammatory gene expression. Arthritis Res 2000;2:172–4.

[74] Gracie JA, Leung BP, McInnes IB. Novel pathways that regulate tumor necrosis factor-alpha production in rheumatoid arthritis. Curr Opin Rheumatol 2002;14:270–5.

RHEUMATIC
DISEASE CLINICS
OF NORTH AMERICA

ELSEVIER
SAUNDERS

Rheum Dis Clin N Am 30 (2004) 41–67

Cytokines in the rheumatic diseases

William P. Arend, MD[a],*, Cem Gabay, MD[b]

[a]Division of Rheumatology, University of Colorado Health Sciences Center B115,
4200 East Ninth Avenue, Denver CO 80262, USA
[b]Division of Rheumatology, University Hospital of Geneva, 26 Avenue Beau-Sejour,
CH-1211 Geneva 14, Switzerland

Cytokines are small molecular weight mediators of cell–cell communication and include interleukins (ILs), interferons (IFNs), growth factors, colony-stimulating factors, and other groups. These molecules are released by a variety of cells and usually act locally in a tissue to affect adjacent cells in a paracrine manner. Cytokines also may act inside a cell (intracrine), affect the same cell after release (autocrine), or travel through the circulation to act at a distance in an endocrine manner. Cytokines bind to specific receptors on target cells and stimulate signal transduction pathways that culminate in regulation of transcription. Cytokines carry out important functions in normal physiology and in host responses to infection or other exogenous threats to the integrity of the organism.

Extensive data has accumulated over the last 10 to 15 years to implicate various cytokines in pathways of pathophysiology in rheumatic diseases. Abnormalities in cytokine production are not the cause of these diseases, but reflect continual production by immune and inflammatory cells. Cytokines are heterogeneous and function in an overlapping and redundant network. An important principle to emerge is that the net biologic response in a diseased organ or tissue reflects a balance between the local levels of proinflammatory and anti-inflammatory cytokines and factors. Thus, a chronic disease may result from the excess production of proinflammatory cytokines or the inadequate production of anti-inflammatory cytokines. This article summarizes the role of cytokines in

Dr. Gabay is supported by a grant from the Swiss National Science Foundation (grant nos. 3200-054955.98 and 3231-05454.98). Dr. Arend is supported by grant nos. AR40135 and AI46374 from the National Institutes of Health.

* Corresponding author.
E-mail address: william.arend@uchsc.edu (W.P. Arend).

rheumatic diseases by focusing on each disease and the involved pathways of pathophysiology.

Rheumatoid arthritis

The cause of rheumatoid arthritis (RA) remains unknown. This disease is believed to involve the action of inflammatory and immune cells against self tissues, possibly triggered by an environmental agent acting in a genetically-predisposed host [1–4]. The initiating events are unclear but may be multiple, which leads to an inflammatory and immune response against self and possibly incites the development of common mechanisms of chronic synovitis [1]. Major hypotheses about this disease process have involved antigen-presenting cell (APC) dysfunction, B-cells and autoantibody production, T-cell reactivities, and, most recently, cytokines. The role of cytokines in RA has been reviewed extensively, particularly the involvement of IL-1 and tumor necrosis factor (TNF)-α [5–10]. The role of cytokines in several steps in the development of rheumatoid synovitis will be discussed, with an emphasis on some of the newer cytokines beyond IL-1 and TNF-α (Table 1).

Initiation of synovial inflammation

The association of certain HLA-DR4 alleles with increased susceptibility to, and severity of, RA has heightened a search for a common antigen that may

Table 1
Cytokines in rheumatoid arthritis

Stage of disease	Cytokines involved
Initiation of synovitis	
Synovial inflammation	IL-1, TNF-α, IL-6, IFNα, and IFNβ
Effector cell function	IFNγ, TGFβ, IL-4, IL-5, IL-10, IL-12, IL-15, and IL-18
Perpetuation of synovitis	IFNγ, IL-1, TNF-α, IL-4, IL-12, IL-15, IL-18, IL-7, and IL-17
Chronic synovitis	
Angiogenesis	VEGF, FGF, IL-18, HGF, Ang-1, CXCL12, TGFβ, and TNF-α
Cell migration	MIP-1α, MIP-1β, MCP-1, IL-8, and ENA-78
Adhesion molecule expression on EC	IL-1, TNF-α, and IFNγ
Induction of MMP production	(Direct) IL-1 and TNF-α (Indirect) IL-17, IL-18, and MIF

Abbreviatons: Ang, angiopoietin; CXCL12, stromal cell-derived factor-1; EC, endothelial cell; ENA, epithelial-derived neutrophil-activating peptide; FGF, fibroblast growth factor; IL, interleukin; IFN, interferon; HGF, hepatic growth factor; MCP, monocyte chemoattractant protein; MIF, macrophage migration inhibitory factor; MIP, macrophage inhibitory protein; MMP, matrix metalloproteinase; TGF, transforming growth factor; TNF, tumor necrosis factor; VEGF, vascular endothelial growth factor.

trigger T-cell reactivity and initiate synovitis. Such a search has largely been fruitless and it is probable that this disease is not initiated by T cells responding to self-determinants.

An alternative hypothesis is that rheumatoid synovitis is initiated by non-antigen-specific mechanisms and later moves through a stage of self-reactivity. The innate immune system functions at mucosal barriers to mediate initial host responses to infectious agents and other exogenous injurious stimuli [11]. Dendritic cells (DCs) and macrophages are the two major cells of the innate immune system that bind materials through pattern recognition receptors, such as toll receptors [12–14]. These are not antigen-specific receptors but bind certain repeating molecular structures on pathogens. The stimulated DCs and macrophages release cytokines that further stimulate cells of the innate immune system and amplify or inhibit inflammation and adaptive immune responses. The cytokines of the innate immune system that mediate inflammatory responses include IL-1, TNF-α, IL-6, IFNα, and IFNβ. The innate immune cytokines that regulate effector functions, including T-cell function, include IFNγ, transforming growth factor (TGF)-β, IL-4, IL-5, IL-10, IL-12, IL-13, IL-15, and IL-18. These cytokines offer important links between innate and adaptive immune responses.

Perpetuation of rheumatoid synovitis

After the initiation of rheumatoid synovitis by possibly nonantigen-specific mechanisms, the perpetuation of this disease process is believed to be T-cell driven. DCs and macrophages are the primary APCs and in their resting state carry self-peptides in the antigen-binding groove of class II major histocompatibility complex (MHC) molecules. In the development of antigen-specific adaptive immune responses, processed peptides, largely of exogenous origin, are exchanged for the self-peptides. It is possible that nonspecific stimulation of costimulatory molecule expression on T cells by innate immune cytokines may result in antigen-specific responses if the T cell receptor (TCR) also is engaged. TCR recognition of self-peptides may result from at least two different mechanisms. Self-reactive T cells may not have been completely deleted during thymic selection and development of the T-cell repertoire and may circulate in the periphery with the capacity to initiate autoimmune responses. Alternatively, T cells may be involved in molecular mimicry whereby their activation is induced by viral or bacterial peptides, but the T cells then cross-react with identical structures on self-peptides.

Rheumatoid synovitis usually is characterized primarily as a T helper (Th)-1 cell response, although a study of tissue cytokine patterns indicated a more heterogeneous picture [15]. The major histologic pattern of diffuse synovitis was marked by low-level transcription of genes for IFNγ, IL-4, IL-1β, and TNF-α. Follicular synovitis was next most common with abundant IL-10 present. Lastly, the minor histologic pattern of granulomatous synovitis was characterized by the high level of transcription of IFNγ, IL-4, IL-1β, and TNF-α. During the early perpetuation of rheumatoid synovitis, however, not reflected in studies on chronic rheumatoid synovium, IL-12, IL-15, and IL-18 play important roles in the attraction and activation of T cells.

IL-12 is released by DCs and macrophages through innate immune mechanisms and induces IFNγ production from natural killer (NK) cells and T cells; this leads to enhanced Th1 cell development [16]. IL-12 levels are elevated in the sera and synovial fluids (SF) of patients who have RA, although in paired samples, higher IL-12 levels were found in SF than in blood which suggested local synthesis in the joint [17]. IL-12 levels correlate with disease activity in RA and decrease in blood and SF after treatment with disease-modifying antirheumatic drugs (DMARDs). The local enhancement of IL-12 production in streptococcal cell wall–induced arthritis in mice through gene transfer converted a transient acute arthritis into a chronic, destructive immune-mediated process [18]. Thus, IL-12 enhancement of Th1 cell development may be involved in T-cell activation during the perpetuation stage of rheumatoid synovitis.

IL-15 is believed to be important in the attraction of T cells into the rheumatoid synovium and in their subsequent activation. IL-15 is present in high concentrations in rheumatoid SF and also can be found in the synovial membrane where it seems to be produced by macrophages, T cells, and NK cells [19,20]. Endothelial cells (ECs) also produce IL-15 and may assist in the transendothelial migration of T cells during their movement from the blood into the inflamed joint [21]. In addition, IL-15 activates T cells to induce TNF-α production in macrophages through a contact-dependent process that may involve upregulation of expression of CD154 (CD40 ligand) on the T cells [22–24]. IL-15 also is produced by synovial fibroblasts that are induced with IL-1 and TNF-α, and IL-15 stimulates synovial fibroblasts to proliferate and resist apoptosis [25,26]. Thus, the effects of IL-15 in the rheumatoid synovium result in the activation of T cells, macrophages, and fibroblasts.

IL-18, originally described as an IFNγ-inducing factor, may play an important upstream stimulatory role in rheumatoid synovitis [27]. IL-18 is an important regulator of innate and adaptive immune responses through inducing proliferation, cytotoxicity, and cytokine production by Th1 and NK cells, primarily in synergy with IL-12 [28]. IL-18 mRNA and protein were present in high levels in rheumatoid synovial tissue, primarily in macrophages; IL-18 receptors were identified on synovial lymphocytes and macrophages [29–32]. The combination of IL-18, IL-15, and IL-12 potently stimulated IFNγ production by synovial tissue in vitro and TNF-α production by synovial macrophages [29]. In addition, IL-18 production by synovial fibroblasts was stimulated by IL-1 and TNF-α; this established a positive feedback loop for IL-18 production. IL-18 also is produced by articular chondrocytes and induces proinflammatory and catabolic responses in these cells [33]. Other possible roles for IL-18 in rheumatoid synovitis include acting as a chemoattractant for T cells and as an angiogenic factor that enhances the growth of new blood vessels [34,35].

The importance of IL-18 in inflammatory arthritis has been examined in experimental animal models of disease. Mice that lack IL-18 exhibited reduced incidence and severity of collagen-induced arthritis (CIA) [36]. These mice exhibited decreased spleen cell proliferative responses to collagen in vitro, decreased levels of IgG2a anticollagen antibodies, and reduced production of IFN-γ, TNF-α, IL-6, and IL-12 by cultured spleen cells in vitro. Blockade of endogenous IL-18 with administration of specific antibodies in streptococcal cell wall–induced arthritis in mice was anti-inflammatory in both intact and IFN-γ-deficient mice; this indicated that IL-18 demonstrated proinflammatory properties separate from its ability to induce IFN-γ production [37]. IL-18 possesses a potent natural inhibitor, the IL-18 binding protein (IL-18BP), which binds IL-18 in the fluid phase and prevents interaction with cell surface receptors. Administration of either recombinant human or murine IL-18BP significantly inhibited the development and severity of CIA in mice [38,39]. Treatment with murine IL-18BP in CIA decreased the production of IL-1 and TNF-α by cultured spleen cells and reduced the mRNA levels for IL-1 and TNF-α in the joints [39]. Lastly, IL-18 in the rheumatoid synovium may be an important stimulant of local IL-1 and TNF-α production, similar to the animal models of arthritis [40]. Thus, IL-18 in RA may enhance Th1 cell development and may directly induce production of proinflammatory cytokines. The importance of IL-18 in RA is being studied through a clinical trial that is administering IL-18BP.

Other cytokines that are released in rheumatoid synovitis may activate T cells and link the stages of perpetuation and chronic synovitis. IL-7 was produced by fibroblast-like synoviocytes in the joints of patients who had RA, with enhanced synthesis after stimulation with IL-1 and TNF-α [25]. IL-7 stimulated the development of T cells and the proliferation of mature T cells that were obtained from synovial tissue. IL-7 also stimulated the production of IL-1, IL-6, and TNF-α by human monocytes and IFN-γ and TNF-α by CD4[+] T cells in rheumatoid SF [41,42]. The stimulatory effects of IL-7 on T cells were enhanced by the presence of IL-12 that is produced by monocytes. Lastly, IL-7 also stimulated the development and function of DCs, which enhanced further innate immune responses [43].

IL-17 is produced by activated memory T cells and may play numerous proinflammatory roles in rheumatoid synovitis [44]. IL-17 was produced by rheumatoid synovial tissue and stimulated the production of IL-1, TNF-α, IL-6, IL-10, IL-12, and IL-1Ra by human monocytes and IL-6 by rheumatoid synoviocytes [45,46]. The combination of IL-17 and TNF-α, however, exhibited synergistic stimulation of IL-1β, IL-6, and IL-8 production in rheumatoid synovial fibroblasts [47,48]. High levels of IL-15 and IL-17 were found in rheumatoid SF; IL-15 was a potent inducer of IL-17 production by T cells [49]. IL-17 seems to be important in cartilage and bone resorption in the rheumatoid joint. IL-17 stimulated matrix metalloproteinase (MMP)-9 production in human monocytes which led to the destruction of collagen and proteoglycans in cartilage and to decreased synthesis of these matrix molecules [50–57]. In addition, IL-17 stimulated osteoclast differentiation and enhanced bone degradation while inhibiting bone formation [54,58,59]. The IL-17R was found on synovial ECs, chondrocytes, and fibroblasts from patients who had various forms of arthritis;

IL-17 stimulated production of IL-8 and other chemokines by the synovial fibroblasts [60,61]. Inhibition of IL-17 by administration of a IL-17R-Fc fusion protein attenuated antigen-induced arthritis in rats [62]. Inhibition of IL-17 has become of great interest as a possible treatment for RA.

Chronic synovitis

Chronic synovitis is the third stage of rheumatoid joint disease, following initiation and T-cell–mediated perpetuation. This phase of the disease process exhibits spontaneous clinical remissions and exacerbations and is characterized by the prominent involvement of macrophages and synovial fibroblasts or synoviocytes. Numerous cytokines are involved in chronic rheumatoid synovitis, particularly in the regulation of migration of blood cells into the joint and in induction of MMP production by synoviocytes and chondrocytes.

Angiogenesis and cell migration

Chronic rheumatoid synovitis is characterized by an intense growth of new blood vessels. The role of ECs in rheumatoid synovitis and the mechanisms of angiogenesis in this disease process have been reviewed regularly [63–68]. The growth of new blood vessels in the rheumatoid synovium reflects the balance between factors that promote or inhibit angiogenesis, the latter are termed "angiostatic factors." The most prominent proangiogenic factors in the rheumatoid synovium are vascular endothelial growth factor (VEGF), fibroblast growth factor, IL-8, and hepatic growth factor. Two new potentially important angiogenic factors in RA are angiopoietin-1 and stromal cell-derived factor-1; both are produced by synovial fibroblasts [69,70]. Other cytokines, including TGFβ and TNF-α, may enhance angiogenesis indirectly through the induction of production of angiogenic factors by macrophages. Angiostatic factors in the rheumatoid synovium include IL-12, IFN-α, -β, and -γ, platelet factor 4, and other cytokines that are induced by IFN. Inhibition of angiogenesis suppressed CIA in rats and represents a potential new treatment approach to RA [71].

Cytokines also enhance migration of blood cells into the joint through the upregulation of expression of adhesion molecules on ECs [72,73]. The major adhesion molecules on rheumatoid synovial ECs are P-selectin, leukocyte function–associated antigen type 3, β1 and β3 integrins, vascular cell adhesion molecule type 1, and intercellular adhesion molecule types 1 and 2. Numerous chemokines attract cells into the joint and enhance the expression of adhesion molecules on ECs, including macrophage inhibitory protein-1α and -1β, monocyte chemoattractant protein (MCP)-1, IL-8, and epithelial-derived neutrophil-activating peptide-78 [74]. These chemokines have been described in the rheumatoid synovium. Cytokines that upregulate the expression of adhesion molecules on ECs include IL-1, TNF-α, and IFNγ. Treatment of antigen-induced arthritis in rabbits with a β3 integrin antagonist suppressed angiogenesis, infiltration of cells into the synovium, pannus formation, and cartilage erosions [75]. A major mechanism of TNF-α inhibition of RA by treatment with the monoclonal antibody, infliximab, is the inhibition of migration of blood cells into the joint [76]. Intense interest exists in the development of new therapeutic agents for RA based on inhibition of angiogenesis or of adhesion molecule expression on ECs.

Induction of matrix metalloproteinase release

The induction of MMP production in synoviocytes and chondrocytes by IL-1 and TNF-α is a major mechanism in the degradation of cartilage, the joint capsule, and periarticular tissues in RA. The roles of IL-1 and TNF-α in RA have been reviewed extensively and will not be reiterated in detail [6,76–79]. The success of inhibitors of IL-1 and TNF-α in the treatment of RA emphasizes the key roles of these cytokines in the disease process. The direct contact between lymphocytes and macrophages in the rheumatoid synovium is probably the most important mechanism that induces IL-1 and TNF-α production by macrophages. Other nonlymphocyte mechanisms exist, however, including macrophage stimulation by immune complexes, complement fragments, and other cytokines, such as IL-1 and TNF-α. The upstream cytokines that are capable of induction of IL-1 and TNF-α production by macrophages include IL-17 and IL-18. Macrophage migration inhibitory factor (MIF) is produced by T cells, macrophages, synoviocytes, and ECs and is capable of inducing production of IL-1 and TNF-α in macrophages [80]. In addition, synoviocyte proliferation was stimulated by MIF directly and indirectly, the latter mechanism through enhancing IL-1 and TNF-α production [81]. Antibodies to MIF suppressed various experimental animal models of RA, including CIA in mice [82], adjuvant-induced arthritis in rats [83], and antigen-induced arthritis in mice [84]. A unique characteristic of MIF is the antagonism or reversal of glucocorticoid effects. Thus, treatment of RA with MIF inhibitors blocks the proinflammatory effects of this cytokine and may allow the anti-inflammatory properties of endogenous glucocorticoids to be unmasked.

The role of IL-6 in inflammatory arthritis has been controversial. The properties of IL-6 include enhancement of B-cell differentiation and stimulation of production of the acute phase proteins (APPs) by hepatocytes. IL-6 is produced constitutively by rheumatoid synoviocytes and is present in high levels in the SF and sera of patients who have RA [85]. IL-6 seemed to play a dual role in experimental arthritis in mice; proinflammatory and anti-inflammatory effects were described [85–87]. The mixed effects of IL-6 may be explained by understanding its mechanism of stimulating cells; IL-6 binds to a single-chain receptor but stimulates cells through an associated gp130 molecule. Through gp130, IL-6 induces two signal transduction pathways, one of which may be stimulatory to inflammatory responses and the other may be inhibitory [88]. Thus, depending on which pathway predominates, IL-6 may enhance or reduce

Table 2
Cytokines in other forms of inflammatory arthritis

Disease	Cytokines
Spondyloarthritis	TNF-α and TGFβ
Juvenile rheumatoid arthritis	IL-1, IL-6, TNF-α, VEGF, IL-8, MCP-1, and IL-18
Osteoarthritis	IL-1, TNF-α, and IL-6

inflammation. Treatment of RA with a monoclonal antibody to the IL-6R binding chain, however, significantly improved the symptoms and signs of the disease and normalized the acute phase proteins [89]. Further clinical trials in patients who have RA to examine this anti–IL-6R antibody are in progress.

Spondyloarthritis

Cytokines also are involved in other forms of inflammatory arthritis besides RA (Table 2). The spondyloarthritides include ankylosing spondylitis, reactive arthritis, and arthritis that is associated with psoriasis or inflammatory bowel disease [90]. The primary pathologic sites in these diseases are the entheses (insertion of ligaments and tendons with bone) and the axial skeleton, as well as peripheral joints and nonarticular structures, such as the eye and aortic valve. Histologic studies on the sacroiliac joints of patients who had ankylosing spondylitis revealed the presence of T cells and macrophages, with abundant TNF-α mRNA and lower amounts of TGFβ mRNA [91]. The results of clinical trials with TNF-blocking agents in ankylosing spondylitis and psoriatic arthritis further substantiated the importance of TNF-α in these diseases [92]. Treatment of ankylosing spondylitis with a monoclonal antibody to TNF-α, infliximab, or with a soluble TNF receptor, etanercept, led to significant improvements in clinical and serologic evidence of active disease in the axial skeleton [92–95]. In a similar fashion, patients who had psoriasis and active peripheral arthritis exhibited significant responses to treatment with etanercept [96]. No clinical trials have been reported with TNF inhibitors in reactive arthritis or on the possible beneficial effect on nonarticular manifestations in the spondyloarthritides.

Juvenile rheumatoid arthritis

Juvenile rheumatoid arthritis (JCA) consists of three clinical subgroups: polyarticular disease with or without the presence of rheumatoid factor, pauci-articular disease often accompanied by iritis, and systemic onset or Still's disease. Several cytokines are elevated in the serum of patients who have JCA, including IL-1, IL-6, and TNF-α [97]. Examination of the synovium of these patients revealed a mixed picture with a Th1 bias that included the presence of IFNγ, IL-12, and IL-18 and low amounts of IL-4 and IL-10. In general, the SF of patients who had JCA demonstrated the presence of chemokines and angiogenic factors, such as VEGF, IL-8, and MCP-1, and low levels of cytokine antagonists, including IL-1Ra. In patients who had Still's disease, elevated serum levels of IL-6, IFNγ, and TNF-α were described, with markedly increased levels of IL-18 [98]. Treatment with etanercept was efficacious in patients who had polyarticular JCA who were intolerant of, or responded poorly to, methotrexate [99].

Osteoarthritis

Although osteoarthritis (OA) is not primarily an inflammatory disease, many studies incriminated IL-1 in cartilage destruction in this disease [100]. Several other cytokines are found in the joints of patients who have OA with lesser roles ascribed to TNF-α and IL-6. The primary role of IL-1 is believed to be stimulation of production of MMPs by chondrocytes with resultant destruction of proteoglycans and collagen. Experimental animal models of OA responded to inhibition of IL-1 by IL-1Ra but this form of therapy has not been studied in the human disease.

Systemic lupus erythematosus

Systemic lupus erythematosus (SLE) is a prototypic autoimmune disease that affects predominantly women in their child-bearing years. The prevalence of SLE varies in different ethnic groups from 1 in 250 black women to 1 in 4300 white women. SLE is an autoimmune disease with involvement of multiple organ systems that is characterized by the production of autoantibodies. Among these antibodies, antidouble stranded (ds)DNA antibodies are most likely to be pathogenic. Although the cause of SLE remains unknown, multiple studies implicated the role of different cytokines in SLE pathogenesis [reviewed in 101]. Cytokines may be involved in the different steps of SLE pathogenesis, including the breakdown of tolerance, the activation of B cells with consequent autoantibody production, and the inflammatory processes that lead to organ damage.

Breakdown of tolerance

Several studies implicated TNF-α and other members of the TNF family of cytokines in the loss of tolerance. The mode of action of TNF in SLE remains unclear, however, because there is evidence both for a protective role and for pathogenic effects in the inflammatory process. TNF-α may exert opposite activities by promoting and inhibiting the adaptive immune responses. TNF-α is required for the development of secondary lymphoid organs and for induction of optimal humoral responses [102,103]. TNF-α induces thymocyte proliferation and acts as a mitogen for T cells [104]. TNF-α also stimulates the recruitment of APCs, thus enhancing T-cell responses [105]. In contrast, TNF-α inhibits T-cell receptor signaling [106]. As with other TNF receptors, TNF-α receptor p55 possesses a cytoplasmic death domain that can induce apoptosis through activation of the enzymatic caspase cascade. TNF-α plays an important role in the termination of lymphocyte responses, as exemplified by its capacity to promote activation-induced cell death in CD8[+] T cells [107,108].

In the classic (NZB × NZW) F1 mouse model of SLE, early administration of TNF-α had a beneficial effect on the onset of lupus nephritis; this suggested that TNF-α can modulate the autoimmune response [109]. The lack of TNF-α in gene knockout mice resulted in the induction of autoimmunity and fatal lupus nephritis in otherwise nonsusceptible offspring that were derived from the cross between NZB and B6/129 mice [110]. The occurrence of antinuclear antibodies and of anti-dsDNA antibodies preceded the deposition of immune complexes on the glomerular basement membrane, thus providing strong evidence for a role for TNF-α in early events that lead to the development of SLE. Similar findings regarding the potential role of TNF-α in the development of autoimmune responses were described in other experimental models of autoimmune diseases, such as allergic encephalomyelitis [111]. Low levels of TNF-α production were observed in some patients who had SLE [112]. In contrast, other investigators observed that serum TNF-α levels in patients who had SLE were not different from healthy controls, but that TNF soluble receptors levels were significantly increased and correlated with the degree of disease activity [113]. TNF-α soluble receptors p55 and p75 are natural inhibitors; the presence of elevated levels of soluble receptors in patients who have SLE represents an additional variable that can modulate the biologic activity of TNF-α.

The use of TNF-α inhibitors in the treatment of RA has provided additional evidence regarding the potential role of TNF-α in the control of autoimmune manifestations. The incidence of antinuclear antibodies and anti-dsDNA antibodies was significantly increased in patients who received either monoclonal antibodies against TNF-α or soluble TNF receptors. Some treated patients developed a lupuslike syndrome; rare cases of neuroinflammatory manifestations also have been reported [114,115]. These observations suggest that a lack of TNF may predispose to autoimmune responses.

Several experimental models of lupus have directly linked genetic abnormalities with defective apoptosis or impaired clearance of apoptotic cells, and then to tolerance breakdown and autoimmune responses to nuclear antigens. Fas/APO-1 (CD95) is a member of the TNF receptor superfamily that, upon activation by specific antibody, triggered cell death by apoptosis. The lpr mutation in the MRL strain of mice results in the absence of Fas expression on resting or activated lymphocytes from MRL lpr/lpr mice. Fas may play a role in thymic selection and T-cell survival in the periphery. The presence of lymphoproliferation and accelerated autoimmunity with renal lupus in MRL lpr/lpr mice is likely to result from a defect in these pathways [116]. Fas ligand is a transmembrane protein that induces apoptosis in Fas-expressing target cells. gld mutation is a point mutation in the Fas ligand gene that abolishes binding to its receptor (Fas) and is associated with lymphoproliferation and autoimmune manifestations [117]. In

MRL lpr/lpr mice, the absence of TNF receptor p55 resulted in greatly accelerated lymphoproliferation and autoimmune disease; this indicated that TNF receptor p55 signaling plays a compensatory role in lymphocyte apoptosis [118].

TNF-related apoptosis-inducing ligand (TRAIL), like other members of the TNF ligand family, induces apoptosis in a variety of tumor cells [119]. TRAIL is expressed by various immune cells, such as CD4[+] T cells, NK cells, macrophages, and DCs [120]. TNF-like weak inducer of apoptosis (TWEAK) was first described in malignant cells [121]. FasL, TRAIL, and TWEAK all contribute to the increased monocyte apoptosis that is induced by lupus T cells [122]. TRAIL, similar to FasL, also may play a role in preventing the development of autoimmunity. Blocking TRAIL in mice enhanced the proliferation of autoreactive lymphocytes, whereas administration of adenoviral vector encoding TRAIL in (NZB × NZW) F1 mice resulted in decreased levels of anti-dsDNA antibodies [123]. Although these observations provide strong evidence that defective apoptosis is implicated in the induction of autoimmunity in experimental animal models, similar genetic defects have been observed rarely in human lupus. Only one patient who had SLE was described with a point mutation in FasL [124]. Mutations of the Fas gene can result in a rare and severe autoimmune lymphoproliferative syndrome (ALPS, Canale-Smith syndrome) in humans, but such mutations have not been detected in human SLE [125,126].

Proinflammatory cytokines also may indirectly contribute to the clearance of apoptotic cells. IL-6, IL-1, and TNF-α stimulate the production of APP, including C-reactive protein (CRP), by hepatocytes [127]. CRP and its mouse homolog, serum amyloid protein (SAP), are involved in the elimination of apoptotic fragments. SAP and CRP bind to nuclear components and stimulate the classical pathway of complement. Together with complement proteins, SAP plays an important role in the clearance of chromatin DNA, and, thus, possibly in the tolerance to nuclear antigens. Knockout mice that are deficient in SAP developed antinuclear antibodies and lupuslike manifestations [128]. The presence of a weak CRP response in SLE may contribute to pathogenesis of the disease through a defective clearance of apoptotic or damaged cells. In contrast, in disorders that are associated with a high acute-phase response, elevated levels of CRP, and possibly other acute-phase proteins, may exert a protective effect on the development of autoimmunity. For example, the prevalence of SLE is reduced among patients who have familial Mediterranean fever [129].

Stimulation of autoreactive B cells

SLE is a prototypical autoimmune disease that is characterized by overt B-cell activation that results in polyclonal hyperglobulinemia and autoantibody production. CD40 ligand (CD40L or CD154) is a member of the TNF ligand superfamily. The interaction of CD40L on activated T cells with CD40 on B cells induces proliferation and formation of germinal centers. Within germinal centers, further CD40/CD40L interactions lead to B-cell maturation through immunoglobulin isotype class switching, somatic mutation, clonal expansion of specific B cells, and terminal differentiation to plasma cells [130–132]. The potential role of CD40/CD40L interaction in the pathogenesis of SLE was supported by studies in experimental animal models of lupus that showed that administration of antibodies against CD40L was effective in delaying the onset of disease and ameliorating the course of established nephritis [133,134]. In patients who had SLE, a brief period of treatment with a humanized monoclonal anti-CD40L antibody resulted in the improvement of serologic markers (levels of anti-DNA antibodies) and hematuria. The occurrence of severe side effects, including myocardial infarctions and thromboembolic events, resulted in premature cessation of the trial [135]. In contrast, the result of a recent trial with another humanized monoclonal anti-CD40L antibody in patients who had SLE was not associated with thrombotic events but did not demonstrate significant effect on disease activity [136]. Thus, further studies are needed to explore the efficacy of targeting CD40/CD40L interactions in the treatment of autoimmune diseases.

B-cell activating factor (BAFF) is a novel member of the TNF family and an essential component of B-cell homeostasis. BAFF is a homotrimer that is found at the cell surface or as a soluble protein that binds three different receptors, including B-cell maturation antigen, transmembrane activator and calcium-modulator and cyclophilin ligand interactor (TACI), and BAFF receptor. These receptors are expressed primarily on the B-cell lineage but are present to a lesser extent on T cells [137,138]. DCs, macrophages, and monocytes produce BAFF; its expression is upregulated by IFNγ and IL-10 [139,140]. BAFF is a crucial mediator for survival of transitional and mature B cells. In contrast, BAFF overexpression leads to B-cell hyperplasia and to the development of autoimmune manifestations that are suggestive of a SLE-like disease, including anti-DNA antibodies and renal deposition of immune complexes [138]. As BAFF transgenic mice get older they develop a condition that is similar to Sjögren's syndrome in humans. In addition, large amounts of BAFF were described in the salivary glands of patients who had Sjögren's syndrome [141]. The administration of TACI-immunoglobulin, a decoy receptor that inhibits the effects of BAFF, ameliorated the course of lupus nephritis in NZB × NXW mice and MRL-lpr/lpr mice. This provided strong support for the pathogenic role of BAFF [142]. A proliferation-inducing ligand (APRIL) is closely related to BAFF and also can form heterotrimeric molecules with BAFF; this heterotrimer can induce B-cell proliferation in vitro. Elevated levels of BAFF/APRIL were detected in the circulation of patients who had inflammatory rheumatic diseases; this suggested that BAFF/APRIL heterotrimers may play a role in the development of autoimmunity [143].

Circulating levels of IL-6 are elevated in patients who have SLE. IL-6 is necessary for plasma cell survival and maturation and was suggested to induce B-cell hyperreactivity. Spontaneous production of IgG was inhibited by the addition of anti–IL-6 antibodies. Administration of neutralizing anti–IL-6 antibodies to MRL mice decreased the production of anti-dsDNA antibodies and the development of renal damage [144].

The role of the Th1/Th2 balance

CD4$^+$ T cells have been divided into two main subsets of helper lymphocytes that possess distinct arrays of cytokine production and function. Th1 and Th2 cytokines illustrate this division. Th1 cytokines include IL-2 and IFNγ; the latter generally promotes macrophage activation and elimination of intracellular pathogens. Th2 cytokines include IL-4, IL-5, IL-6, IL-10, and IL-13, all of which promote humoral immune responses. This clear separation is artificial because IFNγ can induce the production of specific IgG subclasses (IgG2a and IgG3 in the mouse).

The presence of elevated serum levels of IL-4, IL-6, and IL-10 in patients who had SLE suggested that it should be considered as a Th2-driven disease. In addition, the presence of B-cell hyperreactivity and hyperglobulinemia supported this hypothesis. The primary source of IL-6 and IL-10 in SLE are monocytes, not Th2 lymphocytes. In addition, observations regarding the role of IL-4 led to contradictory results. Treatment of MRL-lpr/lpr mice with anti–IL-4 antibodies reduced disease manifestations and mortality [145]. Conversely, IL-4 was shown to be unnecessary in the BXSB male lupus model [146]. Transgenic mice that overexpressed IL-4 could develop a lupuslike disease or could exhibit less disease, according to the genetic background [147,148]. Elevated serum levels of IL-10 were present in patients who had SLE and correlated with disease activity and anti-dsDNA antibody levels [149,150]. Peripheral blood mononuclear cells (PBMC) from patients who have SLE produce high amounts of IL-10. Transfer of PBMC from patients who had SLE to severe combined immunodeficient mice resulted in high titers of anti-dsDNA antibodies, which were abolished almost completely by treatment with anti–IL-10 antibodies [151]. Immune complexes from SLE sera induced the production of IL-10 by a FcγRII mechanism, thus leading to the maintenance of B-cell hyperactivity [152]. Anti–IL-10 antibodies delayed the onset of disease in (NZB × NZW) F1 mice [153]. In an open-label clinical trial, the administration of a murine monoclonal antihuman IL-10 antibody for 21 days ameliorated the SLE disease activity index, thus supporting a role for IL-10 in the pathogenesis of SLE [154].

Other evidence suggests that Th1 cytokines, particularly IFNγ, may play an important role in lupus models and in human SLE. IL-18, a novel member of the IL-1 family of cytokines, induces the production of IFNγ, acting synergistically with IL-12. Serum IL-18 levels were elevated in patients who had SLE and correlated with disease activity and IFNγ levels [155]. By flow cytometry, the intracellular Th1:Th2 ratio was elevated in patients who had renal lupus, with particularly high values in patients who had diffuse proliferative lupus nephritis [156]. The importance of IFNγ in the (NZB × NZW) F1 mice was suggested by acceleration of renal disease after administration of IFNγ, whereas mice that received neutralizing IFNγ antibodies at an early stage exhibited significantly delayed onset [157]. In addition, significant reduction in serologic abnormalities and extended survival was observed in MRL-lpr/lpr mice in which the IFNγ or IFNγ receptor genes had been deleted [158–160].

The inflammatory process

The pattern of cytokines in SLE varies according to the clinical manifestations and the site of inflammation. Elevated IL-6 levels were present in the cerebrospinal fluid of patients who had central nervous system lupus but not in those who did not have neurologic involvement. IL-6 was detected in the urine of patients who had lupus nephritis. These findings suggested that cytokines participated in the inflammatory processes that take place in affected organs. Levels of TNF-α, IL-1β, and other proinflammatory cytokines were increased in the kidneys of MRL-lpr/lpr mice. These cytokines can induce the attraction of inflammatory cells and promote autoimmune organ destruction. TNF-α also was detected in the glomeruli of 52% of patients who had lupus nephritis [161]. The pathogenic role of this local production of TNF-α was recently demonstrated by the beneficial effect of infliximab, a chimeric monoclonal antibody against TNF-α, in patients who had lupus nephritis [162]. The administration of FR167653, an inhibitor of p38 mitogen-activated protein kinases (MAPK), reduced the accumulation of inflammatory cells, prevented kidney pathology, and prolonged the survival of MRL-lpr/lpr mice [163]. This observation further demonstrates the potential contribution of proinflammatory cytokines to autoimmune organ damage in SLE.

Systemic sclerosis

Systemic sclerosis (SSc) is a connective tissue disease of unknown origin that is characterized by fibrosis of the skin and visceral organs. The fibrotic process is probably secondary to an imbalance between excessive collagen synthesis and reduced degradation. SSc fibroblasts are activated and produce increased amounts of collagen as compared with fibroblasts from healthy controls. By in situ hybridization, SSc fibroblasts were shown to express α1 chain types I and III procollagen mRNA [164,165]. Conversely, inhibitors of matrix-degrading enzymes, such as tissue inhibitor of metalloproteinases and plasminogen activator inhibitor-1, are underexpressed by SSc fibroblasts [166]. In addition, the production of collagenase 1 is impaired [167]. IL-1α was expressed by SSc fibroblasts; experiments using antisense oligonucleotides demonstrated that endogenous IL-1α in SSc dermal fibroblasts stimulated IL-6 and platelet-derived growth factor-A (PDGF-A) production [168]. Furthermore, inhibition of IL-6 by the addition of neutralizing antibodies resulted in a significant inhibition of collagen synthesis [169].

Although the pathogenesis of SSc remains largely unknown, immunologic abnormalities were suggested to play an important role in the development of skin and visceral manifestations. It was shown that most cells infiltrating the skin were CD4$^+$ T cells. Th1 and Th2 cytokines were found in the circulation of patients who had SSc and were produced by PBMC in culture [170–172]. IL-4 stimulated the production of collagen by normal and SSc fibroblasts at the level of transcription and mRNA stability [173]. IL-17 is produced by $CD4^+$ Th1 lymphocytes; serum levels were significantly increased in patients who had SSc but not in patients who had SLE or in healthy controls. IL-17 mRNA was detected in the skin and in lymphocytes in bronchoalveolar lavage fluid, particularly in the early stages of SSc; this suggested a role for IL-17 in the early events of SSc. IL-17 induced the proliferation of cultured dermal fibroblasts from healthy donors and patients who had SSc, and IL-17 stimulated the expression of adhesion molecules, IL-1β, and IL-6 by endothelial cells [174]. TGFβ is thought to play an important role in the fibrotic process of SSc [reviewed in 166]. TGFβ is produced by infiltrating inflammatory cells and SSc fibroblasts. In addition, TGFβ induced the production of connective tissue growth factor (CTGF) by fibroblasts [175]. Serum CTGF levels were increased in patients who had SSc and correlated with the extent of skin sclerosis and the degree of pulmonary fibrosis; this suggested that CTGF may play an important role in the development of scleroderma [176]. TGFβ and CTGF stimulated fibroblasts in an autocrine and paracrine manner which resulted in progressive extracellular matrix accumulation. The role of TGFβ in the pathogenesis of fibrosis is supported by experiments that used specific inhibitors in vivo. Administration of TGFβ-soluble receptors, anti-TGFβ antibodies, and overexpression of Smad7, a specific endogenous intracellular TGFβ signaling antagonist, attenuated experimentally-induced tissue fibrosis in animal models [177–179]. Clinical trials are currently being conducted in patients who have SSc using therapies that inhibit the effect of TGFβ.

Idiopathic inflammatory myopathies

Idiopathic inflammatory myopathies (IIM) are characterized by proximal and symmetrical muscle weakness and inflammatory infiltrates in the muscle tissue. Based on clinical and histologic features, three different forms of IIM can be distinguished. These include polymyositis (PM), dermatomyositis (DM), and inclusion body myositis (IBM). Patients who have IBM have distal and asymmetrical muscle involvement and usually are resistant to corticosteroids. Patients who have DM have typical cutaneous lesions. Histologically, the most common infiltrating cells are T cells and macrophages. A higher proportion of $CD8^+$ T cells are present in PM and IBM, whereas B cells are more common in DM. The localization of inflammatory cells varies according to the IIM subset, with a predominance of infiltrates in the endomysium in PM and at perivascular sites in DM.

Despite the histologic differences, the expression of cytokines, as assessed by immunostaining studies, generally were similar in the three IIM subsets [180]. By immunohistochemistry, monokines, including IL-1 and TNF-α, were detected in large amounts in the different IIM subsets. IL-1α was present in endothelial cells in capillaries, perifascicular arterioles, and venules, as well as in infiltrating mononuclear cells. In contrast, the expression of IL-1β and TNF-α was restricted to inflammatory cells [181]. A pathogenic role for these cytokines was suggested by their effects on the recruitment of inflammatory cells through the stimulation of expression of adhesion molecules on ECs and the induction of chemokine production. The presence of chemokines was detected in muscle biopsies from patients who had IIM [182]. MCP-1 was expressed differently in IIM subsets. MCP-1 was expressed strongly in T cells and a subset of macrophages in muscle fibers in PM and IBM, whereas it was primarily located in perimysial ECs [183]. In addition, IL-1 and TNF-α can inhibit glucose transport and lactate production by blocking the effects of insulin-like growth factor [184]. These direct effects on muscle metabolism may explain the poor correlation between clinical symptoms, such as muscle weakness, and the degree of tissue inflammatory infiltration. The importance of the role of IL-1 in the pathophysiology of IIM is supported by the results of a longitudinal study with histologic analysis performed before and after therapy. The expression of IL-1α, IL-1β, and adhesion molecules was significantly decreased in patients who underwent muscle biopsy after treatment with high doses of corticosteroids. IL-1α was expressed in patients who had persisting symptoms despite the disappearance of inflammatory infiltrates, thus supporting a direct effect of IL-1 on muscle metabolism [185].

TGFβ is expressed highly by invading inflammatory cells and ECs and is present in the extracellular matrix [186]. TGFβ also can contribute to the development of fibrosis in myositis [187]. The expression of TGFβ mRNA decreased following treatment with intravenous immunoglobulins in patients who had DM who responded to therapy [186].

IL-15, a pleiotropic cytokine produced by macrophages and fibroblasts, plays an important role in T-cell attraction, survival, and activation. IL-15 was elevated in the circulation of patients who had IIM [188]. Stimulated muscle cells are able to produce IL-15 in response to IL-1 and TNF-α in vitro [189]. In addition, the interaction between CD40L on T cells and CD40 on myocytes stimulated the release of IL-6, IL-8, IL-15, and MCP-1 by muscle cells [190]. These findings indicate that muscle cells are not innocent bystanders and participate in the inflammatory process.

Vasculitis

The vasculitides are a heterogeneous group of syndromes that are classified according to the histologic pattern and the size of blood vessels affected. This classification is useful for clinical purposes and pathogenic studies. Recent studies showed the presence of various cytokines in blood vessel walls in patients who had forms of vasculitis; this suggesting that they may play a role in pathogeneses.

Giant cell arteritis

Large arteries are the target of two distinct types of vasculitis, giant cell arteritis (GCA) and Takayasu's arteritis. GCA preferentially affects medium-sized muscular arteries that possess well-developed internal and external elastic laminae. GCA most often is located in the upper branches of the aorta and in extracranial arteries. The inflammatory infiltrate includes activated T lymphocytes, predominantly CD4$^+$ T cells, macrophages, and, in approximately 50% of cases, multinucleated giant cells. The other pathologic findings include the presence of fragmented external and internal elastic laminae, destruction of the media, and formation of new vasa vasorum. In addition, the mechanism of tissue repair that takes place in the inflamed and damaged arteries includes intimal proliferation that leads to occlusion of the lumen and to clinically relevant ischemic complications. Compared with noninflamed temporal arteries, GCA biopsies demonstrated the presence of IFNγ, IL-2, IL-1β, IL-6, and TGFβ [191]. The subset of T cells that produce IFNγ was detected exclusively in the adventitia [192]. This finding led to the hypothesis that, in the early events of GCA, T cells enter arterial walls through the vasa vasorum that are located in the adventitia of normal arteries. The T cells react with antigens that are present in the outer layers of the blood vessels, produce IFNγ, and activate macrophages which leads to vascular lesions [193]. In addition, high production of IFNγ typically was detected in patients who may develop ischemic symptoms [194]. The production of inflammatory mediators by macrophages was diverse according to their location in the blood vessel wall. In the adventitia, they produced IL-1β, IL-6, and TGFβ, whereas in the media MMP 2 synthesis was detected predominantly and intimal macrophages expressed nitric oxide synthase 2 [195,196]. The secretion of MMP probably is involved in the occurrence of tissue damage with the breakdown of elastic laminae. Multinucleated giant cells produce various growth factors, including PDGF and VEGF [197,198]. PDGFA and PDGFB are involved in the intimal hyperplasia, whereas VEGF may contribute to the proliferation of new vasa vasorum in the vessel walls. Serum levels of IL-6 are elevated in patients who have GCA and correlate with the presence of disease activity [199]. In a recent study, IL-6 was more sensitive than erythrocyte sedimentation rate for detecting disease activity [200].

Wegener's granulomatosis

Wegener's granulomatosis (WG) is an inflammatory disease of unknown origin that is characterized by the presence of disseminated necrotizing granulomas and systemic vasculitis that affect small blood vessels predominantly. The inflammatory infiltrate consists of T cells, macrophages, giant cells, and neutrophils that surround necrotic areas. A marked expansion of CD28^{neg}, CD4$^+$, and CD8$^+$ T cells was observed in the granulomas of patients who had WG [201]. Immunohistochemistry studies demonstrated that CD4$^+$ CD28$^-$ T cells that were present in granulomatous lesions were a major source of IFNγ and TNF-α. Peripheral blood CD4$^+$ CD28$^-$ T cells that were isolated from patients who had WG shared the same cytokine pattern [202]. IL-12 and TNF-α expression by circulating monocytes was elevated in active WG and decreased following treatment with prednisone and cyclophosphamide [203]. The potential role of

TNF-α in the pathophysiology of WG was supported by the results of clinical trials showing that administration of infliximab was of benefit in patients who were refractory to classic treatment with steroids and cytotoxic drugs [204].

Behcet's disease

Behcet's disease (BD) is an inflammatory disease that is associated with several clinical manifestations, including oral and genital ulcerations, uveitis, erythema nodosum, cutaneous pustular lesions, and arthritis. Some of these clinical features can be attributed to underlying vasculitis. Vessels of all sizes can be affected. Activated peripheral neutrophils and infiltration of neutrophils into the lesions also are characteristic findings of BD. IL-8 is a chemokine that is responsible for neutrophil attraction and activation. Cultured PBMC from patients who had BD spontaneously produced IL-8 mRNA and protein [205,206]. In addition, mononuclear cells, ECs, and fibroblasts in BD lesions produced IL-8 [205]. Serum levels of IL-8 were higher in patients who had BD than in controls [207]. Production of IL-6 and TNF-α by unstimulated and lipopolysaccharide (LPS)-stimulated PBMC also was higher than in control PBMC [206]. Circulating levels of several cytokines, including IL-6, IL-10, IL-17, and IL-18, were higher in active BD than in patients who were in remission [208]. These findings and the positive results that were observed after treatment with TNF-α inhibitors support the role of cytokines in the inflammatory manifestations of BD [209].

References

[1] Zvaifler NJ. Immunopathology of inflammatory diseases: rheumatoid arthritis as an example. Adv Inflam Res 1984;7:1–10.

[2] Arend WP. The pathophysiology and treatment of rheumatoid arthritis. Arthritis Rheum 1997; 40:595–7.

[3] VenderBorght A, Geusens P, Stinissen P. The autoimmune pathogenesis of rheumatoid arthritis: role of autoreactive T cells and new immunotherapies. Semin Arthritis Rheum 2001;31: 160–75.

[4] Smith JB, Haynes MK. Rheumatoid arthritis: a molecular understanding. Ann Intern Med 2002; 136:908–22.

[5] Ivashkiv LB. Cytokine expression and cell activation in inflammatory arthritis. Adv Immunol 1996;63:337–76.

[6] Feldmann M, Brennan FM, Maini RN. Role of cytokines in rheumatoid arthritis. Annu Rev Immunol 1996;14:397–440.

[7] Koch AE, Kunkel SL, Strieter RM. Cytokines in rheumatoid arthritis. J Invest Med 1995;43: 28–38.

[8] Arend WP. Physiology of cytokine pathways in rheumatoid arthritis. Arthritis Care Res 2001; 45:101–6.

[9] Choy EHS, Panayi GS. Cytokine pathways and joint inflammation in rheumatoid arthritis. N Engl J Med 2001;344:907–16.

[10] Vervoordeldonk MJBM, Tak PP. Cytokines in rheumatoid arthritis. Curr Rheumatol Rep 2002; 4:208–17.

[11] Arend WP. The innate immune system in rheumatoid arthritis. Arthritis Rheum 2001;44: 2224–34.

[12] Thomas R, Lipsky PE. Presentation of self peptides by dendritic cells. Arthritis Rheum 1996; 39:183–90.

[13] Thomas R, Lipsky PE. Could endogenous self-peptides presented by dendritic cells initiate rheumatoid arthritis? Immunol Today 1996;17:559–64.

[14] Thomas R, MacDonald KPA, Pettit AR, et al. Dendritic cells and the pathogenesis of rheumatoid arthritis. J Leukoc Biol 1999;66:286–92.

[15] Klimiuk PA, Goronzy JJ, Björnsson J, et al. Tissue cytokine patterns distinguish variants of rheumatoid synovitis. Am J Pathol 1997;151:1311–9.

[16] Caspi RR. IL-12 in autoimmunity. Clin Immunol Immunopathol 1998;88:4–13.

[17] Kim W-U, Min S-Y, Cho M-L, et al. The role of IL-12 in inflammatory activity of patients with rheumatoid arthritis (RA). Clin Exp Immunol 2000;119:175–81.

[18] Joosten LAB, Heuvelmans-Jacobs M, Lubberts E, et al. Local interleukin gene transfer promotes conversion of an acute arthritis to a chronic destructive arthritis. Arthritis Rheum 2002; 46:1379–89.

[19] McInnes IB, Al-Mughales J, Field M, et al. The role of interleukin-15 in T-cell migration and activation in rheumatoid arthritis. Nat Med 1996;2:175–82.

[20] Thurkow EW, van der Heijden IM, Breedveld FC, et al. Increased expression of IL-15 in the synovium of patients with rheumatoid arthritis compared with patients with *Yersinia*-induced arthritis and osteoarthritis. J Pathol 1997;181:444–50.

[21] Oppenehimer-Marks N, Brezinschek RI, Mohamadzadeh M, et al. Interleukin 15 is produced by endothelial cells and increases the transendothelial migration of T cells in vitro and in the SCID mouse-human rheumatoid arthritis model in vivo. J Clin Invest 1998;101:1261–72.

[22] McInnes IB, Leung BP, Sturrock RD, et al. Interleukin-15 mediates T cell-dependent regulation of tumor necrosis factor-α production in rheumatoid arthritis. Nat Med 1997;3: 189–95.

[23] McInnes IB, Liew FY. Interleukin 15: a proinflammatory role in rheumatoid arthritis synovitis. Immunol Today 1998;19:75–9.

[24] Möttönen M, Isomäki P, Luukkainen R, et al. Interleukin-15 up-regulates the expression of CD154 on synovial fluid T cells. Immunology 2000;100:238–44.

[25] Harada S, Yamamura M, Okamoto H, et al. Production of interleukin-7 and interleukin-15 by fibroblast-like synoviocytes from patients with rheumatoid arthritis. Arthritis Rheum 1999;42: 1508–16.

[26] Kurowsk M, Rudnicka W, Kontny E, et al. Fibroblast-like synoviocytes from rheumatoid arthritis patients express functional IL-15 receptor complex: endogenous IL-15 in autocrine fashion enhances cell proliferation and expression of Bcl-x_L and Bcl-2. J Immunol 2002;169: 1760–7.

[27] Dayer J-M. Interleukin-18, rheumatoid arthritis, and tissue destruction. J Clin Invest 1999;104: 1337–9.

[28] McInnes IB, Gracie JA, Liew FY. Interleukin-18: a novel cytokine in inflammatory rheumatic disease. Arthritis Rheum 2001;44:1481–3.

[29] Gracie JA, Forsey RJ, Chan WL, et al. A proinflammatory role for IL-18 in rheumatoid arthritis. J Clin Invest 1999;104:1393–401.

[30] Tanaka M, Harigai M, Kawaguchi Y, et al. Mature form of interleukin 18 is expressed in rheumatoid arthritis synovial tissue and contributes to interferon-γ production by synovial cells. J Rheumatol 2001;28:1779–87.

[31] Yamamura M, Kawashima M, Taniai M, et al. Interferon-γ-inducing activity of interleukin-18 in the joint with rheumatoid arthritis. Arthritis Rheum 2001;44:275–85.

[32] Möller B, Kukoc-Zivojnov N, Kessler U, et al. Expression of interleukin-18 and its monokine-directed function in rheumatoid arthritis. Rheumatol 2001;40:302–9.

[33] Olee T, Hashimoto S, Quach J, et al. IL-18 is produced by articular chondrocytes and induces proinflammatory and catabolic responses. J Immunol 1999;162:1096–100.

[34] Komai-Koma M, Gracie JA, Wei X-Q, et al. Chemoattraction of human T cells by IL-18. J Immunol 2003;170:1084–90.

[35] Park CC, Morel JCM, Amin MA, et al. Evidence of IL-18 as a novel angiogenic mediator. J Immunol 2001;167:1644–53.

[36] Wei X-Q, Leung BP, Arthur HML, et al. Reduced incidence and severity of collagen-induced arthritis in mice lacking IL-18. J Immunol 2001;166:517–21.

[37] Joosten LAB, van de Loo FAJ, Lubberts E, et al. An IFN-γ-independent proinflammatory role of IL-18 in murine streptococcal cell wall arthritis. J Immunol 2000;165:6553–8.

[38] Plater-Zyberk C, Joosten LAB, Helsen MMA, et al. Therapeutic effect of neutralizing endogenous IL-18 activity in the collagen-induced model of arthritis. J Clin Invest 2001;108: 1825–32.

[39] Banda NK, Vondracek A, Kraus D, et al. Mechanisms of inhibition of collagen-induced arthritis by murine IL-18 binding protein. J Immunol 2003;170:2100–5.

[40] Joosten LAB, Radstake TRD, Lubberts E, et al. Association of interleukin-18 expression with enhanced levels of both interleukin-1β and tumor necrosis factor α in knee synovial tissue of patients with rheumatoid arthritis. Arthritis Rheum 2003;48:339–47.

[41] Alderson MR, Tough TW, Ziegler SF, et al. Interleukin 7 induces cytokine secretion and tumoricidal activity by human peripheral monocytes. J Exp Med 1991;173:923–30.

[42] Van Roon JAG, Glaudemans KAFM, Bijlsma WJW, et al. Interleukin 7 stimulates tumour necrosis factor α and Th1 cytokine production in joints of patients with rheumatoid arthritis. Ann Rheum Dis 2003;62:113–9.

[43] Fry TJ, Mackall CL. Interleukin-7: from bench to clinic. Blood 2002;99:3892–904.

[44] Aggareal S, Gurney AL. IL-17: prototype member of an emerging cytokine family. J Leukoc Biol 2002;71:1–8.

[45] Chabaud M, Durand JM, Buchs N, et al. Human interleukin-17. A T cell-derived proinflammatory cytokine produced by the rheumatoid synovium. Arthritis Rheum 1999;42:963–70.

[46] Jovanovic DV, Di Battista JA, Martel-Pelletier J, et al. IL-17 stimulates the production and expression of proinflammatory cytokines IL-1β and TNF-α by human macrophages. J Immunol 1998;160:3513–21.

[47] Chabaud M, Fossiez F, Taupin J-L, et al. Enhancing effect of IL-17 on IL-1-induced IL-6 and leukemia inhibitory factor production by rheumatoid arthritis synoviocytes and its regulation by Th2 cytokines. J Immunol 1998;161:409–14.

[48] Katz Y, Nadiv O, Beer Y. Interleukin-17 enhances tumor necrosis factor α-induced synthesis of interleukins 1, 6, and 8 in skin and synovial fibroblasts. Arthritis Rheum 2001;44:2176–84.

[49] Ziolkowska M, Koc A, Luszczykiewicz G, et al. High levels of IL-17 in rheumatoid arthritis patients: IL-15 triggers in vitro IL-17 production via cyclosporin A-sensitive mechanism. J Immunol 2000;164:2832–8.

[50] Jovanovic DV, Martel-Pelletier J, Di Battista JA, et al. Stimulation of 92-kd gelatinase (matrix metalloproteinase 9) production by interleukin-17 in human monocyte/macrophages. Arthritis Rheum 2000;43:1134–44.

[51] Chabaud M, Garnero P, Dayer J-M, et al. Contribution of interleukin 17 to synovium matrix destruction in rheumatoid arthritis. Cytokine 2000;12:1092–9.

[52] Dudler J, Rengli-Zulliger N, Busso N, et al. Effect of interleukin 17 on proteoglycan degradation in murine knee joints. Ann Rheum Dis 2000;59:529–32.

[53] Chabaud M, Aarvak T, Bernero P, et al. Potential contribution of IL-17-producing Th1 cells to defective repair activity in joint inflammation: partial correction with Th2-promoting conditions. Cytokine 2001;13:113–8.

[54] Chabaud M, Lubberts E, Joosten L, et al. IL-17 derived from juxta-articular bone and synovium contributes to joint degradation in rheumatoid arthritis. Arthritis Res 2001;3:168–77.

[55] van Bezooijen RL, van der Wee-pals L, Papapoulos SE, et al. Interleukin17 synergises with tumour necrosis factor α to induce cartilage destruction in vitro. Ann Rheum Dis 2002;61: 870–6.

[56] Honorati MC, Bovara M, Cattini L, et al. Contribution of interleukin 17 to human cartilage

degradation and synovial inflammation in osteoarthritis. Osteoarthritis Cartilage 2002;10: 799–807.

[57] Koshy PJ, Henderson N, Logan C, et al. Interleukin 17 induces cartilage collagen breakdown: novel synergistic effects in combination with proinflammatory cytokines. Ann Rheum Dis 2002;61:704–13.

[58] Kotake S, Udagawa N, Takahashi N, et al. IL-17 in synovial fluids from patients with rheumatoid arthritis is a potent stimulator of osteoclastogenesis. J Clin Invest 1999;103:1345–52.

[59] Lubberts E, van den Bersselaar L, Oppers-Walgreen B, et al. IL-17 promotes bone erosion in murine collagen-induced arthritis through loss of the receptor activator of NF-κB ligand/osteoprotegerin balance. J Immunol 2003;170:2655–62.

[60] Honorati MC, Meliconi R, Pulsatelli L, et al. High in vivo expression of interleukin-17 receptor in synovial endothelial cells and chondrocytes from arthritis patients. Rheumatol 2001;40: 522–7.

[61] Kehlen A, Thiele K, Riemann D, et al. Expression, modulation and signaling of IL-17 receptor in fibroblast-like synoviocytes of patients with rheumatoid arthritis. Clin Exp Immunol 2002; 127:539–46.

[62] Bush KA, Farmer KM, Walker JS, et al. Reduction of joint inflammation and bone erosion in rat adjuvant arthritis by treatment with interleukin-17 receptor IgG1 Fc fusion protein. Arthritis Rheum 2002;46:802–5.

[63] Ziff M. Role of the endothelium in chronic inflammatory synovitis. Arthritis Rheum 1991; 34:1345–52.

[64] Colville-Nash PR, Scott DL. Angiogenesis and rheumatoid arthritis: pathogenic and therapeutic implications. Ann Rheum Dis 1992;51:919–25.

[65] Szakanecz Z, Szegedi G, Koch AE. Angiogenesis in rheumatoid arthritis: pathogenic and clinical significance. J Invest Med 1998;46:27–41.

[66] Koch AE. Angiogenesis. Implications for rheumatoid arthritis. Arthritis Rheum 1998;41: 951–62.

[67] Walsh DA. Angiogenesis and arthritis. Rheumatol 1999;38:103–12.

[68] Brenchley PEC. Angiogenesis in inflammatory joint disease: a target for therapeutic intervention. Clin Exp Immunol 2000;121:426–9.

[69] Gravallese EM, Pettit AR, Lee R, et al. Angiopoietin-1 is expressed in the synovium of patients with rheumatoid arthritis and is induced by tumour necrosis factor α. Ann Rheum Dis 2003;62: 100–7.

[70] Pablos JL, Santiago B, Galindo M, et al. Synoviocyte-derived CXCL12 is displayed on endothelium and induces angiogenesis in rheumatoid arthritis. J Immunol 2003;170:2147–52.

[71] Peacock DJ, Banquerigo ML, Brahn E. Angiogenesis inhibition suppresses collagen arthritis. J Exp Med 1992;175:1135–8.

[72] Oppenheimer-Marks N, Lipsky P. Adhesion molecules as targets for the treatment of autoimmune diseases. Clin Immunol Immunopathol 1996;79:203–10.

[73] Mojcik CF, Shevach EM. Adhesion molecules. A rheumatologic perspective. Arthritis Rheum 1997;40:991–1004.

[74] Luster AD. Chemokines—chemotactic cytokines that mediate inflammation. N Engl J Med 1998;338:436–45.

[75] Storgard CM, Stupack DG, Jonczyk A, et al. Decreased angiogenesis and arthritic disease in rabbits treated with an αvβ3 antagonist. J Clin Invest 1999;103:47–54.

[76] Feldmann M, Maini RN. Anti-TNFα therapy of rheumatoid arthritis: what have we learned? Annu Rev Immunol 2001;19:163–96.

[77] Arend WP, Dayer J-M. Cytokines and cytokine inhibitors or antagonists in rheumatoid arthritis. Arthritis Rheum 1990;33:305–15.

[78] Arend WP, Dayer J-M. Inhibition of the production and effects of interleukin-1 and tumor necrosis factor α in rheumatoid arthritis. Arthritis Rheum 1995;38:151–60.

[79] Iwakura Y. Roles of IL-1 in the development of rheumatoid arthritis: consideration from mouse models. Cytokine Growth Factor Rev 2002;13:341–55.

[80] Morand EF, Bucala R, Leech M. Macrophage migration inhibitory factor. An emerging therapeutic target in rheumatoid arthritis. Arthritis Rheum 2003;48:291–9.

[81] Lacey D, Sampey A, Mitchell R, et al. Control of fibroblast-like synoviocyte proliferation by macrophage migration inhibitory factor. Arthritis Rheum 2003;48:103–9.

[82] Mikulowaska A, Meyz C, Bucala R, et al. Macrophage migration inhibitory factor is involved in the pathogenesis of collagen type II-induced arthritis in mice. J Immunol 1997;158:5514–7.

[83] Leech M, Metz C, Santos L, et al. Involvement of macrophage migration inhibitory factor in the evolution of rat adjuvant arthritis. Arthritis Rheum 1998;41:910–7.

[84] Santos L, Hall P, Metz C, et al. Role of macrophage migration inhibitory factor (MIF) in murine antigen-induced arthritis: interaction with glucocorticoids. Clin Exp Immunol 2001; 123:309–14.

[85] Miyazawa K, Mori A, Yamamoto K, et al. Constitutive transcription of the human interleukin-6 gene by rheumatoid synvoiocytes. Spontaneous activation of NF-κB and CBF1. Am J Pathol 1998;152:793–803.

[86] van de Loo FA, Kuiper S, van Enckevort FHJ, et al. Interleukin-6 reduces cartilage destruction during experimental arthritis. A study in interleukin-6-deficient mice. Am J Pathol 1997;151: 177–91.

[87] de Hooge ASK, van de Loo FAJ, Arntz OJ, et al. Involvement of IL-6, apart from its role in immunity, in mediating a chronic response during experimental arthritis. Am J Pathol 2000; 157:2081–91.

[88] Atsumi T, Ishihara K, Kamimura D, et al. A point mutation of Tyr-759 in interleukin 6 family cytokine receptor subunit gp130 causes autoimmune arthritis. J Exp Med 2002;196:979–90.

[89] Choy EHS, Isenberg DA, Garrood T, et al. Therapeutic benefit of blocking interleukin-6 activity with an anti-interleukin-6 receptor monoclonal antibody in rheumatoid arthritis. Arthritis Rheum 2002;46:3143–50.

[90] Khan MA. Update on spondyloarthropathies. Ann Intern Med 2002;136:896–907.

[91] Braun J, Bollow M, Neure L, et al. Use of immunohistologic and in situ hybridization techniques in the examination of sacroiliac joint biopsy specimens from patients with ankylosing spondylitis. Arthritis Rheum 1995;38:499–505.

[92] Braun J, Sieper J. Therapy of ankylosing spondylitis and other spondyloarthritides: established medical treatment, anti-TNF-α therapy and other novel approaches. Arthritis Res 2002;4: 307–21.

[93] Brandt J, Haibel H, Cornely D, et al. Successful treatment of active ankylosing spondylitis with the anti-tumor necrosis factor α monoclonal antibody infliximab. Arthritis Rheum 2000;43: 1346–52.

[94] Braun J, Brandt J, Listing J, et al. Treatment of active ankylosing spondylitis with infliximab: a randomized controlled multicentre trial. Lancet 2002;359:1187–93.

[95] Gorman JD, Sack KE, Davis Jr JC. Treatment of ankylosing spondylitis by inhibition of tumor necrosis factor α. N Engl J Med 2002;346:1349–56.

[96] Mease PJ, Goffe BS, Metz J, et al. Etanercept in the treatment of psoriatic arthritis and psoriasis: a randomised trial. Lancet 2000;356:385–90.

[97] Woo P. Cytokines and juvenile idiopathic arthritis. Curr Rheumatol Rep 2002;4:452–7.

[98] Kawashima M, Yamamura M, Taniai M, et al. Levels of interleukin-18 and its binding inhibitors in the blood circulation of patients with adult-onset Still's disease. Arthritis Rheum 2001; 44:550–60.

[99] Lovell DJ, Giannini EH, Reiff A, et al. Etanercept in children with polyarticular juvenile rheumatoid arthritis. N Engl J Med 2000;342:763–9.

[100] Westacott CI, Sharif M. Cytokines in osteoarthritis: mediators or markers of joint destruction. Semin Arthritis Rheum 1996;25:254–72.

[101] Dean GS, Tyrrell-Price J, Crawley E, et al. Cytokines and systemic lupus erythematosus. Ann Rheum Dis 2000;59:243–51.

[102] Pasparakis M, Alexopoulou L, Episkopou V, et al. Immune and inflammatory responses in TNF alpha-deficient mice: a critical requirement for TNF alpha in the formation of primary B cell

follicles, follicular dendritic cell networks and germinal centers, and in the maturation of the humoral immune response. J Exp Med 1996;184:1397–411.

[103] Le Hir M, Bluethmann H, Kosco-Vilbois MH, et al. Differentiation of follicular dendritic cells and full antibody responses require tumor necrosis factor receptor-1 signaling. J Exp Med 1996; 183:2367–72.

[104] Ranges GE, Zlotnik A, Espevik T, et al. Tumor necrosis factor alpha/cachectin is a growth factor for thymocytes. Synergistic interactions with other cytokines. J Exp Med 1988;167: 1472–8.

[105] Banchereau J, Steinman RM. Dendritic cells and the control of immunity. Nature 1998;392: 245–52.

[106] Cope AP, Liblau RS, Yang XD, et al. Chronic tumor necrosis factor alters T cell responses by attenuating T cell receptor signaling. J Exp Med 1997;185:1573–84.

[107] Zheng L, Fisher G, Miller RE, et al. Induction of apoptosis in mature T cells by tumour necrosis factor. Nature 1995;377:348–51.

[108] Speiser DE, Sebzda E, Ohteki T, et al. Tumor necrosis factor receptor p55 mediates deletion of peripheral cytotoxic T lymphocytes in vivo. Eur J Immunol 1996;26:3055–60.

[109] Jacob CO, McDevitt HO. Tumour necrosis factor-alpha in murine autoimmune 'lupus' nephritis. Nature 1998;331:356–8.

[110] Kontoyiannis D, Kollias G. Accelerated autoimmunity and lupus nephritis in NZB mice with an engineered heterozygous deficiency in tumor necrosis factor. Eur J Immunol 2000;30: 2038–47.

[111] Kassiotis G, Kollias G. Uncoupling the proinflammatory from the immunosuppressive properties of tumor necrosis factor (TNF) at the p55 TNF receptor level: implications for pathogenesis and therapy of autoimmune demyelination. J Exp Med 2000;193:427–34.

[112] Jacob CO, Fronek Z, Lewis GD, et al. Heritable major histocompatibility complex class II-associated differences in production of tumor necrosis factor alpha: relevance to genetic predisposition to systemic lupus erythematosus. Proc Natl Acad Sci USA 1990;87:1233–7.

[113] Gabay C, Cakir N, Moral F, et al. Circulating levels of tumor necrosis factor soluble receptors in systemic lupus erythematosus are significantly higher than in other rheumatic diseases and correlate with disease activity. J Rheumatol 1997;24:303–8.

[114] Shakoor N, Michalska M, Harris CA, et al. Drug-induced systemic lupus erythematosus associated with etanercept therapy. Lancet 2002;359:579–80.

[115] Robinson WH, Genovese MC, Moreland LW. Demyelinating and neurologic events reported in association with tumor necrosis factor alpha antagonism: by what mechanisms could tumor necrosis factor alpha antagonists improve rheumatoid arthritis but exacerbate multiple sclerosis? Arthritis Rheum 2001;44:1977–83.

[116] Drappa J, Brot N, Elkon KB. The Fas protein is expressed at high levels on CD4[+]CD8[+] thymocytes and activated mature lymphocytes in normal mice but not in the lupus-prone strain, MRL lpr/lpr. Proc Natl Acad Sci USA 1993;90:10340–4.

[117] Takahashi T, Tanaka M, Brannan CI, et al. Generalized lymphoproliferative disease in mice, caused by a point mutation in the Fas ligand. Cell 1994;76:969–76.

[118] Zhou T, Edwards III CK, Yang P, et al. Greatly accelerated lymphadenopathy and autoimmune disease in lpr mice lacking tumor necrosis factor receptor I. J Immunol 1996;156:2661–5.

[119] Gura T. How TRAIL kills cancer cells, but not normal cells. Science 1997;277:768.

[120] Baetu TM, Hiscott J. On the TRAIL to apoptosis. Cytokine Growth Factor Rev 2002;13: 199–207.

[121] Chicheportiche Y, Bourdon PR, Xu H, et al. TWEAK, a new secreted ligand in the tumor necrosis factor family that weakly induces apoptosis. J Biol Chem 1997;272:32401–10.

[122] Kaplan MJ, Lewis EE, Shelden EA, et al. The apoptotic ligands TRAIL, TWEAK, and Fas ligand mediate monocyte death induced by autologous lupus T cells. J Immunol 2000;169: 6020–9.

[123] Zhou T, Mountz JD, Kimberly RP. Immunobiology of tumor necrosis factor receptor superfamily. Immunol Res 2002;26:323–36.

[124] Wu J, Wilson J, He J, et al. Fas ligand mutation in a patient with systemic lupus erythematosus and lymphoproliferative disease. J Clin Invest 1996;98:1107–13.

[125] Drappa J, Vaishnaw AK, Sullivan KE, et al. Fas gene mutations in the Canale-Smith syndrome, an inherited lymphoproliferative disorder associated with autoimmunity. N Engl J Med 1996; 335:1643–9.

[126] Sneller MC, Wang J, Dale JK, et al. Clinical, immunologic, and genetic features of an auto-immune lymphoproliferative syndrome associated with abnormal lymphocyte apoptosis. Blood 1997;89:1341–8.

[127] Gabay C, Kushner I. Acute-phase proteins and other systemic responses to inflammation. N Engl J Med 1997;340:448–54.

[128] Bickerstaff MC, Botto M, Hutchinson WL, et al. Serum amyloid P component controls chromatin degradation and prevents antinuclear autoimmunity. Nat Med 1995;5:694–7.

[129] Swissa M, Schul V, Korish S, et al. Determination of autoantibodies in patients with familial Mediterranean fever and their first degree relatives. J Rheumatol 1991;18:606–8.

[130] Reiser H, Stadecker MJ. Costimulatory B7 molecules in the pathogenesis of infectious and autoimmune diseases. N Engl J Med 1996;335:1369–77.

[131] Lindhout E, Koopman G, Pals ST, et al. Triple check for antigen specificity of B cells during germinal centre reactions. Immunol Today 1997;18:573–7.

[132] Tarlinton D. Germinal centers: form and function. Curr Opin Immunol 1998;10:245–51.

[133] Mohan C, Shi Y, Laman JD, et al. Interaction between CD40 and its ligand gp39 in the development of murine lupus nephritis. J Immunol 1995;154:1470–80.

[134] Kalled SL, Cutler AH, Datta SK, et al. Anti-CD40 ligand antibody treatment of SNF1 mice with established nephritis: preservation of kidney function. J Immunol 1998;160:2158–65.

[135] Boumpas DT, Furie RA, Manzi S, et al. A short course of BG9588 (anti-CD40L antibody) improves serologic activity and decreases hematuria in patients with proliferative lupus glomerulonephritis. Arthritis Rheum 2001;44:S387.

[136] Kalunian KC, Davis Jr JC, Merrill JT, et al. Treatment of systemic lupus erythematosus by inhibition of T cell costimulation with anti-CD154: a randomized, double-blind, placebo-controlled trial. Arthritis Rheum 2002;46:3251–8.

[137] Mackay F, Schneider P, Rennert P, et al. BAFF and APRIL: a tutorial on B cell survival. Annu Rev Immunol 2003;21:231–64.

[138] Mackay F, Browning JL. BAFF: a fundamental survival factor for B cells. Nat Rev Immunol 2002;2:465–75.

[139] Schneider P, MacKay F, Steiner V, et al. BAFF, a novel ligand of the tumor necrosis factor family, stimulates B cell growth. J Exp Med 1999;189:1747–56.

[140] Nardelli B, Belvedere O, Roschke V, et al. Synthesis and release of B-lymphocyte stimulator from myeloid cells. Blood 2001;97:198–204.

[141] Groom J, Kalled SL, Cutler AH, et al. Association of BAFF/BLyS overexpression and altered B cell differentiation with Sjogren's syndrome. J Clin Invest 2002;109:59–68.

[142] Gross JA, Johnston J, Mudri S, et al. TACI and BCMA are receptors for a TNF homologue implicated in B-cell autoimmune disease. Nature 2000;404:995–9.

[143] Roschke V, Sosnovtseva S, Ward CD, et al. BLyS and APRIL form biologically active heterotrimers that are expressed in patients with systemic immune-based rheumatic diseases. J Immunol 2002;169:4314–21.

[144] Kiberd BA. Interleukin-6 receptor blockage ameliorates murine lupus nephritis. J Am Soc Nephrol 1993;4:58–61.

[145] Schorlemmer HU, Dickneite G, Kanzy EJ, et al. Modulation of the immunoglobulin dysregulation in GvH- and SLE-like diseases by the murine IL-4 receptor (IL-4-R). Inflamm Res 1995; 2(Suppl 4):S194–6.

[146] Kono DH, Balomenos D, Park MS, et al. Development of lupus in BXSB mice is independent of IL-4. J Immunol 2000;164:38–42.

[147] Erb KJ, Ruger B, von Brevern M, et al. Constitutive expression of interleukin (IL)-4 in vivo causes autoimmune-type disorders in mice. J Exp Med 1997;185:329–39.

[148] Santiago ML, Fossati L, Jacquet C, et al. Interleukin-4 protects against a genetically linked lupus-like autoimmune syndrome. J Exp Med 1997;185:65–70.

[149] Park YB, Lee SK, Kim DS, et al. Elevated interleukin-10 levels correlated with disease activity in systemic lupus erythematosus. Clin Exp Rheumatol 1998;16:283–8.

[150] Grondal G, Gunnarsson I, Ronnelid J, et al. Cytokine production, serum levels and disease activity in systemic lupus erythematosus. Clin Exp Rheumatol 2000;18:565–70.

[151] Llorente L, Zou W, Levy Y, et al. Role of interleukin 10 in the B lymphocyte hyperactivity and autoantibody production of human systemic lupus erythematosus. J Exp Med 1995;181: 839–44.

[152] Ronnelid J, Tejde A, Mathsson L, et al. Immune complexes from SLE sera induce IL10 production from normal peripheral blood mononuclear cells by an FcgammaRII dependent mechanism: implications for a possible vicious cycle maintaining B cell hyperactivity in SLE. Ann Rheum Dis 2003;62:37–42.

[153] Ishida H, Muchamuel T, Sakaguchi S, et al. Continuous administration of anti-interleukin 10 antibodies delays onset of autoimmunity in NZB/W F1 mice. J Exp Med 1994;179:305–10.

[154] Llorente L, Richaud-Patin Y, Garcia-Padilla C, et al. Clinical and biologic effects of anti-interleukin-10 monoclonal antibody administration in systemic lupus erythematosus. Arthritis Rheum 2000;43:1790–800.

[155] Amerio P, Frezzolini A, Abeni D, et al. Increased IL-18 in patients with systemic lupus erythematosus: relations with Th-1, Th-2, pro-inflammatory cytokines and disease activity. IL-18 is a marker of disease activity but does not correlate with pro-inflammatory cytokines. Clin Exp Rheumatol 2002;20:535–8.

[156] Akahoshi M, Nakashima H, Tanaka Y, et al. Th1/Th2 balance of peripheral T helper cells in systemic lupus erythematosus. Arthritis Rheum 1999;42:1644–8.

[157] Jacob CO, van der Meide PH, McDevitt HO. In vivo treatment of (NZB X NZW)F1 lupus-like nephritis with monoclonal antibody to gamma interferon. J Exp Med 1987;166:798–803.

[158] Balomenos D, Rumold R, Theofilopoulos AN. Interferon-gamma is required for lupus-like disease and lymphoaccumulation in MRL-lpr mice. J Clin Invest 1998;101:364–71.

[159] Haas C, Ryffel B, Le Hir M. IFN-gamma receptor deletion prevents autoantibody production and glomerulonephritis in lupus-prone (NZB × NZW)F1 mice. J Immunol 1998;160:3713–8.

[160] Schwarting A, Wada T, Kinoshita K, et al. IFN-gamma receptor signaling is essential for the initiation, acceleration, and destruction of autoimmune kidney disease in MRL-Fas(lpr) mice. J Immunol 1998;161:494–503.

[161] Herrera-Esparza R, Barbosa-Cisneros O, Villalobos-Hurtado R, et al. Renal expression of IL-6 and TNFalpha genes in lupus nephritis. Lupus 1998;7:154–8.

[162] Aringer M, Zimmermann C, Graninger WB, et al. TNF-alpha is an essential mediator in lupus nephritis. Arthritis Rheum 2002;46:LB08.

[163] Iwata Y, Wada T, Furuichi K, et al. p38 mitogen-activated protein kinase contributes to auto-immune renal injury in MRL-Fas(lpr) mice. J Am Soc Nephrol 2003;14:57–67.

[164] Kahari VM, Sandberg M, Kalimo H, et al. Identification of fibroblasts responsible for increased collagen production in localized scleroderma by in situ hybridization. J Invest Dermatol 1998; 90:664–70.

[165] Scharffetter K, Lankat-Buttgereit B, Krieg T, et al. Localization of collagen mRNA in normal and scleroderma skin by in-situ hybridization. Eur J Clin Invest 1988;18:9–17.

[166] Varga J. Scleroderma and Smads: dysfunctional Smad family dynamics culminating in fibrosis. Arthritis Rheum 2002;46:1703–13.

[167] Takeda K, Hatamochi A, Ueki H, et al. Decreased collagenase expression in cultured systemic sclerosis fibroblasts. J Invest Dermatol 1994;103:359–63.

[168] Kawaguchi Y, Hara M, Kamatani N, et al. Identification of an IL1A gene segment that determines aberrant constitutive expression of interleukin-1 alpha in systemic sclerosis. Arthritis Rheum 2003;48:193–202.

[169] Kawaguchi Y, Hara M, Wright TM. Endogenous IL-1alpha from systemic sclerosis fibroblasts induces IL-6 and PDGF-A. J Clin Invest 1999;103:1253–60.

[170] Valentini G, Baroni A, Esposito K, et al. Peripheral blood T lymphocytes from systemic sclerosis patients show both Th1 and Th2 activation. J Clin Immunol 2001;21:210–7.

[171] Sato S, Hanakawa H, Hasegawa M, et al. Levels of interleukin 12, a cytokine of type 1 helper T cells, are elevated in sera from patients with systemic sclerosis. J Rheumatol 2000;27: 2838–42.

[172] Tsuji-Yamada J, Nakazawa M, Minami M, et al. Increased frequency of interleukin 4 producing CD4+ and CD8+ cells in peripheral blood from patients with systemic sclerosis. J Rheumatol 2001;28:1252–8.

[173] Lee KS, Ro YJ, Ryoo YW, et al. Regulation of interleukin-4 on collagen gene expression by systemic sclerosis fibroblasts in culture. J Dermatol Sci 1996;12:110–7.

[174] Kurasawa K, Hirose K, Sano H, et al. Increased interleukin-17 production in patients with systemic sclerosis. Arthritis Rheum 2000;43:2455–63.

[175] Denton CP, Abraham DJ. Transforming growth factor-beta and connective tissue growth factor: key cytokines in scleroderma pathogenesis. Curr Opin Rheumatol 2001;13:505–11.

[176] Sato S, Nagaoka T, Hasegawa M, et al. Serum levels of connective tissue growth factor are elevated in patients with systemic sclerosis: association with extent of skin sclerosis and severity of pulmonary fibrosis. J Rheumatol 2000;27:149–54.

[177] McCormick LL, Zhang Y, Tootell E, et al. Anti-TGF-beta treatment prevents skin and lung fibrosis in murine sclerodermatous graft-versus-host disease: a model for human scleroderma. J Immunol 1999;163:5693–9.

[178] Wang Q, Wang Y, Hyde DM, et al. Reduction of bleomycin induced lung fibrosis by trans-forming growth factor beta soluble receptor in hamsters. Thorax 1999;54:805–12.

[179] Nakao A, Fujii M, Matsumura R, et al. Transient gene transfer and expression of Smad7 prevents bleomycin-induced lung fibrosis in mice. J Clin Invest 1999;104:5–11.

[180] Lundberg IE, Nyberg P. New developments in the role of cytokines and chemokines in inflam-matory myopathies. Curr Opin Rheumatol 1998;10:521–9.

[181] Lundberg I, Ulfgren AK, Nyberg P, et al. Cytokine production in muscle tissue of patients with idiopathic inflammatory myopathies. Arthritis Rheum 1997;40:865–74.

[182] Adams EM, Kirkley J, Eidelman G, et al. The predominance of beta (CC) chemokine transcripts in idiopathic inflammatory muscle diseases. Proc Assoc Am Physicians 1997;109:275–85.

[183] De Bleecker JL, De Paepe B, Vanwalleghem IE, et al. Differential expression of chemokines in inflammatory myopathies. Neurology 2002;58:1779–85.

[184] Fang CH, Li BG, James JH, et al. Cytokines block the effects of insulin-like growth factor-I (IGF-I) on glucose uptake and lactate production in skeletal muscle but do not influence IGF-I-induced changes in protein turnover. Shock 1997;8:362–7.

[185] Lundberg I, Kratz AK, Alexanderson H, et al. Decreased expression of interleukin-1alpha, interleukin-1beta, and cell adhesion molecules in muscle tissue following corticosteroid treat-ment in patients with polymyositis and dermatomyositis. Arthritis Rheum 2000;43:336–48.

[186] Amemiya K, Semino-Mora C, Granger RP, et al. Downregulation of TGF-beta1 mRNA and protein in the muscles of patients with inflammatory myopathies after treatment with high-dose intravenous immunoglobulin. Clin Immunol 2000;94:99–104.

[187] Confalonieri P, Bernasconi P, Cornelio F, et al. Transforming growth factor-beta 1 in poly-myositis and dermatomyositis correlates with fibrosis but not with mononuclear cell infiltrate. J Neuropathol Exp Neurol 1997;56:479–84.

[188] Suzuki J, Morimoto S, Amano H, et al. Serum levels of interleukin 15 in patients with rheumatic diseases. J Rheumatol 2000;28:2389–91.

[189] Sugiura T, Harigai M, Kawaguchi Y, et al. Increased IL-15 production of muscle cells in polymyositis and dermatomyositis. Int Immunol 2002;14:917–24.

[190] Sugiura T, Kawaguchi Y, Harigai M, et al. Increased CD40 expression on muscle cells of polymyositis and dermatomyositis: role of CD40–CD40 ligand interaction in IL-6, IL-8, IL-15, and monocyte chemoattractant protein-1 production. J Immunol 2000;164:6593–600.

[191] Weyand CM, Hicok KC, Hunder GG, et al. Tissue cytokine patterns in patients with poly-myalgia rheumatica and giant cell arteritis. Ann Intern Med 1994;121:484–91.

[192] Wagner AD, Bjornsson J, Bartley GB, et al. Interferon-gamma-producing T cells in giant cell vasculitis represent a minority of tissue-infiltrating cells and are located distant from the site of pathology. Am J Pathol 1996;148:1925–33.

[193] Weyand CM, Goronzy JJ. Pathogenic principles in giant cell arteritis. Int J Cardiol 2000; 75(Suppl 1):S9–15 [discussion S17–9].

[194] Weyand CM, Tetzlaff N, Bjornsson J, et al. Disease patterns and tissue cytokine profiles in giant cell arteritis. Arthritis Rheum 1997;40:19–26.

[195] Wagner AD, Goronzy JJ, Weyand CM. Functional profile of tissue-infiltrating and circulating CD68$^+$ cells in giant cell arteritis. Evidence for two components of the disease. J Clin Invest 1994;94:1134–40.

[196] Weyand CM, Wagner AD, Bjornsson J, et al. Correlation of the topographical arrangement and the functional pattern of tissue-infiltrating macrophages in giant cell arteritis. J Clin Invest 1996;98:1642–9.

[197] Kaiser M, Weyand CM, Bjornsson J, et al. Platelet-derived growth factor, intimal hyperplasia, and ischemic complications in giant cell arteritis. Arthritis Rheum 1998;41:623–33.

[198] Kaiser M, Younge B, Bjornsson J, et al. Formation of new vasa vasorum in vasculitis. Production of angiogenic cytokines by multinucleated giant cells. Am J Pathol 1999;155:765–74.

[199] Roche NE, Fulbright JW, Wagner AD, et al. Correlation of interleukin-6 production and disease activity in polymyalgia rheumatica and giant cell arteritis. Arthritis Rheum 1993;36:1286–94.

[200] Weyand CM, Fulbright JW, Hunder GG, et al. Treatment of giant cell arteritis: interleukin-6 as a biologic marker of disease activity. Arthritis Rheum 2000;43:1041–8.

[201] Lamprecht P, Moosig F, Csernok E, et al. CD28 negative T cells are enriched in granulomatous lesions of the respiratory tract in Wegener's granulomatosis. Thorax 2001;56:751–7.

[202] Komocsi A, Lamprecht P, Csernok E, et al. Peripheral blood and granuloma CD4($^+$)CD28($^-$) T cells are a major source of interferon-gamma and tumor necrosis factor-alpha in Wegener's granulomatosis. Am J Pathol 2002;160:1717–24.

[203] Lamprecht P, Kumanovics G, Mueller A, et al. Elevated monocytic IL-12 and TNF-alpha production in Wegener's granulomatosis is normalized by cyclophosphamide and corticosteroid therapy. Clin Exp Immunol 2002;128:181–6.

[204] Lamprecht P, Voswinkel J, Lilienthal T, et al. Effectiveness of TNF-alpha blockade with infliximab in refractory Wegener's granulomatosis. Rheumatol 2002;41:1303–7.

[205] Itoh R, Takenaka T, Okitsu-Negishi S, et al. Interleukin 8 in Behcet's disease. J Dermatol 1994; 21:397–404.

[206] Mege JL, Dilsen N, Sanguedolce V, et al. Overproduction of monocyte derived tumor necrosis factor alpha, interleukin (IL) 6, IL-8 and increased neutrophil superoxide generation in Behcet's disease. A comparative study with familial Mediterranean fever and healthy subjects. J Rheumatol 1993;20:1544–9.

[207] Zouboulis CC, Katsantonis J, Ketteler R, et al. Adamantiades Behcet's disease: interleukin-8 is increased in serum of patients with active oral and neurological manifestations and is secreted by small vessel endothelial cells. Arch Dermatol Res 2000;292:279–84.

[208] Hamzaoui K, Hamzaoui A, Guemira F, et al. Cytokine profile in Behcet's disease patients. Relationship with disease activity. Scand J Rheumatol 2002;31:205–10.

[209] Sfikakis PP. Behcet's disease: a new target for anti-tumour necrosis factor treatment. Ann Rheum Dis 2002;61(Suppl 2):51–3.

ELSEVIER
SAUNDERS

RHEUMATIC
DISEASE CLINICS
OF NORTH AMERICA

Rheum Dis Clin N Am 30 (2004) 69–95

Novel endogenous small molecules as the checkpoint controllers in inflammation and resolution: entrée for resoleomics

Charles N. Serhan, PhD*, Nan Chiang, PhD

The Center for Experimental Therapeutics and Reperfusion Injury, Department of Anesthesiology, Perioperative and Pain Medicine, Brigham and Women's Hospital, Harvard Medical School, 75 Francis Street, Boston, MA 02115, USA

Resolution of an acute inflammatory response was, until recently, believed to rely solely on the dissipation or "burning out" of the initiating exogenous stimuli or signals [1]. Results from many experimental systems now point to the mounting of the resolution phase as activation of a well-orchestrated series of temporal events that is initiated by novel host mechanisms. Studies in our laboratory have focused on the identification and structural elucidation of endogenous autacoids that are involved in anti-inflammation and led to the recognition that specific cellular and biochemical circuits have evolved to activate resolution (reviewed in [2]). These, in some cases, novel molecules and "stop signaling" pathways were recently referred to as checkpoint controllers in inflammation (reviewed in [3]). The mapping of these resolution circuits by way of lipidomics and cellular and molecular approaches provides the informatic basis for resolution circuits from molecular autacoid to gene and back; hence entrée for resoleomics[1]. This article reviews recent findings from the authors' laboratory and others that are currently involved in the identification of endogenous mediators of anti-inflammation and promoters of resolution.

Acute inflammation in healthy individuals is normally a localized protective mechanism in response to microbial invasion, trauma/injury, or chemical stimuli. Excessive and prolonged inflammatory responses may lead to diverse disorders that underlie the pathogenesis of some of the most prevalent diseases, such as rheumatic diseases, diabetes, Alzheimer's disease, reperfusion injury, and athero-

This work was supported in part by National Institutes of Health grant no. GM38765.

* Corresponding author.

E-mail address: cnserhan@zeus.bwh.harvard.edu (C.N. Serhan).

[1] Resoleomics is the systematic analysis of the resolution phase in inflammation using combined proteomics, lipidomics, and genomics to establish the temporal relationship of the key components to homeostasis.

sclerosis. The accumulation and activation of leukocytes are central in most of the inflammatory disorders. It is now clear that a diverse range of endogenous chemical mediators control these events and orchestrate the host response (reviewed in [3]). These small chemical signals regulate leukocyte traffic as well as the cardinal signs of inflammation—heat, redness, swelling, pain, and loss of function. It is well-established that the classic eicosanoids, such as prostaglandins (PGs) and leukotrienes (LTs), play important roles as local mediators and exert a wide range of actions in responses of interest in inflammation [4]. In recent years, the scope and range of chemical mediators that have been identified has expanded considerably (reviewed in [3]). These include novel lipid mediators, many new cytokines (eg, interleukin [IL]-10, transforming growth factor-β), gases (eg, nitric oxide, carbon monoxide), as well as new roles for nucleosides, nucleotides, and polyisoprenyl phosphates (Table 1). The identification of these novel endogenous small molecules opens many new levels for checkpoint controls as well as novel signaling mechanism in inflammation-resolution and the potential to exploit them in therapeutics.

A body of new evidence demonstrates that endogenous mediators are generated and actively participate in dampening host responses to orchestrate resolution

Table 1
Novel endogenous small molecules in check-point controls of inflammation

Class	Molecule	Action
Lipid	Lipoxins (A_4 and B_4)	Anti-inflammation and proresolution (see Tables 2, 3, and 4)
	Aspirin-triggered lipoxins (A_4 and B_4)	Anti-inflammation and proresolution (see Tables 2, 3, and 4)
	Resolvins E (18R-series)	Stop human PMN transendothelial migration and infiltration in vivo [5]
	Resolvins D (17-series)	Block microglial cell cytokine expression and PMN infiltration in dermal inflammation and peritonitis [6]
	Presqualene diphosphate	Inhibits recombinant PLD and superoxide anion generation [7,8]
Nucleotide	IMP	Downregulates neutrophil recruitment in reperfusion injury [9]
	Inosine	Reduces inflammation in colitis and acute lung injury [10] Inhibits inflammatory cytokine production [11]
	Adenosine	Inhibits AA release and LT synthesis in vitro [12] Regulates inflammation and tissue damage in vivo [13,14]
Protein (small peptides)	Annexin-derived peptides (Ac2–26)	Inhibit PMN activation, transmigration, and phagocytic functions in vitro and in vivo [15]

Abbreviations: AA, arachidonic acid; IMP, inosine monophosphate; PLD, phopholipase D; PMN, polymorphonuclear leukocytes.

(reviewed in [2,3]). In this context, the lipoxins (LXs) and aspirin-triggered LXs (ATLs) were the first to be recognized as endogenous anti-inflammatory lipid mediators that are relevant in resolution because hey can function as "braking signals" or chalones in inflammation (Fig. 1) [16]. Aspirin (ASA), the widely used nonsteroidal anti-inflammatory drug with many beneficial properties [17], in addition to its well-appreciated ability to inhibit PG [18], also acetylates cyclo-oxygenase-2 (COX-2) and triggers the formation of 15-epimeric LXs, ATLs [19]. As a new class of compounds, LXs, ATLs, and their stable analogs possess physiologic, pathophysiologic, and pharmacologic actions in several target tissues [20,21]. More recently, we found that ASA-acetylated COX-2 also produces an array of novel local autacoids from omega-3 polyunsaturated fatty acid (PUFA) [5,6]. Some of these new compounds display potent anti-inflammatory and pro-resolving actions, and, thus, were termed "resolvins" (see Fig. 1). These pre-viously unappreciated mechanisms have intriguing implications for targeting drug design specifically toward resolution as a novel means to control inflammation.

Nucleosides function as signaling molecules and can regulate polymorpho-nuclear leukocytes (PMNs) in inflammation. Adenosine, for example, suppresses leukotriene biosynthesis in neutrophils and regulates the severity of inflammation that is associated with reperfusion injury and certain infectious agents [12,13,22]. Also, adenosine can protect tissues from ischemic damage and displays chemo-protective properties [12]. We recently found that inosine monophosphate inhibited cytokine-initiated neutrophil infiltration in vivo and selectively attenu-ated neutrophil rolling by 90% in microvessels. These results bring forth a

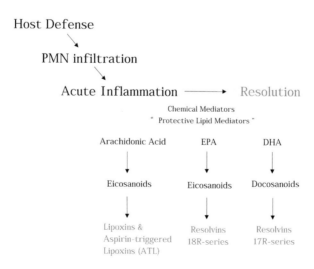

Fig. 1. Overview of endogenous lipid mediators on anti-inflammation and resolution. During cell-cell interactions, lipid-derived mediators (eg, PG, LT) can be amplified to enhance the actions of signal molecules or braking signals (eg, LX, ATL, resolvins) that can be generated by way of cell-cell interactions to limit further PMN recruitment and promote resolution. DHA, docosahexaenoic acid; EPA, eicosapentaenoic acid.

previously unrecognized mechanism that may protect tissues from the potentially deleterious consequences of aberrant neutrophil accumulation [9]. Moreover, the most recently uncovered of this class, inosine [10,11] also inhibits inflammatory cytokine production in vitro and regulates neutrophil (PMN) trafficking in murine models of acute lung injury and colitis (see Table 1). Together, these selective nucleotides and nucleosides can function as "negative checkpoint regulators" for limiting inflammatory responses.

Traditional approaches to anti-inflammatory drug development relied heavily on the use of inhibitors of biosynthesis pathways and receptor antagonists of "pro-inflammatory mediators." These drugs are, however, not without significant unwanted side effects. Therefore, a more comprehensive understanding of the endogenous pathways and cellular mechanisms that counterregulate inflammatory responses and govern the natural resolution phase is needed to uncover the unappreciated sides of human biology and pathogenesis of human disease. Here, we provide an overview and updates of the actions of LXs and their association with human disease as well as on the actions of recently uncovered omega-3 derived lipid signals, resolvins. These pathways and compounds represent new opportunities to explore therapeutic approaches for the design of "resolution-targeted" therapeutics that may reduce unwanted side effects and control, with a high degree of precision, inflammatory responses.

Cell-cell interaction theme in formation of bioactive autacoids

Transcellular biosynthesis of lipoxins

Formation of LXs are promoted during platelet-leukocyte interactions by transcellular conversion of the leukocyte 5-lipoxygenase (LO) product, leukotriene A_4 (LTA_4) (Fig. 2). When platelets are adherent, their 12-LO converts LTA_4 to lipoxin A_4 and B_4. For a review and mechanistic details with recombinant 12-LO, see reference [23]. Human platelets do not produce LX on their own, but become a major source of LX when they adhere to PMN. The second classical pathway for LX production is initiated by 15-LO (see Fig. 2) in airway epithelial cells, monocytes, or eosinophils which upregulate their 15-LO when exposed to cytokines, such as IL-4 or IL-13 (reviewed in [19]). The 15-LO, by definition, inserts molecular oxygen at the carbon 15 position of, for example, arachidonic acid, in the "S" configuration. When these cell types are activated, they generate and release 15S-hydroxy eicosatetraenoic acid (HETE), which is rapidly taken up and converted by PMN to LX by way of the action of their 5-LO. This event leads to LX biosynthesis and reduces LT formation.

Eicosanoid class switching during acute focal inflammation: a matter of timing

Recent evidence obtained with clinical and experimental exudates revealed the early coordinate appearance of LT and PG coincident with PMN infiltration to

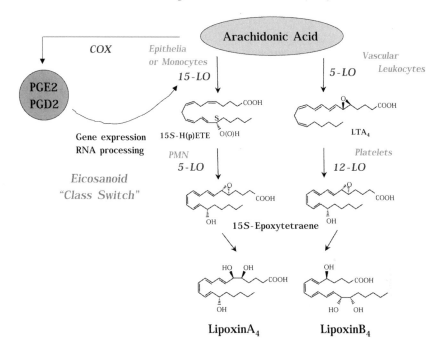

Fig. 2. Eicosanoid class switch: lipoxin formation by way of transcellular biosynthesis. During cell-cell interactions, lipoxins can be amplified by transcellular biosynthesis by way of the interactions of two or more cell types. Two main pathways seem to be used in human cells and tissues to generate LX. PGE_2 triggers eicosanoid class switch by regulating 15-LO. This event also blocks LT formation, and, therefore, regulates leukocytes. HETE, hydroxy eicosatetraenoic acid; PGD_2, prostaglandin D_2.

site of inflammation. This was followed by LX biosynthesis, which was concurrent with spontaneous resolution [24]. Human peripheral blood PMN that was exposed to PGE_2 (as in exudates) switched eicosanoid biosynthesis from predominantly LTB_4 and 5-lipoxygenase-initiated pathways to LXA_4, a 15-lipoxygenase product that "stops" PMN infiltration (see Fig. 2). In addition, PGE_2 initiates 15-LO gene expression and RNA processing in vitro in a temporal frame that is consistent with the "switching on" of lipoxin production in vivo. These results indicate that functionally distinct lipid mediator profiles switch during acute exudate formation to "reprogram" the exudate PMN to promote resolution. Also inhibition of PG products might alter the duration of resolution.

Novel mechanism of action for an old drug: aspirin-triggered lipid mediators

Aspirin-triggered 15–epi-lipoxins by way of acetylated cyclooxygenase-2

Inhibition of cyclooxygenase and biosynthesis of prostaglandins account for many of ASA's therapeutic properties [25]. Its ability to regulate neutrophil-mediated inflammation or cell proliferation remains a topic of interest and debate,

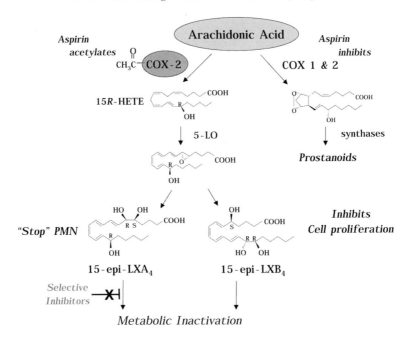

Fig. 3. Generation of ATL mediators, 15-epi-LXs, when COX-2 is upregulated and acetylated by ASA. Irreversible acetylation of COX-2 by aspirin changes the enzyme's product from prostaglandin intermediate to precursors of ATL. The acetylated COX-2 remains catalytically active to generate 15R-HETE.

however. We uncovered a new action of ASA that involves COX-2–bearing cells, such as vascular endothelial cells or epithelial cells, and their coactivation with PMN (Fig. 3). Hence, inflammatory stimuli (eg, tumor necrosis factor [TNF]-α, lipopolysaccharide) induce COX-2 to generate 15R-HETE when ASA is administered [19]. This intermediate carries a carbon-15 alcohol in the "R" configuration that is converted rapidly by 5-LO in activated PMN to 15 epimeric-LX or ATLs that carry their 15 position alcohol in the "R" configuration (reviewed in [23]), rather than 15S native LX. This is likely to provide alternate explanations for ASA's therapeutic actions; many beneficial new actions were documented in recent clinical studies, including decreasing incidence of lung, colon, and breast cancer (reviewed in [26]) and prevention of cardiovascular diseases.

LXB$_4$ is a positional isomer of LXA$_4$ (see Fig. 2), that carries alcohol groups at carbon 5S, 14R, and 15S positions, instead of the carbon 5S, 6R, and 15S positions as in LXA$_4$. ASA-triggered LXB$_4$ carries a 15R alcohol, hence 15–epi-LXB$_4$ (see Fig. 3). Although LXA$_4$ and LXB$_4$ show similar activities in some biologic systems, in many other systems each shows distinct actions (reviewed in [23]). 15–epi-LXB$_4$, for example, is a more potent inhibitor of cell proliferation than LXA$_4$ or 15–epi-LXA$_4$ [23].

Novel agonists in anti-inflammation and pro-resolution: metabolically stable analogs of lipoxin A₄ and aspirin-triggered lipoxins

Pathways of enzymatic inactivation of lipoxins

Like other autacoids, lipoxins are generated rapidly in response to stimuli, act locally, and are inactivated rapidly by metabolic enzymes. The major route of LX inactivation is through dehydrogenation by monocytes that convert LXA_4 to 15-oxo-LXA_4, followed by specific reduction of the double bond that is adjacent to the ketone [21]. 15-hydroxyprosglandin dehydrogenase (15-PGDH) catalyzes the oxidation of LXA_4 to 15-oxo-LXA_4 (Fig. 4). This compound is biologically inactive and is converted further to 13,14-dihydro-15-oxo-LXA_4 by the action of eicosanoid oxidoreductase (EOR) (also known as LXA_4/PGE 13,14-reductase/LTB_4 12-hydroxydehydrogenase [PGR/LTB_4DH]). Moreover, reduction of the 15-oxo-group by 15-PGDH yields 13,14-dihydro-LXA_4, which reveals an additional catalytic activity for this enzyme [27]. When compared with the native LXs, the ATLs are converted less effectively in vitro to their 15-oxo-metabolite [21]. This indicates that the dehydrogenation step is highly stereospecific and suggests that when ATLs are generated in vivo, their biologic half-life is increased by about twofold greater compared with that of native LXA_4, thereby enhancing their ability to evoke bioactions. LXB_4 also can be dehydrogenated

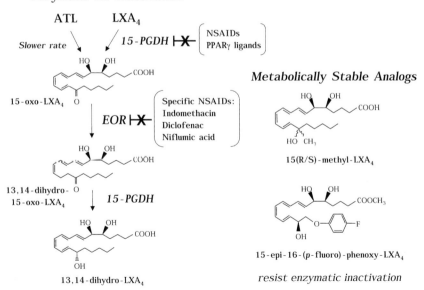

Fig. 4. Design of LX and ATL stable analogs to resist rapid enzyme inactivation The initial step in LXA_4 inactivation is dehydrogenation of the 15-hydroxyl group, catalyzed by 15-PGDH, followed by reduction of 13,14-double bond by EOR. Metabolic stable analogs of LXA_4 and 15-epi-LXA_4 were designed to resist rapid inactivation at carbon 15 and the ω-end of the molecule.

by 15-PGDH at carbon-5 to produce 5-oxo-LXB$_4$, therefore sharing a common route of inactivation [28].

Each action of lipoxins is stereoselective; changes in potencies accompany double bond isomerization and change in alcohol chirality (R or S) at key positions as well as selective dehydrogenation of alcohols and reduction of double bonds. For example, the 15-hydroxyl group is important for anti-inflammatory properties because ASA-triggered LXA$_4$ (15R-LXA$_4$) with the 15-hydroxyl group in the R-configuration was established in several experimental settings to be more potent than native LXA$_4$ (15S-LXA$_4$) in vitro and in vivo [19]. Also, 15-oxo-LXA$_4$ [27] and 15-deoxy-LXA$_4$ [21] are biologically inactive in inhibiting superoxide anion generation and transmigration in PMN, respectively. The 13, 14-double bond is important because 13, 14-dihydro-LXA$_4$ proved to be inactive in inhibiting superoxide anion generation [27]. These pharmacophores for LX's anti-inflammatory action also are required for their interaction with the specific cell surface receptor, namely lipoxin A$_4$ receptor (ALX). These biologically inactive isomers (eg, 15-oxo-LXA$_4$, 15-deoxy-LXA$_4$ and 13, 14-dihydro-LXA$_4$) did not bind to ALX, whereas the active ones (eg, 15R-LXA$_4$ and 15(R/S)-methyl-LXA$_4$) gave specific receptor binding to ALX, as demonstrated by specific [^{3}H] LXA$_4$ binding [23].

Selective nonsteroidal anti-inflammatory drugs also block enzymes that inactivate lipoxins: 15-hydroxyprosglandin dehydrogenase and lipoxin A$_4$/prostaglandin E 13,14-reductase/leukotriene B$_4$ 12-hydroxydehydrogenase (eicosanoid oxidoreductase)

15-PGDH and EOR (PGR/LTB4DH) act on main series of eicosanoids (eg, leukotrienes, prostaglandins) and recently were found to act in lipoxin inactivation. 15-PGDH was induced by androgens in hormone-sensitive human prostate cancer cells [29] and also may be involved in prostate tumorigenesis. Selective nonsteroidal anti-inflammatory drugs (NSAIDs) and some chemopreventive agents (eg, peroxisome proliferator-activated receptor (PPAR) gamma agonists, flavanoids, and phytophenolic compounds) gave potent inhibition of 15-PGDH. This suggested that regulation of 15-PGDH may be involved in the chemopreventive action of these agents [30]. A panel of NSAIDs was assessed to determine each compound's ability to inhibit recombinant EOR [31]. Several of the widely-used NSAIDs were potent inhibitors of the EOR that metabolizes 15-oxo-PGE$_2$, LTB$_4$, and 15-oxo-LXA$_4$ (see Fig. 4). Diclofenac and indomethacin each inhibited EOR-catalyzed conversion of 15-oxo-PGE$_2$ to 13,14-dihydro-15-oxo-PGE$_2$ by 70% and 95%, respectively. Also, a COX-2 inhibitor, niflumic acid, inhibited the EOR by 80%, whereas other COX-2 inhibitors, such as nimesulide and NS-398, did not inhibit this enzyme. These results indicate that certain clinically useful NSAIDs, such as diclofenac and indomethacin, inhibit COX-1 and COX-2 and interfere with eicosanoid degradation by blocking EOR; they are members of a new class of dual COX-EOR inhibitors. It is possible that selective NSAIDs, in addition to inhibiting PG generation (by way of the COX pathway), also increase LX accumulation by blocking its enzymatic inactivation (by 15-PGDH and EOR).

Design of stable analogs of lipoxin A_4 and 15–epi-lipoxin A_4

Because LXs are transformed rapidly and inactivated by monocytes, and, potentially, other cells in vivo, it was highly desirable to design LX analogs that could resist this form of metabolism, maintain their structural integrity, and potentially enhance beneficial bioactions. LX analogs were constructed with specific modifications of the native structures of LXA_4 and LXB_4, such as the addition of methyl groups on carbon-15 and carbon-5 of LXA_4 and LXB_4 structures, respectively, to block dehydrogenation by 15-PGDH. For example, 15(R/S)-methyl-LXA_4 is a racemic stable analog of LXA_4 and 15–epi-LXA_4 (see Fig. 4). Additional analogs of LXA_4 were synthesized with a phenoxy group bonded to carbon-16 and replacing the ω-end of the molecule to protect from dehydrogenation in vivo. Fluoride was added to the para-position of the phenoxy ring to hinder its degradation (see Fig. 4). These modifications prolonged the half-life of the compounds in blood and enhanced their bioavailabilities and bioactivities [32]. This suggested that they are useful tools and offers leads for developing novel therapeutic modalities. These analogs proved to be active and acted by way of competition at endogenous and recombinant ALX.

Lipoxins and aspirin-triggered lipoxins are associated with human diseases

Generation of lipoxin A_4 and 15–epi-lipoxin A_4 in animal models and in human diseases

Animal models

LXA_4 is produced in vivo during the course of inflammation, such as in an experimental immune complex glomerulonephritis model [33] and in pleural exudate upon allergen challenge in rats [34]. Also, endogenous LXA_4 was produced in ischemic lungs and elevated by reperfusion in a hind limb ischemia reperfusion model [35]. A recent report demonstrated that LXA_4 was generated during microbial infection in a *T gondii*–exposed murine model [36,37] as well as in a murine model of asthma [38]. In addition, LXA_4 is formed in rat brain and elevated in focal cerebral ischemia [23]. Recently, using a newly-developed specific ELISA method and liquid chromatography–tandem mass spectrometry (LC-MS-MS) system [39], 15–epi-LXA_4 could be detected in vivo. For example, 15–epi-LXA_4 was generated in an ASA-dependent manner in murine peritonitis [39] and murine dorsal air pouches [40] and was detected in rat kidney [33] and liver [41]. ASA also upregulated COX-2 expression in the stomach rapidly and caused a significant increase in gastric 15–epi-LXA_4 production in rats [42].

Human diseases

In human subjects, a reduction and alteration in LX generation was found in patients who had chronic liver disease and chronic myelogenous leukemia [23]. These diseases contrast with recent findings that LXA_4 production is upregulated in localized juvenile periodontitis [43] and mild asthma [44], as well as following atherosclerotic plaque rupture and with nasal polyps (Table 2). Moreover, ATL and LXA_4 formation was evaluated in ASA-tolerant and ASA-intolerant asthmatics. The ASA-tolerant subjects generated LX and ATL, but the ASA-intolerant patients had a diminished capacity to generate ATL and LX upon ASA challenge [45]. The lower levels of these potentially protective mediators (ie, LX and ATL) could contribute to the pathobiology of this chronic disorder. Together, these results indicate that alterations in LX and ATL levels may be linked to the pathophysiology of several human diseases and may display local organ-specific functions that stand apart from their roles in inflammation and within local inflammatory lesions (see Table 2; Table 3).

Actions of LX and ATL in cellular systems

LXA_4 and ATL display counterregulatory roles in various cell types in vitro (Table 4).

Myeloid cells

LXA_4 and ATL display counter-regulatory roles in various cell types in vitro (see Table 4; Fig. 5). With human peripheral blood leukocytes, LXA_4 inhibits isolated PMN and eosinophil chemotaxis in vitro in the nanomolar

Table 2
Lipoxins and human diseases — generation and impact in vivo

Organ/System	Impact in vivo
Hematologic	Defect in LX production with cells from patients who have chronic myeloid leukemia in blast crisis
	LX stimulate nuclear form of PKC in erythroleukemia cells
	Formation of LX by granulocytes from eosinophilic donors
Cardiovascular	Angioplasty-induced plaque rupture triggers LX formation
Dermatologic	LXA_4 regulates delayed hypersensitive reactions in skin
Pulmonary	LXA_4 detected in bronchoalveolar lavage fluids from patients who have pulmonary disease and asthma
	Production of LX by nasal polyps and bronchial tissue
	LXA_4 inhalation shifts and reduces leukotriene C_4-induced contraction in patients who have asthma
	ASA-intolerant asthmatics display a lower biosynthetic capacity than ASA-tolerant patients [45]
	LXA_4 inhibits IL-8 release by monocytes in patients who have asthma [44]
Hepatic	LX generation decreased in cirrhotic patients
Rheumatoid arthritis	LX levels increase with recovery
Oral	LXA_4 production is upregulated in localized juvenile periodontitis [43]

Table 3
Actions of LXs and ATL in disease models in vivo

Target organ/tissue	Animal model	Action
Acute inflammation	Peritonitis (M, R)	Promote macrophage phagocytosis of PMN [46] Inhibit PMN infiltration and vascular leakage [47]
	Dorsal air pouch (M)	Inhibit TNF-α–induced PMN infiltration [32]
	Dermal inflammation (M)	Inhibit LTB$_4$ induced PMN infiltration into ear skin and vascular permeability
Lung	Asthma (M)	Inhibit airway hyperresponsiveness and pulmonary inflammation [38]
	Ischemia and reperfusion (M)	Inhibit PMN infiltration into lungs [35]
Kidney	Glomerulonephritis (R)	Reduce leukocyte rolling and adherence
	Ischemia and reperfusion (R)	Reduce PMN infiltration and is protective against acute renal failure [48]
Microbial infection	*T gondii* infection (M)	Block dendritic cell migration and IL-12 production [36,37]
	A costaricensis infection (R)	Shorten the duration of pleural exudation [34]
Endothelium	Granuloma (M)	Reduce angiogenic phenotype [49]
Eye (Ra)		Lower intraocular pressure
Gastrointestinal tract	Colitis (M)	Attenuate induction of proinflammatory gene expression and reduce severity of DSS-induced colitis [50]
	Mesenteric ischemia-reperfusion (M)	Detachment of adherent leukocytes [51]
	Aspirin-induced gastric damage (R)	Reduce the severity of gastric damage and suppress aspirin-induced leukocyte adherence [42]

Abbreviations: DSS, dextran sodium sulfate; M, mouse; R, rat; Ra, rabbit.

range and blocks human natural killer (NK) cell cytotoxicity in a stereoselective fashion and stimulates myeloid bone marrow–derived progenitors. LXA$_4$ stimulates chemotaxis and adherence in monocytes but no apparent "proinflammatory" responses of these cells in vitro or in vivo; this may relate to the recruitment of monocytes to sites of wound healing and clearance. LXs and ATLs stimulate the uptake of apoptotic PMN by macrophages in a nonphlogistic fashion [54]. These are key events in clearance and resolution.

Nonmyeloid cells

With human enterocytes and fibroblasts, LXA$_4$ regulates proinflammatory cytokine release as well as gene expression (see later discussion). In hepatocytes, ATL significantly reduces PPARα and cytokine-induced neutrophil chemoattractant (CINC)-1 [58]. With other cell types, such as endothelial and mesangial cells, LXA$_4$ evokes bioactions and interacts with a subclass of peptido-LT receptors (CysLT$_1$) [23].

Table 4
Actions of LXs and ATL in cellular systems

Cell type/tissue	Action
Whole blood	Downregulate CD11/CD18, prevent shedding of L-selectin and reduce peroxynitrite generation on PMN, monocytes, and lymphocytes [52,53]
Neutrophils	Inhibit chemotaxis, adherence, and transmigration
	Inhibit PMN-epithelial and endothelial cell interactions
	Block superoxide anion generation [7]
	Inhibit CD11b/CD18 expression and IP_3 formation
	Inhibit peroxynitrite generation [52]
	Attenuate AP-1 and NF-kB accumulation and inhibit IL-8 gene expression [52]
Monocytes	Stimulate chemotaxis and adhesion to laminin without increase in cytotoxicity
	Inhibit peroxynitrite generation [52]
	Inhibit IL-8 release by cells obtained from patients who have asthma [44]
Macrophages	Stimulate nonphlogistic phagocytosis of apoptotic PMN [46,54]
Dendritic cells	Block IL-12 production [36,37]
Eosinophils	Stop migration/chemotaxis [55]
NK cells	Block cytotoxicity
Myeloid progenitors	Stimulate myeloid bone marrow–derived progenitors
Enterocytes	Inhibit TNF-α–induced IL-8 expression and release
	Inhibit *Salmonella typhimurium*–induced IL-8
Fibroblasts	Inhibit IL-1β-induced IL-6, IL-8, and MMP-3 production [56]
Endothelia (HUVEC)	Stimulate protein kinase C–dependent prostacyclin formation
	Block P-selectin expression
Mesangial cells	Inhibit LTD_4-induced proliferation [57]
Pulmonary artery	Induce relaxation and reverse precontraction by PGF_2 or endothelin-1
Hepatocytes	Reduce PPARa and CINC-1 levels [58]
Bronchi	Relaxation after precontraction by blocking peptido-leukotrienes in human airway

Abbreviations: AP, activator protein; CINC, cytokine-induced neutrophil chemoattractant; HUVEC, human umbilical vein endothelial cells; MMP, matrix metalloproteinase; PGF, prostaglandin F; PPAR, peroxisome proliferator-activated receptor.

Actions of lipoxins and aspirin-triggered lipoxins in disease models

The metabolic stable analogs of LXs and ATLs have been useful tools in the examination of the role and local actions of lipoxins in several experimental animal models. See Table 3 for a summary of the findings.

Acute inflammation

In dermal inflammation, when LX stable analogs were applied topically to mouse ears PMN infiltration and vascular permeability changes were inhibited. Also, the fluorinated analog of ATL, at levels as low as approximately 24 nmol per mouse, potently inhibited TNF-α–induced leukocyte recruitment into the dorsal air pouch [32]. Inhibition was evident by local intra–air pouch delivery or

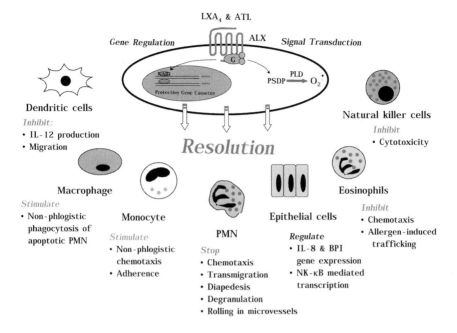

Fig. 5. LXs action by way of ALX in regulating inflammation and resolution. Upon ligand activation, ALX-initiated signaling pathways (eg, presqualene disphosphate; PSDP) or gene regulation (expression of a "protective gene cassette", eg, NAB1) in leukocytes and human epithelial cells to promote resolution. BPI, bactericidal/permeability-increasing protein; NAB, NGFI-A-binding protein; PLD, phospholipase D.

by way of systemic delivery by intravenous (IV) injection and proved more potent than local delivery of ASA. Recently, using a casein-induced peritonitis model in rats, ATL significantly inhibited neutrophil infiltration (~43%) and protein extravasation (~42%) when two consecutive doses of approximately 60 μg/kg IV were administered [47]. Transgenic expression of the human ALX (ie, the human receptor expressed in the mouse model) markedly decreased PMN infiltration to the peritoneum in zymosan-initiated peritonitis and displayed increased sensitivity to suboptimal doses of ATL stable analog [59]. ATL analogs rapidly promoted macrophage phagocytosis of apoptotic PMN in a thioglycollate-induced peritonitis; this supported a role for LXs as proresolution signals in inflammation [46].

Lung (endogenous versus exogenous stimuli)

Because LXA₄ and ATL selectively regulate leukocyte responses, they were tested in BLT1 transgenic mice that have increased PMN trafficking to lungs after high limb ischemia-reperfusion. Despite excessive PMN recruitment in BLT1 transgenic mice, IV injection of ATL sharply diminished reperfusion-initiated PMN trafficking to lungs; this revealed a novel protective role for LXs and ATLs in stress responses that has applications in perioperative medicine [35]. With exogenous allergen challenge in a murine model of asthma, LXA_4 biosynthesis and ALX expression was increased. Also, transgenic expression of human ALX led to significant inhibition of pulmonary inflammation and eicosanoid-initiated eosinophil infiltration. Administration of a stable analog of ATL blocked airway hyperresponsiveness and pulmonary inflammation, which highlighted a unique counterregulatory role for LX in airway responses [38]. In these experiments, LXA_4/ATL analogs dramatically blocked allergic pleural eosinophil influx on allergen-induced eosinophilic pleurisy in sensitized rats [55].

Kidney

LXA_4 and ATL display physiologic and pathophysiologic roles in kidney, including regulation of renal functions by increasing glomerular filtration rate and renal plasma flow rate. In ischemic acute renal failure, ATL stable analog shows functional and morphologic protection and reduces PMN infiltration. In addition, ATL-treated mice display increased renal mRNA levels for suppressors of cytokine signaling (SOCS)-1 and SOCS-2 [48].

Gastrointestinal

LXA_4 attenuates leukocyte rolling and adherence in rat mesenteric micro-vasculature. Recently, using an ischemia-reperfusion procedure to promote leu-kocyte-endothelium interactions in the mouse mesenteric microcirculation, Gavin and colleagues [51] reported that LXA_4 evoked detachment of adherent leuko-cytes; this demonstrated that endogenous regulatory autacoids, such as LXA_4, function to disengage adherent cells during cell-cell interactions. Also, LXA_4 exhibits potent protective action on gastric mucosa by reducing the severity of gastric damage and suppressing leukocyte adherence during ASA-induced gas-tric damage in rats [42]. Furthermore, ATL is protective in intestinal inflammation in a mouse model of dextran sodium sulfate–induced colitis. As little as 10 µg/d ATL analog, by mouth, significantly reduced the weight loss, hematochezia, and mortality that characterize dextran sodium sulfate-induced colitis [50].

Microbial infection

In rats that were infected with *Angiostrongylus costaricensis*, two stable LXA_4 analogs did not alter the magnitude of pleural exudation response, but clearly shortened its duration. The early resolution of allergic pleural edema that was observed during *A costaricensis* infection coincided with a selective local eosinophilia and seemed to be mediated by COX-2–derived PGE_2 and LXA_4 [34]. ATL stable analog caused reduced splenic dendritic cell mobilization and IL-12 response in *T gondii*–infected mice; this demonstrated a novel role for LXs in regulating proinflammatory responses during microbial infection [36,37].

Endothelium

ATL analog inhibits endothelial cell proliferation and vascular endothelial growth factor-induced endothelial cell chemotaxis. In a granuloma in vivo model of inflammatory angiogenesis, ATL treatment (10 μg/mouse) reduced the angiogenic phenotype, as assessed by vascular casting and fluorescence. Together, these results identify a previously unappreciated novel and potent action of ATL in angiogenesis [49].

Eye

LXA$_4$ and LXB$_4$ and their stable analogs lower intraocular pressure in rabbits; that may underlie their role in the physiology of ocular pressure regulation. In human eye tissue, the receptor ALX is present and seems to be associated with corneal epithelial cells [60].

Specific receptors for lipoxin A$_4$ and aspirin-triggered lipoxin

Molecular cloning, ligand specificity, and receptor expression

The specific LXA$_4$ binding sites that are likely to mediate many of its selective actions were first characterized on human PMN. Intact PMN demonstrate specific and reversible [11,12-^{3}H]-LXA$_4$ binding; these LXA$_4$ binding sites are inducible in promyelocytic lineage (HL-60) cells that are exposed to differentiating agents (eg, retinoic acid, dimethyl sulphoxide [DMSO], phorbol 12-myristate 13-acetate [PMA]) and confer LXA$_4$-stimulated phospholipase activation. One of the orphan G protein–coupled receptors (GPCR) that was cloned earlier from myeloid lineages (also known as formyl peptide receptor like-1 and formyl peptide receptor-2), displayed specific [^{3}H]-LXA$_4$ binding with high affinity (Kd = 1.7 nM) and demonstrated selectivity when compared with LXB$_4$, LTB$_4$, LTD$_4$, and PGE$_2$ [23]. This recombinant receptor transmits signal with LXA$_4$, and activates guanosine triphosphotase (GTPase) and the release of arachidonic acid (C20:4) from membrane phospholipid; this indicated that this cDNA encodes a functional receptor for LXA$_4$ in myeloid cells, and, thus, is denoted lipoxin A$_4$ receptor (ALX). ALX has identified and cloned in various cells types, including PMN, monocytes, enterocytes, and synovial fibroblasts [56]. The finding that LXA$_4$ blocks platelet-activating factor and formyl-Met-Len-Phe-stimulated eosinophil chemotaxis [61] suggests that functional ALXR also is present on eosinophils.

The mouse ALX cDNA subsequently was cloned from a spleen cDNA library and displays specific [^{3}H]-LXA$_4$ binding as well as LXA$_4$-initiated GTPase activity. The human and mouse LXA$_4$ receptors represented the first cloned LO-derived eicosanoid receptors. Most recently, an ortholog of ALX was isolated from rat leukocytes and proved to be functional as demonstrated by radioligand binding as well as LXA$_4$-dependent inhibition of TNF-α–mediated nuclear factor κB activity [47]. Alignment of the deduced amino acid sequences revealed that the rat ortholog of ALX shares 74% and 84% homology with human and mouse ALX, respectively. The highest homology is found in their second intracellular loop (identical, 100%) followed by the sixth transmembrane segment (93%). A phylogenetic tree that was constructed with related GPCR demonstrated that this rat receptor is most closely related to mouse and human ALX, followed by formyl peptide receptors (FPR) (~60% identity in amino acid sequences) (Fig. 6). As a class, human, mouse, and rat ALX is related distantly to prostanoid receptors and belongs to the cluster of chemoattractant peptide receptors that are exemplified by fMLP and C5a receptors and also include leukotriene B_4 receptors (BLT).

Although ALX shares high homology with FPR, ALX binds [^{3}H]-fMLP with low affinity (Kd ~5 μM) and proves to be selective for LXA_4 by three log orders of magnitude. More recently, it was reported that certain peptides/proteins also can interact with ALX in vitro and in vivo. For example, major histocompatibility complex binding peptide (a potent necrotactic peptide that is derived from NADH dehydrogenase subunit 1 from mitochondria) directly binds to human ALX and evokes PMN chemotaxis that is inhibited by ATL analog [62]; it also stimulates macrophage phagocytosis of PMN [46]. In addition, naturally-produced, cleaved forms [ie, D2D3(88-274)] of urokinase-type plasminogen activa-

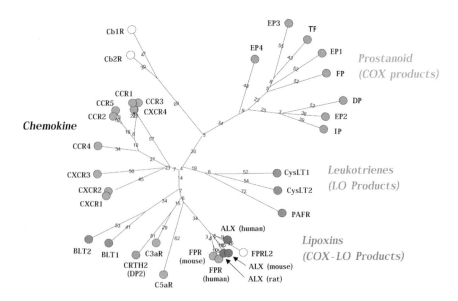

Fig. 6. Phylogenetic tree of GPCRs for chemokines and lipid mediators. This tree is constructed with deduced amino acid sequences of human eicosanoid and chemokine receptors using the "All All Program" at the Computational Biochemistry Server at ETHZ (http://cbrg.inf.ethz.ch/Server/AllAll.html). ALX, lipoxin A_4 receptor; Cb1R/Cb2R, cannabinoid receptors; CCR, receptors for CC chemokines; $CRTH_2$, chemoattractant receptor-homologous molecule expressed on T-helper type 2 cells; CXCR, receptors for CXC chemokines; CysLT, cysteinyl leukotrienes; DP, prostaglandin D_2 receptor; DP_2, prostaglandin D_2 receptor 2; EP_1/EP_2/EP_3/EP_4, subtypes of prostaglandin E_2 receptor; FPRL, formyl peptide receptor like; FP, prostaglandin F_2 receptor; FPR, formyl peptide receptor; IP, prostacyclin receptor; PAFR, platelet-activating factor receptor; TP, thromboxane A_2 receptor.

tor directly binds to ALX and is a unique endogenous chemotactic agonist for ALX; this provided the first direct link between the fibrinolytic machinery and the inflammatory response [63]. These endogenously-generated peptides evoke their bioaction by way of ALX in the subnanomolar range. Additional peptides in the micromolar range also can interact with ALX in some in vitro model systems, including HIV envelope peptides (eg, T21, N36, V3, and F peptides), bacterial-derived peptides (eg, Hp2-20 from *Helicobacter pylori*), and host-derived peptides (eg, serum amyloid A, PrP106-126, and Aβ) [64]. The functional roles of these peptides in human biology remain of interest.

These new findings suggest that small peptides and bioactive lipids can function as ligands for the same receptor. These occur with different affinities or distinct interaction sites within the receptor and evoke separate intracellular signaling that depends on the cell type and system. Probably the intracellular protein interactions that follow ligand-receptor binding are different for peptide and lipid ligands of the receptor because different conformations of the ligand-receptors are likely to be formed. Taken together, the finding that specific LXA$_4$-related structures and certain peptides interact with ALX may reflect the need for multirecognition and receptor redundancies in the immune system.

Retinoic acid, PMA, and DMSO, which lead to granulocytic phenotypes in HL-60 cells, induce an approximately threefold to fivefold increase in the expression of ALX as monitored by specific [^{3}H]-LXA$_4$ binding. Also, ALX transcription is upregulated dramatically by cytokines in human enterocytes; lymphocyte-derived IL-13 and interferon-γ are the most potent, followed by IL-4 and IL-6. IL-1β and LPS also showed moderate induction of ALX mRNA [60]. In view of the cytokine regulation of ALX, it is likely that the expression of these receptors will change dramatically in disease states, which, in turn, might attenuate mucosal inflammatory and allergic responses.

Signal transduction of lipoxin A$_4$ receptor: novel anti-inflammatory proresolving signal transduction

Recent results from this laboratory indicate that, with PMN, ALX interaction with LX and ATL analogs regulates a newly-described polyisoprenyl phosphate signaling pathway [7]. ALX activation reverses LTB$_4$-initiated polyisoprenyl phosphate remodeling which leads to accumulation of presqualene diphosphate, a potent negative intracellular signal in PMN that inhibits recombinant phospholipase D (PLD) and superoxide anion generation. LXA$_4$ reduces peroxynitrite formation, and, thus, can oppose peroxynitrite signaling in leukocytes [52]. Recent findings by Maderna et al [65] demonstrated that LX induces cytoskeleton reorganization and an increase in membrane-associated ρA GTPase as well as ρA activity in monocytes and macrophages by way of inhibition of cyclic adenosine monophosphate; this revealed a potential mechanism of LXs in promoting resolution. In retinoic acid–differentiated HL-60 cells, LXA$_4$ stimulated PLD activation that was staurosporine sensitive; this suggested the involvement of protein kinase C (PKC) in signal transduction in these cells. It also was demonstrated that LXA$_4$ blocks LTB$_4$ or fMLP-stimulated PMN transmigration or adhesion by regulation of β2 integrin–dependent PMN adhesion. This modulatory action is reversed partially by previous exposure to genistein, a tyrosine kinase inhibitor.

Aspirin-triggered lipoxins regulate proinflammatory gene expression

Leukocytes

Using differential display reverse transcription-polymerase chain reaction (RT-PCR), a subset of genes was identified that was selectively upregulated upon short exposure of PMN to ATL analog (ATLa). Among them, a transcriptional corepressor, NGFI-A-binding protein 1 (NAB1), which was identified previously as a glucocorticoid-responsive gene in hamster smooth muscle cells, was investigated further and also was found to be upregulated by ATLa in murine lung vascular smooth muscle in vivo [66]. These findings provide evidence for rapid transcriptional induction of a cassette of genes by way of an ATLa-stimulated G protein–coupled receptor pathway. In addition, ATLa attenuates nuclear accumulation of activator protein-a and nuclear factor (NF)-kB in PMN and monocytes and inhibits IL-8 mRNA expression [52].

Epithelial cells

Microarray analysis revealed that epithelial cells of wide origin express bactericidal/permeability-increasing protein (BPI), an antibacterial and endo-toxin-neutralizing molecule that is transcriptionally regulated by ATL. A BPI-neutralizing antiserum revealed that surface BPI blocks endotoxin-mediated signaling in epithelia and kills Salmonella typhimurium [67]. These studies identified a previously unappreciated "molecular shield" for protection of mucosal surfaces against gram-negative bacteria and their endotoxin. In human enterocytes, ALX activation by LXA$_4$ and LX analogs diminished S typhimu-rium–induced IL-8 transcription [68]. The reduction of IL-8 mRNA level parallels decrements in IL-8 secretion which indicated that in these cells, ALX's mecha-nism of action for blocking this chemokine is at the gene transcriptional level. In an effort to elucidate the mechanism by which these lipid mediators modulate cellular proinflammatory programs, global epithelial gene expression was sur-veyed using microarray analysis. ATL analog pretreatment attenuated the induc-tion of approximately 50% of S typhimurium–induced gene expression [50]. A major subset of genes whose induction was reduced by ATL analog pretreatment is regulated by NF-kB; this suggested that ATL analog was influencing the activity of this transcription factor. Nanomolar amounts of ATL analog reduced NF-kB–mediated transcriptional activation in an ALX-dependent manner and inhibited degradation of IkBα.

Resident cell types

In human synovial fibroblasts, LXA$_4$ inhibited IL-1β responses with reduc-tion of IL-6 and IL-8 synthesis and prevented IL-1β-induced matrix metalloproteinase 3 synthesis at nanomolar concentrations [56]. Also, LXA_4 induces increases of tissue inhibitor of metalloproteinase (TIMP)-1 and TIMP-2 protein. These findings suggested that LXA_4 may be involved in a negative feedback loop that opposes inflammatory cytokine–induced activation of synovial fibroblasts. In addition, LXA_4 induced tissue factor activity by increasing its mRNA level in EC304 cells (nonendothelial parenchymal cells) by way of a pertussis toxin-sensitive and PKC-dependent mechanism [69]. The ability of LXA_4 to induce tissue factor is an intriguing result. Its physiologic role remains to be established in relation to LX generation and proximity to tissue factor–releasing cells in vivo.

Combination therapies: aspirin and glucocorticoids to endogenous resolvins?

Endogenous lipid and peptide anti-inflammatory pathways share common target

Certain stress hormones also play important roles in controlling inflammation, such as adrenal glucocorticoids, adrenaline, and a melanocyte-stimulating hormone (see Table 1). Among them, glucocorticoids are used widely to treat inflammatory diseases. ASA and glucocorticoids share the ability to inhibit a key first step in inflammation—leukocyte-endothelial adhesion. Prolonged treatment with ASA or glucocorticoids is associated with an unacceptably high level of adverse side effects. Therefore, the molecular basis that underlies their anti-PMN activity is of great interest; its elucidation could shed light on novel pathways that might be useful in sparing unwanted side effects of these agents.

We recently reported that glucocorticoid-induced annexin 1 (ANXA1)–derived peptides (eg, Ac2–26) are generated in vivo and act at the ALX to halt PMN diapedesis [40]. These peptides specifically interact with recombinant human ALX as demonstrated by radioligand binding and function as well as immunoprecipitation of PMN receptors. In addition, the combination of ATL and ANXA1-derived peptides limited PMN infiltration and reduced production of inflammatory mediators in murine dorsal air pouches. LXA_4 and ANXA1-derived peptide induced detachment of adherent leukocytes in the mesenteric microcirculation [51]. By convergence at the same anti-inflammatory receptor, these two structurally distinct endogenous systems, lipid-derived (eg, ATL) and protein-derived (eg, ANXA1) mediators, limit PMN in vivo. This overlap may have evolved to ensure that inflammation loci remain local, walled off, and self-limited as well as to protect from self-damage from within. Moreover, impingement of these natural endogenous systems by popular therapies, such as ASA and dexamethasone (DEX), may, at least in part, underlie the proven efficacy of the combination of DEX and ASA in controlling rheumatic diseases and the success of their individual use. These systems likely represent functional redundancies in endogenous anti-inflammation circuits that unveil presently unappreciated mech-

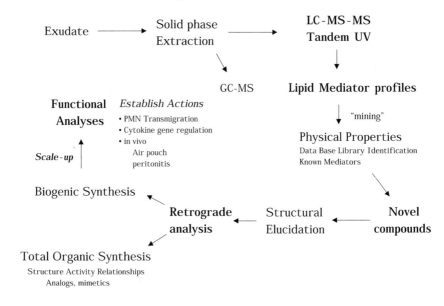

Fig. 7. Lipidomics: liquid chromatography–tandem mass spectrometry (LC-MS-MS)–based analysis. GC-MS, gas chromatography–mass spectrometry; UV, ultraviolet.

anisms that are operative in governing PMN responses in host defense and open new avenues for approaches, such as combination therapies.

Novel omega-3 polyunsaturated fatty acid–derived lipid mediators: resolvins

What about other precursors and substrates?

With new lipidomic analyses that use liquid chromatography–photodiode array detector–tandem mass spectrometry (LC-PDA-MS-MS) (Fig. 7), a novel array of endogenous lipid mediators was identified (Fig. 8) during multicellular events within the early phase of resolution. These biosynthetic pathways use omega-3 docosahexaenoic acid (DHA) and eicosapentaenoic acid (EPA) to produce a family of protective compounds, termed "resolvins," that include resolvin-E (18R-series from EPA, C20:5) and resolvin-D (17-series from DHA, C22:6).

Human endothelial cells with upregulated COX-2 that were treated with ASA converted C20:5 omega-3 PUFA, namely EPA, to 18R-hydroxyeicosapentaenoic acid (HEPE) and 15R-HEPE. 18R-HEPE and 15R-HEPE were used by polymor-

Fig. 8. Proposed biosynthetic scheme for resolvins. Interactions of omega-3 PUFA with ASA-acetylated COX-2 generate novel arrays of bioactive compounds, which inhibits PMN transmigration in vitro and inflammation in vivo. A prototypic oxygenation with DHA is depicted as an omega-3–containing fatty acid. HDHA, hydroxy docosahexaenoic acid; HEPE, hydroxy eicosapentaenoic acid.

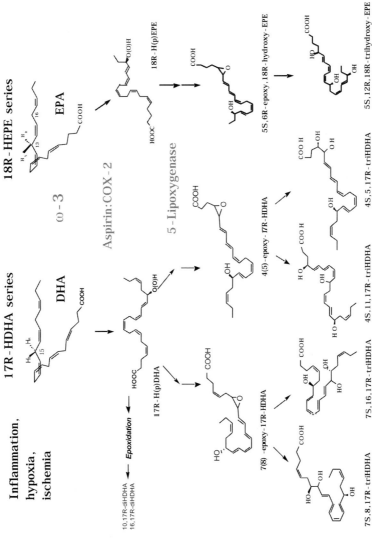

phonuclear leukocytes to generate separate classes of novel trihydroxy-containing mediators, including 5-series 15R-LX(5) and 5,12,18R-triHEPE [70]. These new compounds proved to be potent inhibitors of human polymorphonuclear leukocyte transendothelial migration and infiltration in vivo (ATL analog more so than 5,12,18R-triHEPE more so than 18R-HEPE). These findings established new transcellular routes for producing arrays of bioactive lipid mediators by way of COX-2 and NSAID-dependent oxygenations and cell-cell interactions that impact microinflammation.

DHA (C22:6) is highly enriched in brain, synapses, and retina and is a major omega-3 fatty acid. Deficiencies in this essential fatty acid are associated with neuronal function, cancer, and inflammation. Lipidomic analysis of exudates that were obtained in the resolution phase from mice that were treated with ASA and DHA produced a novel family of bioactive 17R-hydroxy–containing di– and tri–hydroxy-docosanoids [6]. Murine brain that was treated with ASA produced endogenous 17R-hydroxydocosahexaenoic acid, as did human microglial cells. Human neutrophils transformed COX-2–ASA–derived 17R–hydroxy-DHA into novel di- and trihydroxy products. These compounds inhibited microglial cell cytokine expression and in vivo dermal inflammation and peritonitis at nanogram doses and reduced leukocytic exudates by 40% to 80% [6]. An additional series of resolvins (17S series) was identified in blood, leukocytes, brain, and glial cells. These novel mediators were biosynthesized by way of epoxide-containing intermediates and proved to be potent (pico- to nanomolar range) regulators of leukocytes; they reduced infiltration in vivo and glial cells by blocking their cytokine production [71]. Together, these results indicate that DHA is a precursor to potent protective mediators that are generated, by way of enzymatic oxygenations, to novel 17S series resolvins that regulate events of interest in inflammation and resolution. In addition, generation of these and related compounds provides a novel mechanism for the therapeutic benefits of omega-3 dietary supplementation, which may be important in inflammation, neoplasia, and vascular diseases.

Summary

Endogenously-generated small chemical mediators or autacoids play key roles in controlling inflammation and its organized resolution. Among them, lipoxins are the trihydroxy-tetraene–containing eicosanoids that are generated primarily by tight cell-cell interactions by way of transcellular biosynthesis and serve as local endogenous anti-inflammatory mediators. These "stop signals" in inflammation and other related processes may be involved in switching the cellular response from additional PMN recruitment toward monocytes (in a nonphlogistic fashion) that could lead to resolution of the inflammatory response or promotion of repair and healing. ASA impinges on this homeostatic system and evokes the endogenous biosynthesis of the carbon 15 epimers of lipoxins, namely ATLs, that mimic the bioactions of native LX in several biologic systems and, thus, can modulate in part, the beneficial actions of ASA in humans. Moreover, the temporal and spatial components in LX formation and actions are important determinants of their impact during an acute inflammatory reaction [24]. Generation of lipid (ie, ATL) versus protein (ie, ANXA1) mediators during the host inflammatory response display different time courses. The temporal difference suggests that ALX could regulate PMN by interacting with each class of ligands within specific phases of the inflammatory response.

ALX is the first cloned lipoxygenase-derived eicosanoid receptor. The signaling pathways and bioactions of ALX are cell type–specific. In agreement with in vitro results, ALX agonists, namely LXA_4 and 15-epi-LXA_4 and their stable analogs, regulate PMN during acute inflammation. In addition, it seems that LXs also display organ-specific actions, in addition to host defense and immune roles in the eye, kidney, lung, and oral and gastrointestinal tract and within bone marrow progenitors, possibly involving stem cells. The development of these few synthetic stable analogs has provided valuable tools to evaluate the biologic roles, significance, and pharmacologic actions of ALX and provided novel therapies for inflammatory diseases.

The relationship between LX generation and current NSAID therapies is more intertwined than currently appreciated [72]. ASA inhibits COX-1 and converts COX-2 into an ASA-triggered lipid mediator–generating system that produces an array of novel endogenous local autacoids from dietary omega-3 PUFA. Some of the local autacoids display potent anti-inflammatory or antineutrophil recruitment activity [5,6] as well as impinge on the role of these compounds in resolution, and, thus, are termed "resolvins." It is not surprising that investigators recently found a protective action for COX-2 in cardiovascular disease. Together with the lipoxins and 15-epi-lipoxins, the identification of the resolvins [5] gives us new avenues of approach in considering therapies for inflammation, cardiovascular diseases and cancer.

Acknowledgments

We thank Mary Halm Small for expert assistance in the preparation of this manuscript. Because of space limitations, all original references could not be cited. Apologies to our colleagues if reviews that incorporate their original references were substituted.

References

[1] Cotran RS, Kumar V, Collins T, editors. Robbins pathologic basis of disease. 6th edition. Philadelphia: W.B. Saunders Co.; 1999.
[2] Serhan CN. Endogenous chemical mediators in anti-inflammation and pro-resolution. Curr Med Chem 2002;1:177–92.
[3] Nathan C. Points of control in inflammation. Nature 2002;420:846–52.

[4] Samuelsson B, Dahlén SE, Lindgren JÅ, Rouzer CA, Serhan CN. Leukotrienes and lipoxins: structures, biosynthesis, and biological effects. Science 1987;237:1171–6.

[5] Serhan CN, Clish CB, Brannon J, Colgan SP, Chiang N, Gronert K. Novel functional sets of lipid-derived mediators with antiinflammatory actions generated from omega-3 fatty acids via cyclooxygenase 2-nonsteroidal antiinflammatory drugs and transcellular processing. J Exp Med 2000;192:1197–204.

[6] Serhan CN, Hong S, Gronert K, Colgan SP, Devchand PR, Mirick G, et al. Resolvins: a family of bioactive products of omega-3 fatty acid transformation circuits initiated by aspirin treatment that counter pro-inflammation signals. J Exp Med 2002;196:1025–37.

[7] Levy BD, Fokin VV, Clark JM, Wakelam MJO, Petasis NA, Serhan CN. Polyisoprenyl phosphate (PIPP) signaling regulates phospholipase D activity: a "stop" signaling switch for aspirin-triggered lipoxin A_4. FASEB J 1999;13:903–11.

[8] Levy BD, Petasis NA, Serhan CN. A role for polyisoprenyl phosphates in intracellular signaling. Nature 1997;389:985–90.

[9] Qiu F-H, Wada K, Stahl GL, Serhan CN. IMP and AMP deaminase in reperfusion injury downregulates neutrophil recruitment. Proc Natl Acad Sci USA 2000;97:4267–72.

[10] Liaudet L, Mabley JG, Pacher P, Virag L, Soriano FG, Marton A, et al. Inosine exerts a broad range of antiinflammatory effects in a murine model of acute lung injury. Ann Surg 2002;235: 568–78.

[11] Hasko G, Kuhel DG, Nemeth ZH, Mabley JG, Stachlewitz RF, Virag L, et al. Inosine inhibits inflammatory cytokine production by a posttranscriptional mechanism and protects against endotoxin-induced shock. J Immunol 2000;164:1013–9.

[12] Krump E, Picard S, Mancini J, Borgeat P. Suppression of leukotriene B_4 biosynthesis by endogenous adenosine in ligand-activated human neutrophils. J Exp Med 1997;186:1401–6.

[13] Linden J. Molecular approach to adenosine receptors: receptor-mediated mechanisms of tissue protection. Annu Rev Pharmacol Toxicol 2001;41:775–87.

[14] Ohta A, Sitkovsky M. Role of G-protein-coupled adenosine receptors in downregulation of inflammation and protection from tissue damage. Nature 2001;414:916–20.

[15] Pitzalis C, Pipitone N, Perretti M. Regulation of leukocyte-endothelial interactions by glucocorticoids. Ann N Y Acad Sci 2002;966:108–18.

[16] Serhan CN. Lipoxin biosynthesis and its impact in inflammatory and vascular events. Biochim Biophys Acta 1994;1212(1):1–25.

[17] Marcus AJ. Aspirin as prophylaxis against colorectal cancer. N Engl J Med 1995;333:656–8.

[18] Vane JR. 1982. Adventures and excursions in bioassay: the stepping stones to prostacyclin. In: les Prix Nobel: Nobel Prizes, presentations, biographies and lectures. Stockholm (Sweden): Almqvist & Wiksell; 1982. p. 181–206.

[19] Clària J, Serhan CN. Aspirin triggers previously undescribed bioactive eicosanoids by human endothelial cell-leukocyte interactions. Proc Natl Acad Sci USA 1995;92:9475–9.

[20] Schottelius AJ, Giesen C, Asadullah K, Fierro IM, Colgan SP, Bauman J, et al. An aspirin-triggered lipoxin A4 stable analog displays a unique topical anti-inflammatory profile. J Immunol 2002;169:7063–70.

[21] Serhan CN, Maddox JF, Petasis NA, Akritopoulou-Zanze I, Papayianni A, Brady HR, et al. Design of lipoxin A_4 stable analogs that block transmigration and adhesion of human neutrophils. Biochemistry 1995;34:14609–15.

[22] Cronstein BN, Montesinos MC, Weissmann G. Salicylates and sulfasalazine, but not glucocorticoids, inhibit leukocyte accumulation by an adenosine-dependent mechanism that is independent of inhibition of prostaglandin synthesis and p105 of NFκB. Proc Natl Acad Sci USA 1999; 96:6377–81.

[23] Serhan CN. Lipoxins and novel aspirin-triggered 15-epi-lipoxins (ATL): a jungle of cell-cell interactions or a therapeutic opportunity? Prostaglandins 1997;53:107–37.

[24] Levy BD, Clish CB, Schmidt B, Gronert K, Serhan CN. Lipid mediator class switching during acute inflammation: signals in resolution. Nat Immunol 2001;2:612–9.

[25] Samuelsson B. From studies of biochemical mechanisms to novel biological mediators: prosta-

glandin endoperoxides, thromboxanes and leukotrienes. In: Les Prix Nobel: Nobel Prizes, presentations, biographies and lectures. Stockholm (Sweden): Almqvist & Wiksell; 1982. p. 153–74.

[26] Levy GN. Prostaglandin H synthases, nonsteroidal anti-inflammatory drugs, and colon cancer. FASEB J 1997;11:234–47.

[27] Clish CB, Levy BD, Chiang N, Tai H-H, Serhan CN. Oxidoreductases in lipoxin A_4 metabolic inactivation. J Biol Chem 2000;275:25372–80.

[28] Maddox JF, Colgan SP, Clish CB, Petasis NA, Fokin VV, Serhan CN. Lipoxin B_4 regulates human monocyte/neutrophil adherence and motility: design of stable lipoxin B_4 analogs with increased biologic activity. FASEB J 1998;12:487–94.

[29] Tong M, Tai HH. Induction of $NAD(^+)$-linked 15-hydroxyprostaglandin dehydrogenase expression by androgens in human prostate cancer cells. Biochem Biophys Res Commun 2000; 276:77–81.

[30] Cho H, Tai H-H. Thiazolidinediones as a novel class of NAD^+-dependent 15-hydroxyprostaglandin dehydrogenase inhibitors. Arch Biochem Biophys 2002;405:247–51.

[31] Clish CB, Sun YP, Serhan CN. Identification of dual cyclooxygenase-eicosanoid oxidoreductase inhibitors: NSAIDs that inhibit PG-LX reductase/LTB(4) dehydrogenase. Biochem Biophys Res Commun 2001;288(4):868–74.

[32] Clish CB, O'Brien JA, Gronert K, Stahl GL, Petasis NA, Serhan CN. Local and systemic delivery of a stable aspirin-triggered lipoxin prevents neutrophil recruitment in vivo. Proc Natl Acad Sci USA 1999;96:8247–52.

[33] Munger KA, Montero A, Fukunaga M, Uda S, Yura T, Imai E, et al. Transfection of rat kidney with human 15-lipoxygenase suppresses inflammation and preserves function in experimental glomerulonephritis. Proc Natl Acad Sci USA 1999;96:13375–80.

[34] Bandeira-Melo C, Serra MF, Diaz BL, Cordeiro RSB, Silva PMR, Lenzi HL, et al. Cyclooxygenase-2-derived prostaglandin E_2 and lipoxin A_4 accelerate resolution of allergic edema in *Angiostrongylus costaricensis*-infected rats: relationship with concurrent eosinophilia. J Immunol 2000;164:1029–36.

[35] Chiang N, Gronert K, Clish CB, O'Brien JA, Freeman MW, Serhan CN. Leukotriene B_4 receptor transgenic mice reveal novel protective roles for lipoxins and aspirin-triggered lipoxins in reperfusion. J Clin Invest 1999;104:309–16.

[36] Aliberti J, Serhan C, Sher A. Parasite-induced lipoxin A(4) is an endogenous regulator of IL-12 production and immunopathology in Toxoplasma gondii infection. J Exp Med 2002;196: 1253–62.

[37] Aliberti J, Hieny S, Reis e Sousa C, Serhan CN, Sher A. Lipoxin-mediated inhibition of IL-12 production by DCs: a mechanism for regulation of microbial immunity. Nat Immunol 2002;3:76–82.

[38] Levy BD, De Sanctis GT, Devchand PR, Kim E, Ackerman K, Schmidt BA, et al. Multi-pronged inhibition of airway hyper-responsiveness and inflammation by lipoxin A_4. Nat Med 2002;8: 1018–23.

[39] Chiang N, Takano T, Clish CB, Petasis NA, Tai H-H, Serhan CN. Aspirin-triggered 15-epi-lipoxin A4 (ATL) generation by human leukocytes and murine peritonitis exudates: development of a specific 15-epi-LXA_4 ELISA. J Pharmacol Exp Ther 1998;287:779–90.

[40] Perretti M, Chiang N, La M, Fierro IM, Marullo S, Getting SJ, et al. Endogenous lipid- and peptide-derived anti-inflammatory pathways generated with glucocorticoid and aspirin treatment activate the lipoxin A(4) receptor. Nat Med 2002;8:1296–302.

[41] Titos E, Chiang N, Serhan CN, Romano M, Gaya J, Pueyo G, et al. Hepatocytes are a rich source of novel aspirin-triggered 15-epi-lipoxin A_4 (ATL). Am J Physiol 1999;277:C870–7.

[42] Fiorucci S, De Lima Jr OM, Mencarelli A, Palazzetti B, Distrutti E, McKnight W, et al. Cyclooxygenase-2-derived lipoxin A_4 increases gastric resistance to aspirin-induced damage. Gastroenterology 2002;123:1598–606.

[43] Pouliot M, Clish CB, Petasis NA, Van Dyke TE, Serhan CN. Lipoxin A_4 analogues inhibit leukocyte recruitment to *Porphyromonas gingivalis*: a role for cyclooxygenase-2 and lipoxins in periodontal disease. Biochemistry 2000;39:4761–8.

[44] Bonnans C, Vachier I, Chavis C, Godard P, Bousquet J, Chanez P. Lipoxins are potential endoge-
     nous antiinflammatory mediators in asthma. Am J Respir Crit Care Med 2002;165:1531–5.

[45] Sanak M, Levy BD, Clish CB, Chiang N, Gronert K, Mastalerz L, et al. Aspirin-tolerant
     asthmatics generate more lipoxins than aspirin-intolerant asthmatics. Eur Respir J 2000;16:
     44–9.

[46] Mitchell S, Thomas G, Harvey K, Cottell D, Reville K, Berlasconi G, et al. Lipoxins, aspirin-
     triggered epi-lipoxins, lipoxin stable analogues, and the resolution of inflammation: stimulation
     of macrophage phagocytosis of apoptotic neutrophils in vivo. J Am Soc Nephrol 2002;13:
     2497–507.

[47] Chiang N, Takano T, Arita M, Watanabe S, Serhan CN. Cloning and characterization of a novel
     rat lipoxin A_4 receptor that is conserved in structure and function. Br J Pharmacol 2003;139:
     89–98.

[48] Leonard MO, Hannan K, Burne MJ, Lappin DW, Doran P, Coleman P, et al. 15-epi-16-(para-
     fluorophenoxy)-lipoxin A_4-methyl ester, a synthetic analogue of 15-epi-lipoxin A_4, is protec-
     tive in experimental ischemic acute renal failure. J Am Soc Nephrol 2002;13:1657–62.

[49] Fierro IM, Kutok JL, Serhan CN. Novel lipid mediator regulators of endothelial cell prolifera-
     tion and migration: aspirin-triggered-15R-lipoxin A_4 and lipoxin A_4. J Pharmacol Exp Ther
     2002;300:385–92.

[50] Gewirtz AT, Collier-Hyams LS, Young AN, Kucharzik T, Guilford WJ, Parkinson JF, et al.
     Lipoxin A_4 analogs attenuate induction of intestinal epithelial proinflammatory gene expres-
     sion and reduce the severity of dextran sodium sulfate-induced colitis. J Immunol 2002;168:
     5260–7.

[51] Gavins FN, Yona S, Kamal AM, Flower RJ, Perretti M. Leukocyte anti-adhesive actions
     of annexin 1: ALXR and FPR related anti-inflammatory mechanisms. Blood 2003;101:
     4140–7.

[52] Jozsef L, Zouki C, Petasis NA, Serhan CN, Filep JG. Lipoxin A4 and aspirin-triggered 15-epi-
     lipoxin A4 inhibit peroxynitrite formation, NF-kappa B and AP-1 activation, and IL-8 gene
     expression in human leukocytes. Proc Natl Acad Sci USA 2002;99:13266–71.

[53] Filep JG, Zouki C, Petasis NA, Hachicha M, Serhan CN. Anti-inflammatory actions of
     lipoxin A_4 stable analogs are demonstrable in human whole blood: modulation of leukocyte
     adhesion molecules and inhibition of neutrophil-endothelial interactions. Blood 1999;94:
     4132–42.

[54] Godson C, Mitchell S, Harvey K, Petasis NA, Hogg N, Brady HR. Cutting edge: lipoxins rap-
     idly stimulate nonphlogistic phagocytosis of apoptotic neutrophils by monocyte-derived mac-
     rophages. J Immunol 2000;164:1663–7.

[55] Bandeira-Melo C, Bozza PT, Diaz BL, Cordeiro RSB, Jose PJ, Martins MA, et al. Cutting
     edge: lipoxin (LX) A_4 and aspirin-triggered 15-epi-LXA_4 block allergen-induced eosinophil traf-
     ficking. J Immunol 2000;164:2267–71.

[56] Sodin-Semrl S, Taddeo B, Tseng D, Varga J, Fiore S. Lipoxin A_4 inhibits IL-1 beta-induced
     IL-6, IL-8, and matrix metalloproteinase-3 production in human synovial fibroblasts and en-
     hances synthesis of tissue inhibitors of metalloproteinases. J Immunol 2000;164:2660–6.

[57] McMahon B, Stenson C, McPhillips F, Fanning A, Brady HR, Godson C. Lipoxin A_4 antago-
     nizes the mitogenic effects of leukotriene D_4 in human renal mesangial cells: differential acti-
     vation of MAP kinases through distinct receptors. J Biol Chem 2000;275:27566–75.

[58] Planagumà A, Titos E, López-Parra M, Gaya J, Pueyo G, Arroyo V, et al. Aspirin (ASA) regulates
     5-lipoxygenase activity and peroxisome proliferator-activated receptor α-mediated CINC-1 re-
     lease in rat liver cells: novel actions of lipoxin A_4 (LXA_4) and ASA-triggered 15-epi-LXA_4.
     FASEB J 2002;16:1937–9.

[59] Devchand PR, Arita M, Hong S, Bannenberg G, Moussignac R-L, Gronert K, et al. Human
     ALX receptor regulates neutrophil recruitment in transgenic mice: roles in inflammation and
     host-defense. FASEB J 2003;17:652–9.

[60] Gronert K, Gewirtz A, Madara JL, Serhan CN. Identification of a human enterocyte lipoxin

A_4 receptor that is regulated by IL-13 and IFN-γ and inhibits TNF-α-induced IL-8 release. J Exp Med 1998;187:1285–94.

[61] Soyombo O, Spur BW, Lee TH. Effects of lipoxin A_4 on chemotaxis and degranulation of human eosinophils stimulated by platelet-activating factor and N-formyl-L-methionyl-L-leucyl-L-phenylalanine. Allergy 1994;49:230–4.

[62] Chiang N, Fierro IM, Gronert K, Serhan CN. Activation of lipoxin A_4 receptors by aspirin-triggered lipoxins and select peptides evokes ligand-specific responses in inflammation. J Exp Med 2000;191:1197–207.

[63] Resnati M, Pallavicini I, Wang JM, Oppenheim JJ, Serhan CN, Romano M, et al. The fibrinolytic receptor for urokinase activates the G protein-coupled chemotactic receptor FPRL1/LXA4R. Proc Natl Acad Sci USA 2002;99:1359–64.

[64] Le Y, Murphy PM, Wang JM. Formyl-peptide receptors revisited. Trends Immunol 2002;23: 541–8.

[65] Maderna P, Cottell DC, Berlasconi G, Petasis NA, Brady HR, Godson C. Lipoxins induce actin reorganization in monocytes and macrophages but not in neutrophils: differential involvement of rho GTPases. Am J Pathol 2002;160:2275–83.

[66] Qiu F-H, Devchand PR, Wada K, Serhan CN. Aspirin-triggered lipoxin A_4 and lipoxin A_4 upregulate transcriptional corepressor NAB1 in human neutrophils. FASEB J 2001;15:2736–8.

[67] Canny G, Levy O, Furuta GT, Narravula-Alipati S, Sisson RB, Serhan CN, et al. Lipid mediator-induced expression of bactericidal/permeability-increasing protein (BPI) in human mucosal epithelia. Proc Natl Acad Sci USA 2002;99:3902–7.

[68] Gewirtz AT, McCormick B, Neish AS, Petasis NA, Gronert K, Serhan CN, et al. Pathogen-induced chemokine secretion from model intestinal epithelium is inhibited by lipoxin A_4 analogs. J Clin Invest 1998;101:1860–9.

[69] Maderna P, Godson C, Hannify G, Murphy M, Brady HR. Influence of lipoxin A(4) and other lipoxygenase-derived eicosanoids on tissue factor expression. Am J Physiol Cell Physiol 2000; 279:C945–53.

[70] Serhan CN, Prescott SM. The scent of a phagocyte: advances on leukotriene B_4 receptors. J Exp Med 2000;192:F5–8.

[71] Hong S, Gronert K, Devchand P, Moussignac R-L, Serhan CN. Novel docosatrienes and 17S-resolvins generated from docosahexaenoic acid in murine brain, human blood and glial cells: autacoids in anti-inflammation. J Biol Chem 2003;278:14677–87.

[72] FitzGerald GA, Patrono C. The coxibs, selective inhibitors of cyclooxygenase-2. N Engl J Med 2001;345:433–42.

RHEUMATIC
DISEASE CLINICS
OF NORTH AMERICA

ELSEVIER
SAUNDERS

Rheum Dis Clin N Am 30 (2004) 97–114

Vascular endothelium and immune responses: implications for inflammation and angiogenesis

Zoltán Szekanecz, MD, PhD[a,*], Alisa E. Koch, MD[b,c]

[a]Division of Rheumatology, Third Department of Medicine, University of Debrecen Medical and Health Sciences Center, 22 Moricz Street, Debrecen H-4004, Hungary
[b]Division of Arthritis and Connective Tissue Diseases, Department of Medicine, Northwestern University Medical School, Ward Building 3-315, 303 East Chicago Avenue, Chicago, IL 60611, USA
[c]Lakeside Division, Veterans' Administration Chicago Healthcare System, Chicago, IL, USA

Endothelial cells (ECs) line the lumina of arteries, veins, and capillaries, thus separating and connecting the blood and the extravascular tissues. In inflammatory processes (eg, arthritis, vasculitis), ECs are involved passively and they interact with other cells and mediators that are found in the surrounding tissues. ECs are active responders to external stimuli and are targets for leukocytes and mediators that are secreted by these inflammatory cells. On the other hand, ECs produce several inflammatory mediators and express cellular adhesion molecules (CAMs), and, thus, directly influence the action of leukocytes [1,2].

ECs are involved in several mechanisms that underlie inflammation. Various mediators may stimulate ECs. EC stimulation occurs within minutes and is induced by vasoactive substances, such as histamine or serotonin [2]. In contrast, EC activation requires hours to days to occur and is triggered mostly by pro-inflammatory cytokines, such as tumor necrosis factor (TNF)-α, interleukin (IL)-1, or interferon (IFN)-γ [2,3].

We briefly review the mechanisms that are most relevant for the involvement of ECs in inflammation and immune responses. Leukocytes and their mediators cause morphologic changes of ECs, affect vascular permeability, and result in vascular injury. Leukocytes also adhere to, and transmigrate through, the EC layer of the vessel wall. Several mediators may trigger the formation of new

This work was supported by grant no. F 025813 from the Hungarian National Scientific Research Fund (OTKA) (Z.S.), grant no. 0018 from the Research and Development Fund for Highest Education (FKFP) (Z.S.); NIH grant nos. HL-58695 and AI-40987 (A.E.K.), funds from the Veterans' Administration Research Service (A.E.K.), and the Gallagher Professorship for Arthritis Research (A.E.K).

* Corresponding author.
E-mail address: szekanecz@iiibel.dote.hu (Z. Szekanecz).

vessels, termed "angiogenesis." ECs play a crucial role in neovascularization. Eventually, all these mechanisms lead to the progression of inflammation. Although these events are discussed separately, most of the mechanisms may overlap with each other.

Endothelial cell morphology and permeability in inflammation

The endothelium may undergo numerous morphologic changes during inflammation (Box 1). These changes include vasodilatation and increased vascular permeability (vascular leakage). Vascular leakage can result from EC contraction and retraction, as well as leukocyte or anti-EC antibody (AECA)–mediated vascular injury [2]. In addition, vasodilatation may indirectly enhance vascular permeability. Most vasodilatory mediators originate from the plasma or blood cells. ECs also release vasodilators, including prostacyclin (PGI$_2$), nitric oxide (NO) and platelet-activating factor (PAF) [4].

Several key mechanisms may play a role in increased vascular permeability. The most important morphologic basis for vascular leakage is the formation and widening of intercellular gaps between ECs [2]. Histamine, serotonin, C3a, C5a, bradykinin, leukotrienes, and PAF may cause such leakage [5]. This type of leakage, also termed "histamine-mediated injury," occurs mostly in smaller venules [2]. EC retraction, associated with cytoskeletal reorganization, occurs in vitro upon exposure to IL-1, TNF-α, or IFN-γ [6]. EC retraction is a good example of EC stimulation, whereas EC contraction is a manifestation of EC activation [2].

Leukocytes that interact with the vascular wall may cause EC injury that leads to increased vascular permeability. The key mediators in this process are reactive oxygen intermediates and some matrix metalloproteinases (MMPs) [7]. Resting leukocytes extravasate without causing vascular leakage, whereas white cells that are activated by immune complexes or chemotactic complement fragments results in increased vascular permeability [8]. Inhibition of inflammatory leukocyte adhesion suppress plasma exudation and edema formation [9].

The production of AECAs was described in several inflammatory rheumatic conditions, including rheumatoid arthritis (RA), scleroderma, and systemic lupus

---

Box 1. Morphologic changes of blood vessels in inflammation

Vasodilatation
Increased vascular permeability (vascular leakage)
Endothelial contraction ("histamine-mediated injury")
Endothelial retraction ("cytokine-mediated injury")
Leukocyte-mediated endothelial injury
Antiendothelial antibody-mediated injury
Endothelial regeneration

erythematosus [10,11]. The presence of these antibodies in the sera may be a marker of vascular damage.

Capillary regeneration after vascular injury and angiogenesis also is associated with leakage. Neovascularization is characterized by the increased permeability of newly-formed vessels that results from open intercellular junctions and the incomplete basement membranes in differentiating ECs [12,13]. Furthermore, in some cases, EC regeneration may occur without the formation of new blood vessels; regeneration is accompanied by increases in capillary permeability. Such events may transpire in the vicinity of necrotic or infarcted tissues [2,3,5].

In summary, distinct mechanisms may be responsible for the increased vascular permeability that is seen in inflammation. These processes may involve different types of vessels and various soluble mediators.

The role of endothelial adhesion molecules in leukocyte-endothelial interactions

Adhesion of peripheral blood inflammatory leukocytes to endothelium is a key event in inflammation that leads to the process of leukocyte transendothelial emigration into inflammatory sites (Fig. 1) [14–19]. For example, in the inflamed synovium, the cascade of events begins with the adhesion of neutrophils, lymphocytes, and monocytes to the specialized, fenestrated EC [18,19]. High endothelial venule (HEV)–like microvessels, similar to HEV in the primary lymphoid organs, are present in the synovial tissue [18,19]. Thus, the process of

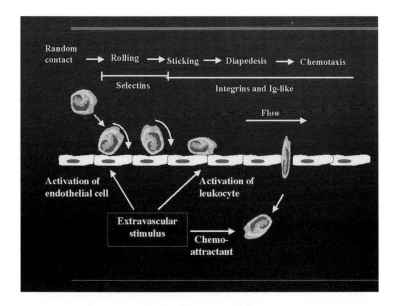

Fig. 1. The four-step model of leukocyte extravasation (see Refs. [17,46]).

leukocyte extravasation into inflammatory sites resembles physiologic lympho-cyte "homing" and may be considered as "pathologic homing." After adhesion, leukocytes transmigrate through the vessel wall into the inflamed tissue (see Fig. 1) [17–19]. In addition to leukocyte-EC interactions, EC adhesion to the extracellular matrix (ECM) is also important for EC activation, migration, and angiogenesis. EC adhesion to leukocytes and to the ECM is mediated by CAMs. CAMs have been classified into several superfamilies; the most relevant EC CAMs belong to three families, the integrins, selectins, and immunoglobulins [14–17] (Table 1). Integrins mainly are involved in EC adhesion to ECM macromolecules, whereas immunoglobulins and selectins play a role in EC ad-hesion to other cells [14–17].

Selectins contain an extracellular N-terminal domain related to lectins, hence the designation. This CAM superfamily includes E-, P-, and L-selectin. E- and P-selectin are present on endothelia [14–17]. E-selectin is not expressed on resting cultured endothelial cells; however, IL-1 and TNF-α stimulate EC E-se-lectin expression within a few hours [3]. Thus, E-selectin is a marker of cytokine-dependent EC activation. In addition, cytokine-activated ECs shed soluble E-selectin [18,20]. Ligands for E-selectin, such as E-selectin ligand-1, P-selectin ligand-1 (PSGL-1), and cutaneous leukocyte antigen, contain sialylated glycan motifs, such as sialyl Lewis-X [21,22]. There is evidence for the role of E-selectin in leukocyte-EC adhesion in vivo. E-selectin has been associated with rheumatoid synovitis, as well as dermal and pulmonary inflammation [9,18,20,23]. P-selectin is constitutively present on the membrane of endothelial

Table 1
Some important endothelial adhesion molecules in inflammation

Adhesion molecule superfamily	Receptor on endothelium	Ligands
Integrins	β_1 Integrins (most)	ECM components (laminin, fibronectin, collagen, vitronectin, etc.)
	$\alpha_4\beta_1$ Integrin	VCAM-1, fibronectin
	$\alpha_V\beta_3$ Integrin	ECM components (fibronectin, fibrinogen, thrombospondin)
Immunoglobulins	ICAM-1	β_2 Integrins: LFA-1, Mac-1
	VCAM-1	$\alpha_4\beta1$ and $\alpha_4\beta_7$
	LFA-3	CD2
	PECAM-1 (CD31)	Homophilic, $\alpha_V\beta_3$
Selectins	E-selectin	ESL-1, PSGL-1, CLA
	P-selectin	PSGL-1
Cadherins	VE-cadherin	Homophilic
Others	CD44	Hyaluronic acid
	Endoglin	TGF-β
	VAP-1	?

Abbreviations: CLA, cutaneous leukocyte antigen; ESL, E-selectin ligand; ICAM, intercellular adhesion molecule; LFA, lymphocyte function-associated antigen; PECAM, platelet-endothelial cell adhesion molecule; PSGL, P-selectin ligand 1; TGF-β, transforming growth factor-β; VCAM, vascular cell adhesion molecule; VAP, vascular adhesion protein; VE, vascular endolethial.

Weibel-Palade bodies [18,24]. P-selectin is involved in neutrophil and monocyte adhesion to EC in vitro [25]. PSGL-1 is a known ligand for P-selectin [22]. Cytokines upregulate P-selectin expression on EC within seconds. This CAM is believed to be involved in the early phases of adhesion [26]. P-selectin also has been implicated in synovial inflammation [27]. L-selectin is absent from EC, but is present on most leukocytes. L-selectin serves as a lymphocyte homing receptor, where it mediates the physiologic recirculation of naive lymphocytes through specialized HEV-expressing L-selectin ligands, including CD34, Mad-CAM-1, and GlyCAM-1 [14–17]. In addition, L-selectin also is involved in leukocyte-EC interactions that underlie inflammation [17]. Studies using E- and P-selectin–deficient, L-selectin–transfected cell lines revealed that L-selectin is able to mediate leukocyte rolling [28]. L-selectin expression on leukocytes is downregulated upon cytokine activation, however [29]; therefore, the exact role of L-selectin in inflammation is not yet clear.

Integrins are $\alpha\beta$ heterodimers; each of the common β subunits is associated with one or more α chains [14–17]. β_1 and β_3 integrins are expressed on ECs. These integrins ($\alpha_{1-9}\beta_1$, $\alpha_V\beta_3$) mediate cell adhesion to ECM components, including various types of collagen, laminin, fibronectin, fibrinogen, tenascin, vitronectin, and thrombospondin. The $\alpha_1\beta_1$ and $\alpha_2\beta_1$ integrins mediate EC adhesion to types I and IV collagen and laminin [14–17,30]. The main EC laminin receptor, however, is $\alpha_6\beta_1$. There are two important receptors for fibronectin—$\alpha_4\beta_1$ and $\alpha_5\beta_1$ [14–17,30]. All of these integrins, as well as $\alpha_3\beta_1$, a receptor for laminin, collagen and fibronectin, are expressed on ECs [30,31]. β_3 integrins mediate EC adhesion to fibronectin, vitronectin, thrombospondin, von Willebrand factor, and fibrinogen. The α_V integrin subunit can be associated with several β chains (ie, β_1, β_3, β_5, β_6, β_8), and, thus, is involved in EC adhesion to various ECM components, depending on the β subunit [14–17,30,31]. Microvascular and macrovascular ECs may express different integrins; this suggests that ECs have a potential to alter their CAM profile during vascular morphogenesis [31]. In addition, most β_1 integrins, as well as $\alpha_V\beta_3$, are involved in EC migration and angiogenesis (see later discussion) and are required for the survival and maturation of new blood vessels [30,32]. Integrin-mediated adhesion has been implicated in leukocyte-EC interactions during inflammation (eg, abundant expression of EC integrins in arthritis) [18,19,27,33].

Regarding members of the immunoglobulin superfamily of CAMs, vascular cell adhesion molecule-1 (VCAM-1), a ligand for the integrins $\alpha_4\beta_1$ and $\alpha_4\beta_7$, is expressed constitutively on resting ECs; its expression is markedly upregulated by proinflammatory cytokines [18,34]. Antibodies to VCAM-1 inhibit leukocyte adhesion to EC [2]. Abundant in situ VCAM-1 expression was associated with synovitis, scleroderma, and various other types of inflammation [18,23,35,36]. Intercellular adhesion molecule-1 (ICAM-1) is a ligand for all β_2 integrins [14–17]. The expression of ICAM-1 on ECs can be induced by IL-1, TNF-α, and IFN-γ [37]. The maximal expression of ICAM-1 on ECs is observed later (>24 hours) than that of E-selectin [1]. ICAM-1 is expressed highly on ECs in inflammatory sites in situ [18,23].

Other CAMs that mediate EC adhesion during inflammation include lymphocyte function-associated antigen-3 (LFA-3), platelet-endothelial cell adhesion molecule-1 (PECAM-1; CD31), CD44, vascular adhesion protein (VAP)-1 and -2, endoglin, vascular endolethial (VE)-cadherin, and, possibly, ICAM-3 [14–17, 38–40]. LFA-3, an EC CAM, and its counterreceptor on T cells, CD2, are members of the immunoglobulin superfamily. The CD2/LFA-3 adhesion pathway is involved in various inflammatory responses, including synovitis [18,41]. PECAM-1, another member of the immunoglobulin superfamily, mediates homotypic adhesion by binding to PECAM-1, as well as heterotypic adhesion by recognizing the $\alpha_V\beta_3$ integrin [14–17,42]. PECAM-1 is found in large quantities in the RA synovium [27]. CD44 is a receptor for hyaluronate [14–17]. CD44 is present on activated ECs in inflammatory synovitis [27,43]. VAP-1 originally was isolated from synovial endothelial cells. The expression of VAP-1 is increased in inflammation [38]. Endoglin is a receptor for transforming growth factor (TGF)-β_1 and TGF-β_3, and is involved in EC adhesion. Endoglin is expressed by most ECs in the inflamed synovium [40]. VE-cadherin, a major constituent of EC junctions, mediates homophilic binding between ECs and is involved in EC migration and polarization during inflammation [44]. ICAM-3 is a leukocyte CAM, which is a known ligand for LFA-1. It is absent from resting ECs; however, it was detected on some RA synovial ECs [39,45]. Thus, several CAMs may play a role in the adhesive interactions of ECs.

The process of leukocyte adhesion to EC occurs in at least four distinct steps (see Fig. 1; Table 2) [17,46]. An early, weak adhesion, termed "rolling," that occurs within the first 1 to 2 hours is mediated by selectins and their ligands. Leukocyte activation and triggering occurs next as a result of the interactions between chemokine receptors on leukocytes and proteoglycans on ECs. PECAM-1 and PAF also are involved in this step. Activation-dependent, firm adhesion that occurs within 4 to 6 hours is mediated mostly by $\alpha_4\beta_1$ integrin/VCAM-1 and

Table 2
Distinct steps during leukocyte emigration

Step	Factors on endothelium	Factors on leukocytes
Rolling	P-selectin	PSGL-1
	E-selectin	ESL-1
	L-selectin ligand?	Sialyl Lewis-X
		CLA
		L-selectin
Activation	Chemokines (eg, IL-8, MCP-1)	Cytokine and chemokine receptors
	PAF	PECAM-1
	PECAM-1	PSGL-1, ESL-1
	E-selectin	
Firm adhesion	ICAM-1	β_1, β_2, and β_7 integrins
	VCAM-1	
Diapedesis	ICAM-1	β_1, β_2, and β_7 integrins
	VCAM-1	PECAM-1
	PECAM-1	

LFA-1/ICAM-1 interactions; this also is accompanied by the secretion of various chemokines. Transendothelial migration or diapedesis that involves integrins occurs when secreted chemokines bind to endothelial heparan sulfate. Chemokines preferentially attract endothelium-bound leukocytes [17,46].

Regulation of leukocyte-endothelial adhesion during inflammation

Several soluble and cell surface–bound factors may be involved in leukocyte adhesion to, and migration through, endothelium (see Fig. 1; see Table 1). Pro-inflammatory cytokines, including IL-1, TNF-α, and, in some cases, IFN-γ, may upregulate EC CAM expression and stimulate leukocyte-EC adhesion [18,34, 37,46]. ECs also release several inflammatory mediators (Box 2). Some of these endogenous mediators also may be involved in EC adhesion. For example, PAF and chemokines have been implicated in P-selectin–dependent rolling and integrin-dependent firm adhesion, respectively [46,47].

Certain CAMs can also cross-talk with each other which results in strengthened intercellular adhesion. For example, E- and P-selectin stimulate the adhesive activity of β_2 integrins on neutrophils [47,48]. EC selectins mediate adhesion and are signaling receptors [49]. The cross-talk between selectins and integrins is crucial for the transition from rolling to firm adhesion.

Box 2. Some endothelial-derived inflammatory mediators

Cytokines

    IL-1, IL-6, IL-8

Chemokines

    Monocyte chemoattractant protein-1 (MCP-1)
    Growth-regulated oncogene-α (groα)

Growth factors

    Endothelial cell-derived growth factor (ECGF)
    TGF-β

Colony-stimulating factors

    Granulocyte colony-stimulating factor (G-CSF)
    Granulocyte-macrophage colony-stimulating factor (GM-CSF)

Others

    PAF, NO, and PGI_2

Finally, intercellular contact itself may result in increased cytokine release and CAM expression [18,50]. These regulatory mechanisms may synchronize the sequence of events described above and they may be important in the perpetuation of leukocyte extravasation and the inflammatory process.

The role of endothelium in angiogenesis

Angiogenesis is an important process in several physiologic processes, such as reproduction, development, and tissue repair, as well as in disease states, including inflammation and malignancies. The outcome of neovascularization depends on the balance or imbalance between angiogenic mediators and inhibitors. The process of neovascularization, the role of angiogenic factors and inhibitors, the role of ECs, and the potential intervention strategies are discussed extensively in several articles [13,51–55].

Angiogenesis is a program of several distinct steps. First, ECs are activated by angiogenic stimuli which results in the secretion of EC proteases, which degrade the EC basement membrane and ECM. The emigration of ECs results in the formation of primary capillary sprouts followed by further EC proliferation, migration, synthesis of new basement membrane, and lumen formation within the sprout. Two sprouts then link to form capillary loops. Finally, the emigration of ECs out of these sprouts results in the development of second and further generation of capillary sprouts [13,51,55].

Recent studies revealed that preferential EC precursors may exist within the population of blood stem cells. The reports suggested that a distinct subpopulation of $CD34^+$ cells that are carrying receptors for vascular endothelial growth factor (VEGF) may, under certain circumstances, develop into ECs [55–58]. These cells may be important in the growth of vessels during angiogenesis and may also be used for the induction of neovascularization in future therapeutic trials that are performed in patients who have certain vascular disorders [55,59,60]. VEGF and basic fibroblast growth factor (bFGF) have been introduced into animal models and into human trials to induce angiogenesis by stimulating endothelial morphogenesis from stem cells in coronary disease as well as obliterative arteriosclerosis [55,59,60].

Several in vitro and in vivo models are available to study angiogenesis. In vitro systems include EC cultures that are grown on extracellular matrix, such as the laminin-containing Matrigel, tissue culture systems, or EC chemotaxis assays [13,20,53–55,61,62]. In vivo neovascularization was investigated using the rat, murine, rabbit, or guinea pig corneal micropocket, the chick embryo chorioallantoic membrane, the hamster cheek pouch, the mesenteric, the aortic ring, the implanted matrix assays, sponge models, as well as other systems [13,53–55]. These models are suitable to test soluble or cell-bound mediators for their capacity to induce or suppress angiogenesis. Using these assays may be important to investigate the role of angiogenesis in the pathogenesis of certain diseases and to design strategies for antiangiogenesis therapies [54,55].

Table 3
Some mediators of angiogenesis

Growth factors	bFGF, aFGF, VEGF, ECGF, PD-ECGF, PDGF, HGF, IGF-I, TGF-β[a]
Cytokines	TNF-α[a], IL-1[a], IL-6[a], IL-8, IL-15, G-CSF, GM-CSF
Chemokines	IL-8, ENA-78, groα, groβ, CTAP-III
ECM macromolecules	Type I collagen, fibronectin, laminin, tenascin, heparin, heparan sulfate, fibrinogen
Proteolytic enzymes	MMPs, plasminogen activators
CAMs	β_1 And β_3 integrins, E-selectin, VCAM-1, PECAM-1, CD34, Sialyl Lewis-X, endoglin
Other mediators	Angiogenin, angiotropin, PAF, histamine, substance P, erythropoetin, prostaglandins, adenosine

Abbreviations: CTAP, connective tissue activating protein; ENA, endothelial neutrophil activating protein.

[a] Exhibits variable stimulatory and inhibitory activity (see text).

Angiogenic mediators (Table 3) may act directly on EC proliferation and migration or may indirectly stimulate the production of other angiogenic factors [13,51–55,61]. Growth factors are the most potent mediators of angiogenesis. Some of them, such as bFGF, acidic FGF (aFGF), VEGF, ECGF, and hepatocyte growth factor (HGF) are bound to heparin and heparan sulfate in the ECM. During neovascularization, these mediators are mobilized by EC-derived heparanase and plasmin [13,51–55]. Other angiogenic growth factors do not bind heparin. Platelet-derived growth factor (PDGF), platelet-derived endothelial cell growth factor (PD-ECGF)/gliostatin, epidermal growth factor, and insulin-like growth factor are less potent than heparin-binding factors [13,54]. TGF-β has a bifunctional, dose-dependent effect on angiogenesis [13,54,55,61].

Among pro-inflammatory cytokines, TNF-α, IL-1, IL-6, IL-8, IL-15, and IL-18 are involved in angiogenesis [13,51–55,61,63,64]. The effects of IL-1 and IL-6 on angiogenesis may be similar to that of TGF-β [52,54,65]. IL-13, under certain circumstances, also may promote angiogenesis [66]. Other angiogenic cytokines include G-CSF, GM-CSF, and oncostatin M [13,54,61,67].

Chemotactic cytokines termed "chemokines" have been divided into families based on the location of cysteine residues. Several C-X-C chemokines that contain the ELR (glutamyl-leucyl-arginyl-) amino acid sequence, such as IL-8, epithelial neutrophil activating protein (ENA)-78, groα, groβ, and connective tissue activating protein III have been implicated in neovascularization [13, 53–55,68–70]. In contrast, other C-X-C chemokines that lack the ELR motif, are potent angiostatic factors [54,55,68–70]. Stromal cell-derived factor-1 is the only angiogenic C-X-C chemokine that lacks ELR [55,70]. In the inflamed synovium, chemokine-expressing cells were localized in the proximity of factor VIII–related antigen-expressing ECs [71]. There is little information available on the possible role of C-C chemokines in angiogenesis. MCP-1 induces EC chemotaxis in vitro and angiogenesis in the chick chorioallantoic membrane assay in vivo. Fractalkine is the only characterized C-X3-C chemokine that is expressed on cytokine-activated ECs [72–74]. Fractalkine mediates neovascularization [73,74].

Regarding the possible role of chemokine receptors in angiogenesis, several of these receptors may be detected on ECs, thus playing a role in chemokine-derived angiogenesis. There is a growing body of evidence that CXCR2 may be the most important EC receptor for angiogenic C-X-C chemokines that contain the ELR amino acid sequence, including IL-8, ENA-78 and groα [69,70,75,76].

Certain ECM components also mediate angiogenesis. It was suggested that EC migration and chemotaxis are stimulated by type I, and, to a lesser extent types II, III, IV, and V collagen [13,77]. Other ECM macromolecules, such as fibronectin, laminin, tenascin, fibrinogen, heparin, and numerous proteoglycans, also promote neovascularization [13,54,61,78,79].

EC invasion and angiogenesis require ECM-degrading proteolytic enzymes, such as MMPs; including collagenase, gelatinase, and stromelysin; as well as urokinase-plasminogen activators and tissue-type plasminogen activators [13,54]. A novel family of metalloproteinases, a disentigrin and metalloprotease with thrombospondin motifs (ADAMTS) proteinases, includes aggrecanase-1 and -2. These aggrecanases are expressed in inflammation at sites of neovascularization [80].

Among EC CAMs, most β_1 integrins, the $\alpha_V\beta_3$ integrin, E-selectin, the L-selectin ligand CD34, VCAM-1, PECAM-1, endoglin, and VE-cadherin have been associated with enhanced angiogenesis [13,30–32,44,51–55,61,81,82]. Certain glycoconjugates also may serve as angiogenic mediators. Lewis^y/H, which is structurally related to the E-selectin ligand, sialyl Lewis^x, promotes neovascularization and is expressed abundantly in synovitis [83]. MUC18 (CD146) is a marker for melanoma metastatic potential. This molecule has adhesive properties and its levels in RA synovial fluids correlate with synovial angiogenesis [55,84].

The cyclooxygenase (COX)/prostaglandin system also is involved in angiogenesis. Prostaglandin E2 is angiogenic [54,55]. COX-2 has been implicated in VEGF-dependent neovascularization [85].

Other angiogenic mediators include angiogenin, angiotropin, substance P, prolactin, PAF, adenosine, and histamine [13,51–55,86].

Table 4
Some inhibitors of angiogenesis

Growth factors	TGF-β[a]
Cytokines	IL-1[a], IL-4, IL-6[a], IL-12, IFN-α, IFN-γ, LIF
Chemokines	IP-10, PF4, MIG
ECM molecules	Thrombospondin-1
Protease inhibitors	TIMP-1, TIMP-2, PAI-1, PAI-2
Tissue-derived inhibitors	Cartilage, lens, vitreous
Others	Angiostatin, endostatin, SPARC, opioids, retinoids, antirheumatic drugs

Abbreviations: IP, interferon-γ inducible protein; MIG, monokine induced by interferon-γ; PAI, plasminogen activator inhibitors; PF4, platelet factor-4; SPARC, secreted protien acidic and rich in cysteine; TIMP, tissue inhibitors of metalloproteinases.

[a] Exhibits variable stimulatory and inhibitory activity (see text).

Angiogenesis inhibitors (Table 4) include some cytokines, such as IFN-α, IFN-γ, IL-4, IL-12, and leukemia inhibitory factor (LIF) [13,52–55,61,87,88].

C-X-C chemokines that lack the ELR motif, such as platelet factor-4 (CXCL4), monokine induced by interferon-γ (MIG; CXCL9), and interferon-γ–inducible protein (IP-10; CXCL10) also inhibit neovascularization [68,70,89]. Regarding chemokine receptors, because angiostatic chemokines, such as IP-10, MIG, and the recently described secondary lymphoid-tissue chemokine (SLC), all bind to CXCR3, this receptor may play a role in chemokine-mediated angiogenesis inhibition [55,90,91].

The ECM molecule, thrombospondin-1, binds to, and blocks the effects of, heparin [13,52,92]. Protease inhibitors, such as tissue inhibitors of metalloproteinases and plasminogen activator inhibitors, inhibit EC migration [52,55]. Tissue-derived natural inhibitors have been isolated from the cartilage, vitreous, lens, epithelia, and other tissues [13,52,55].

Additional angiostatic factors include derivatives of antibiotics, including fumagillin and minocycline; cytoskeleton-dissembling agents, including taxol; secreted protein acidic and rich in cysteine (SPARC)/osteonectin; angiostatin; endostatin; retinoids; opioids; troponin I; as well as numerous antirheumatic or anti-inflammatory agents, such as dexamethasone, indomethacin, sulphasalazine, methotrexate, gold compounds, thalidomide, anti-TNF biologicals, and others [13,51–55,61].

The regulation of angiogenesis during inflammation is based on a complex network of angiogenic and angiostatic factors (Box 3).

In conclusion, a regulatory network of leukocytes and ECs, as well as soluble, cell- and ECM-bound angiogenic and angiostatic factors, exists in most types of inflammatory responses. Naturally-occurring angiogenesis inhibitors or exoge-

---

Box 3. Important mechanisms in the regulation of angiogenesis

Balance between antagonistic angiogenic and angiostatic couples

Concentration-dependent regulation of neovascularization by bifunctional mediators

Direct or indirect interactions between soluble and cell-bound angiogenic factors

Stimulation of angiostatic factor production by angiogenic mediators

Downregulation of the production of angiogenic mediators by angiostatic agents

Angiogenesis stimulation or inhibition by administered drugs or other compounds

Data from Refs. [13,51–55]

nous angiostatic compounds can interfere with pathologic neovascularization which indicates potentially new strategies in anti-inflammatory therapy.

Clinical perspectives of endothelial adhesion and angiogenesis targeting

The aforementioned cellular and molecular mechanisms may have important clinical relevance. EC adhesion, migration, and angiogenesis may be targeted specifically using biologic agents to control inflammation. As one example of antiadhesion targeting, an antihuman ICAM-1 antibody (enlimomab) was used to treat refractory RA; many patients reported improvement in their status. A transient increase in the number of circulating T cells after the administration of the antibody suggested that leukocyte extravasation into the RA synovium was inhibited [18,93]. Anti–ICAM-1 antibodies may activate blood neutrophils, as evidenced by increased β_2 integrin and decreased L-selectin expression on these cells, which may, at least in part, account for the side effects that were observed during antibody treatment [94]. Antibodies to various integrins abrogated animal models of arthritis, colitis, peritonitis, glomerulonephritis, meningitis, and encephalomyelitis [17,93,95,96]. Anti–ICAM-1 antibodies that were administered in vivo prevented experimental arthritis, allergic encephalomyelitis, and glomerulonephritis in animal models [17,93,97]. Antibodies to VCAM-1 could suppress experimental colitis [98] and murine cardiac allograft rejection [99]. Peptides that contain the arginyl-glycyl-aspartate sequence, a motif that is recognized by several integrins on EC, suppressed arthritis in rats [18,54].

Angiogenesis research also may have important therapeutic relevance in inflammatory diseases. For example, two central mechanisms may be targeted when developing antiangiogenic therapy. First, switch from the resting to the angiogenic endothelial phenotype could be inhibited by blocking the secretion, transport, and ECM binding of angiogenic factors. Alternatively, vascular EC response to these mediators could be suppressed by substances that regulate migration, proliferation, basement membrane production and degradation, and expression of EC CAMs [61]. Several immunosuppressive, anti-inflammatory agents, including corticosteroids, nonsteroidal anti-inflammatory drugs, or disease-modifying agents, inhibit angiogenesis or the production of macrophage-derived angiogenic mediators [13,52,54,55]. The inhibition of several soluble cytokines, growth factors, and chemokines can suppress the pathologic angiogenesis that underlies inflammation. TNF-α seems to be a primary target for therapeutic trials, although IL-1, IL-6, IL-8, and other angiogenic mediators recently were targeted [100]. For example, trials with infliximab showed that blocking of TNF-α reduced synovial VEGF expression [101]. A humanized anti-VEGF antibody successfully suppressed neovascularization [101]. Other angiostatic compounds also could be used to target neovascularization. For example, experimental arthritis in rats was suppressed by a fumagillin-derivative antibiotic angiogenesis inhibitor, as well as by taxol [13,54,55]. MMP inhibitors have been tried in several models of angiogenesis [102]. Theoretically, most angiogenesis inhibitors that were described may undergo trials in various inflammatory diseases.

Summary

ECs are involved in several mechanisms during the immune response, particularly in inflammation. These cells are able to produce vasodilatory mediators and several factors lead to increased vascular permeability. ECs play a central role in leukocyte extravasation, a key feature of inflammation. Several adhesion molecules, termed integrins, selectins, immunoglobulins, and others, act in concert and regulate the sequence of distinct steps. Leukocyte-EC adhesion is regulated by the interactions of receptor-ligand CAM pairs, as well as by soluble mediators, such as proinflammatory cytokines. ECs are active participants in angiogenesis. The outcome of neovascularization is highly dependent on the balance or imbalance between angiogenic mediators and inhibitors. Angiogenic mediators form a complex interactive network that regulates the perpetuation of angiogenesis. Naturally-produced or administered angiostatic agents downregulate the effects of angiogenic factors.

There have been several attempts to therapeutically interfere with the cellular and molecular mechanisms described above. Most studies were performed using animal models of various types of inflammation. A limited number of human clinical trials, such as the one using anti–ICAM-1 antibody in RA, had promising results. Specific targeting of pathologic endothelial function may be useful for the future management of various inflammatory diseases.

References

[1] Pober JS, Cotran RS. Cytokines and endothelial cell biology. Physiol Rev 1990;70:427–34.

[2] Cotran RS. Endothelial cells. In: Kelley WN, Harris Jr ED, Ruddy S, Sledge C, editors. Textbook of rheumatology. 4th edition. Philadelphia: W.B. Saunders Co.; 1993. p. 327–36.

[3] Bevilacqua MP, Pober JS, Mendrick DL, Cotran RS, Gimbrone Jr MA. Identification of an inducible endothelial-leukocyte adhesion molecule. Proc Natl Acad Sci USA 1987;84:9238–42.

[4] Brenner BM, Troy JL, Ballermann BJ. Endothelium-dependent vascular responses. Mediators and mechanisms. J Clin Invest 1989;84:1373–8.

[5] Joris I, Majno G, Corey EJ, Lewis RA. The mechanism of vascular leakage induced by leukotriene E4. Endothelial contraction. Am J Pathol 1987;126:19–24.

[6] Brett J, Gerlach H, Nawroth P, Steinberg S, Godman G, Stern D. Tumor necrosis factor/cachectin increases permeability of endothelial cell monolayers by a mechanism involving regulatory G proteins. J Exp Med 1989;169:1977–91.

[7] Varani J, Ginsburg I, Schuger L, Gibbs DF, Bromberg J, Johnson KJ, et al. Endothelial cell killing by neutrophils. Synergistic interaction of oxygen products and proteases. Am J Pathol 1989;135:435–8.

[8] Hurley JV. Acute inflammation. Baltimore (MD): Williams and Wilkins; 1972.

[9] Mulligan MS, Varani J, Dame MK, Lane CL, Smith CW, Anderson DC, et al. Role of endothelial-leukocyte adhesion molecule 1 (ELAM-1) in neutrophil-mediated lung injury in rats. J Clin Invest 1991;88:1396–406.

[10] Antibodies to endothelial cells [editorial]. Lancet 1991;337:649–50.

[11] Westphal JR, Boerbooms AMTH, Schalkwijk CJM, Kwast H, De Weijert M, Jacobs C, et al. Anti-endothelial cell antibodies in sera of patients with autoimmune diseases: comparison between ELISA and FACS analysis. Clin Exp Immunol 1994;96:444–9.

[12] Schoefl G. Studies on inflammation. III. Growing capillaries. Virchows Arch 1963;A337: 97–100.

[13] Szekanecz Z, Halloran MM, Haskell CJ, Shah MR, Polverini PJ, Koch AE. Mediators of angiogenesis: the role of cellular adhesion molecules. Trends Glycosci Glycotechnol 1999; 11:73–93.

[14] Albelda SM, Buck CA. Integrins and other cell adhesion molecules. FASEB J 1990;4: 2868–80.

[15] Springer TA. Adhesion receptors of the immune system. Nature 1990;346:425–33.

[16] Szekanecz Z, Szegedi G. Cell surface adhesion molecules: structure, function, clinical importance. Orv Hetil 1992;133:135–42.

[17] Carlos TM, Harlan JM. Leukocyte-endothelial adhesion molecules. Blood 1994;84:2068–101.

[18] Szekanecz Z, Szegedi G, Koch AE. Cellular adhesion molecules in rheumatoid arthritis. Regulation by cytokines and possible clinical importance. J Invest Med 1996;44:124–35.

[19] Haskard DO. Cell adhesion molecules in rheumatoid arthritis. Curr Opin Rheumatol 1995;7: 229–34.

[20] Koch AE, Turkiewicz W, Harlow LA, Pope RM. Soluble E-selectin in arthritis. Clin Immunol Immunopathol 1993;69:29–35.

[21] Walz G, Aruffo A, Kolanus W, Bevilacqua M, Seed B. Recognition by ELAM-1 of the sialyl-Lex determinant on myeloid and tumor cells. Science 1990;250:1132–5.

[22] Borges E, Tietz W, Steegmaier M, Moll T, Hallmann R, Hamann A, et al. P-selectin glycoprotein ligand-1 (PSGL-1) on T helper 1 but not on T helper 2 cells binds to P-selectin and supports migration into inflamed skin. J Exp Med 1997;185:573–8.

[23] Koch AE, Burrows JC, Haines GK, Carlos TM, Harlan JM, Leibovich SJ. Immunolocalization of leukocyte and endothelial adhesion molecules in human rheumatoid and osteoarthritic synovial tissue. Lab Invest 1991;64:313–20.

[24] McEver RP, Beckstead JH, Moore KL, Marshall-Carlson L, Bainton DF. GMP-140, a platelet alpha-granule membrane protein, is also synthesized by vascular endothelial cells and is localized in Weibel-Palade bodies. J Clin Invest 1989;84:92–9.

[25] Geng JG, Bevilacqua MP, Moore KL, McIntyre TM, Prescott SM, Kim JM, et al. Rapid neutrophil adhesion to activated endothelium mediated by GMP-140. Nature 1990;343: 757–60.

[26] Lawrence MB, Springer TA. Leukocytes roll on a selectin at physiologic flow rates: distinction from and prerequisite for adhesion through integrins. Cell 1991;65:859–73.

[27] Johnson B, Haines GK, Harlow LA, Koch AE. Adhesion molecule expression in human synovial tissues. Arthritis Rheum 1993;36:137–46.

[28] Ley K, Tedder TF, Kansas GS. L-selectin can mediate leukocyte rolling in untreated mesenteric venules in vivo independent of E- or P-selectin. Blood 1993;82:1632–8.

[29] Ichikawa Y, Shimizu H, Yoshida M, Takaya M, Arimori S. Accessory molecules expressed on the peripheral blood or synovial fluid T lymphocytes from patients with Sjogren's syndrome or rheumatoid arthritis. Clin Exp Rheumatol 1992;10:447–54.

[30] Bischoff J. Approaches to studying cell adhesion molecules in angiogenesis. Trends Cell Biol 1995;5:69–74.

[31] Albelda SM. Differential expression of integrin cell-substratum adhesion receptors on endothelium. EXS 1991;59:188–92.

[32] Brooks PC, Clark RA, Cheresh DA. Requirement of vascular integrin alpha v beta 3 for angiogenesis. Science 1994;264:569–71.

[33] El Gabalawy H, Wilkins J. Beta 1 (CD29) integrin expression in rheumatoid synovial membranes. J Rheumatol 1993;20:231–7.

[34] Thornhill MH, Haskard DO. IL-4 regulates endothelial cell activation by IL-1, tumor necrosis factor, or IFN-gamma. J Immunol 1990;145:865–72.

[35] Wilkinson LS, Edwards JC, Poston RN, Haskard DO. Expression of vascular cell adhesion molecule-1 in normal and inflamed synovium. Lab Invest 1993;68:82–8.

[36] Koch AE, Kronfeld-Harrington LB, Szekanecz Z, Cho MM, Haines GK, Harlow LA, et al. In situ expression of cytokines and cellular adhesion molecules in the skin of patients with systemic sclerosis. Pathobiology 1993;61:239–46.

[37] Pober JS, Gimbrone Jr MA, Lapierre LA, Mendrick DL, Fiers W, Rothlein R, et al. Overlapping patterns of activation of human endothelial cells by interleukin 1, tumor necrosis factor, and immune interferon. J Immunol 1986;137:1893–6.

[38] Salmi M, Kalimo K, Jalkanen S. Induction and function of vascular adhesion protein-1 at sites of inflammation. J Exp Med 1993;178:2255–60.

[39] Szekanecz Z, Haines GK, Lin TR, Harlow LA, Goerdt S, Rayan G, et al. Differential distribution of ICAM-1, ICAM-2 and ICAM-3, and the MS-1 antigen in normal and diseased human synovia. Arthritis Rheum 1994;37:221–31.

[40] Szekanecz Z, Haines GK, Harlow LA, Shah MR, Fong TW, Fu R, et al. Increased synovial expression of transforming growth factor (TGF)-β receptor endoglin and TGF-β1 in rheumatoid arthritis: possible interactions in the pathogenesis of the disease. Clin Immunol Immunopathol 1995;76:187–94.

[41] Haynes BF, Hale LP, Denning SM, Le PT, Singer KH. The role of leukocyte adhesion molecules in cellular interactions: implications for the pathogenesis of inflammatory synovitis. Springer Semin Immunopathol 1989;11:163–85.

[42] Piali L, Hammel P, Uherek C, Bachmann F, Gisler RH, Dunon D, et al. CD31/PECAM-1 is a ligand for alpha v beta 3 integrin involved in adhesion of leukocytes to endothelium. J Cell Biol 1995;130:451–60.

[43] Haynes BF, Hale LP, Patton KL, Martin ME, McCallum RM. Measurement of an adhesion molecule as an indicator of inflammatory disease activity. Up-regulation of the receptor for hyaluronate (CD44) in rheumatoid arthritis. Arthritis Rheum 1991;34:1434–43.

[44] Dejana E. Endothelial adherens junctions: implications in the control of vascular permeability and angiogenesis. J Clin Invest 1996;98:1949–53.

[45] Szekanecz Z, Koch AE. Intercellular adhesion molecule (ICAM)-3 expression on endothelial cells. Am J Pathol 1997;151:313–4.

[46] Butcher EC. Leukocyte-endothelial cell recognition: three (or more) steps to specificity and diversity. Cell 1991;67:1033–6.

[47] Lorant DE, Patel KD, McIntyre TM, McEver RP, Prescott SM, Zimmerman GA. Coexpression of GMP-140 and PAF by endothelium stimulated by histamine or thrombin: a juxtacrine system for adhesion and activation of neutrophils. J Cell Biol 1991;115:223–34.

[48] Lo SK, Lee S, Ramos RA, Lobb R, Rosa M, Chi-Rosso G, et al. Endothelial-leukocyte adhesion molecule 1 stimulates the adhesive activity of leukocyte integrin CR3 (CD11b/CD18, Mac-1) on human neutrophils. J Exp Med 1991;173:1493–500.

[49] Lorenzon P, Vecile E, Nardon E, Ferrero E, Harlan JM, Tedesco F, et al. Endothelial cell E- and P-selectin and vascular cell adhesion molecule-1 function as signaling receptors. J Cell Biol 1998;142:1381–91.

[50] Bombara MP, Webb DL, Conrad P, Marlor CW, Sarr T, Ranges GE, et al. Cell contact between T cells and synovial fibroblasts causes induction of adhesion molecules and cytokines. J Leukoc Biol 1993;54:399–406.

[51] Folkman J, Klagsbrun M. Angiogenic factors. Science 1987;235:442–7.

[52] Auerbach W, Auerbach R. Angiogenesis inhibition: a review. Pharmacotherapy 1994;63: 265–311.

[53] Koch AE. Angiogenesis: implications for rheumatoid arthritis. Arthritis Rheum 1998;41: 951–62.

[54] Szekanecz Z, Szegedi G, Koch AE. Angiogenesis in rheumatoid arthritis: pathogenic and clinical significance. J Invest Med 1998;46:27–41.

[55] Szekanecz Z, Koch AE. Chemokines and angiogenesis. Curr Opin Rheumatol 2001;13:202–8.

[56] Peichev M, Naiyer AJ, Pereira D, Zhu Z, Lane WJ, Williams M, et al. Expression of VEGFR-2

and AC133 by circulating human CD34(+) cells identifies a population of functional endothelial precursors. Blood 2000;95:952–8.

[57] Gehling UM, Ergun S, Schumacher U, Wagener C, Pantel K, Otte M, et al. In vitro differentiation of endothelial cells from AC133-positive progenitor cells. Blood 2000;95:3106–12.

[58] Eichmann A, Corbel C, Nataf V, Vaigot P, Breant C, Le-Douarin NM. Ligand-dependent development of the endothelial and hemopoietic lineages from embryonic mesodermal cells expressing vascular endothelial growth factor receptor 2. Proc Natl Acad Sci USA 1997;94:5141–6.

[59] Freedman SB, Isner JM. Therapeutic angiogenesis for ischemic cardiovascular disease. J Mol Cell Cardiol 2001;33:379–93.

[60] Isner JM, Baumgartner I, Rauh G, Schainfeld R, Blair R, Manor O, et al. Treatment of thromboangiitis obliterans (Buerger's disease) by intramuscular gene transfer of vascular endothelial growth factor: preliminary clinical results. J Vasc Surg 1998;28:964–73.

[61] Folkman J. Angiogenesis - retrospect and outlook. EXS 1991;59:4–13.

[62] Jackson CJ, Jenkins K, Schrieber L. Possible mechanisms of type I collagen-induced vascular tube formation. EXS 1991;59:198–204.

[63] Angiolillo AL, Kanegane H, Sgadari C, Reaman GH, Tosato G. Interleukin-15 promotes angiogenesis in vivo. Biochem Biophys Res Commun 1997;233:231–7.

[64] Park CC, Morel JC, Amin MA, Connors MA, Harlow LA, Koch AE. Evidence of IL-18 as a novel angiogenic mediator. J Immunol 2001;167:1644–53.

[65] Sachs L. Angiogenesis - cytokines as part of a network. EXS 1991;59:20–2.

[66] Halloran MM, Haskell CJ, Woods JM, Hosaka S, Koch AE. Interleukin-13 is an endothelial chemotaxin. Pathobiology 1997;65:287–92.

[67] Wijelath ES, Carlsen B, Cole T, Chen J, Kothari S, Hammond WP. Oncostatin M induces basic fibroblast growth factor expression in endothelial cells and promotes endothelial cell proliferation, migration and spindle morphology. J Cell Sci 1997;110:871–9.

[68] Strieter RM, Kunkel SL, Shanafelt AM, Arenberg DA, Koch AE, Polverini PJ. The role of C-X-C chemokines in regulation of angiogenesis. In: Koch AE, Strieter RM, editors. Chemokines in disease. Austin (TX): R.G. Landes Company; 1996. p. 195–209.

[69] Walz A, Kunkel SL, Strieter RM. C-X-C chemokines - an overview. In: Koch AE, Strieter RM, editors. Chemokines in disease. Austin (TX): R.G. Landes Company; 1996. p. 1–25.

[70] Moore BB, Keane MP, Addison CL, Arenberg DA, Strieter RM. CXC chemokine modulation of angiogenesis: the importance of balance between angiogenic and angiostatic members of the family. J Invest Med 1998;46:113–20.

[71] Koch AE, Volin MV, Woods JM, Kunkel SL, Connors MA, Harlow LA, et al. Regulation of angiogenesis by the C-X-C chemokines interleukin-8 and epithelial neutrophil activating peptide-78 in the rheumatoid joint. Arthritis Rheum 2001;44:31–40.

[72] Bazan JF, Bacon KB, Hardiman G, Wang W, Soo K, Rossi D, et al. A new class of membrane bound chemokine with a CX3C motif. Nature 1997;385:640–4.

[73] Ruth JH, Volin MV, Haines III GK, Woodruff DC, Katschke Jr KJ, Woods JM, et al. Fractalkine, a novel chemokine in rheumatoid arthritis and rat adjuvant-induced arthritis. Arthritis Rheum 2001;44:1568–81.

[74] Volin MV, Woods JM, Amin MA, Connors MA, Harlow LA, Koch AE. Fractalkine: a novel angiogenic chemokine in rheumatoid arthritis. Am J Pathol 2001;159:1521–6.

[75] Schonbeck U, Brandt E, Petersen F, Flad HD, Loppnow H. IL-8 specifically binds to endothelial but not to smooth muscle cells. J Immunol 1995;154:2375–83.

[76] Rinaldi N, Schwarz-Eywill M, Weis D, Leppelmann-Jansen P, Lukoschek M, Keilholz U, et al. Increased expression of integrins on fibroblast-like synoviocytes from rheumatoid arthritis in vitro correlates with enhanced binding to extracellular matrix proteins. Ann Rheum Dis 1991;56:45–51.

[77] Madri JA, Williams KS. Capillary endothelial cell cultures: phenotypic modulation by matrix components. J Cell Biol 1983;97:153–65.

[78] Nicosia RF, Bonanno E, Smith M. Fibronectin promotes the elongation of microvessels during angiogenesis in vitro. J Cell Physiol 1993;154:654–61.

[79] Canfield AE, Schor AM. Evidence that tenascin and thrombospondin-1 modulate sprouting of endothelial cells. J Cell Sci 1995;108:797–809.

[80] Vankemmelbeke MN, Holen I, Wilson AG, Ilic MZ, Handley CJ, Kelner GS, et al. Expression and activity of ADAMTS-5 in synovium. Eur J Biochem 2001;268:1259–68.

[81] Horak ER, Leek R, Klenk N, LeJeune S, Smith K, Stuart N, et al. Angiogenesis, assessed by platelet/endothelial cell adhesion molecule antibodies, as indicator of node metastases and survival in breast cancer. Lancet 1992;340:1120–4.

[82] Maier JA, Delia D, Thorpe PE, Gasparini G. In vitro inhibition of endothelial cell growth by the antiangiogenic drug AGM-1470 (TNP-470) and the anti-endoglin antiody TEC-11. Anti-cancer Drugs 1997;8:238–44.

[83] Halloran MM, Carley WW, Polverini PJ, Haskell CJ, Phan S, Anderson BJ, et al. Ley/H: an en-dothelial-selective, cytokine-inducible, angiogenic mediator. J Immunol 2000;164:4868–77.

[84] Neidhart M, Wehrli R, Bruhlmann P, Michel BA, Gay RE, Gay S. Synovial fluid CD146 (MUC18), a marker for synovial membrane angiogenesis in rheumatoid arthritis. Arthritis Rheum 1999;42:622–30.

[85] Leahy KM, Koki AT, Masferrer JL. Role of cyclooxygenases in angiogenesis. Curr Med Chem 2000;7:1163–70.

[86] Camussi G, Montrucchio G, Lupia E, De Martino A, Perona L, Arese M, et al. Platelet-activating factor directly stimulates in vitro migration of endothelial cells and promotes in vivo angiogenesis by a heparin-dependent mechanism. J Immunol 1995;154:6492–501.

[87] Waring PM, Carroll GJ, Kandiah DA, Buirski G, Metcalf D. Increased levels of leukemia inhibitory factor in synovial fluid from patients with rheumatoid arthritis and other inflamma-tory arthritides. Arthritis Rheum 1993;36:911–5.

[88] Volpert OV, Fong T, Koch AE, Peterson JD, Waltenbaugh C, Tepper RI, et al. Inhibition of angiogenesis by interleukin 4. J Exp Med 1998;188:1039–46.

[89] Strieter RM, Polverini PJ, Kunkel SL, Arenberg DA, Burdick MD, Kasper J, et al. The func-tional role of the ELR motif in CXC chemokine-mediated angiogenesis. J Biol Chem 1995; 270:27348–57.

[90] Szekanecz Z, Kunkel SL, Strieter RM, Koch AE. Chemokines in rheumatoid arthritis. Springer Semin Immunopathol 1998;20:115–32.

[91] Vicari AP, Ait-Yahia S, Chemin K, Mueller A, Zlotnik A, Caux C. Antitumor effects of the mouse chemokine 6Ckine/SLC through angiostatic and immunological mechanisms. J Immu-nol 2000;165:1992–2000.

[92] Dameron KM, Volpert OV, Tainsky MA, Bouck N. Control of angiogenesis in fibroblasts by p53 regulation of thrombospondin-1. Science 1994;265:1582–4.

[93] Kavanaugh AF, Davis LS, Nichols LA, Norris SH, Rothlein R, Scharschmidt LA, et al. Treat-ment of refractory rheumatoid arthritis with a monoclonal antibody to intercellular adhesion molecule 1. Arthritis Rheum 1994;37:992–9.

[94] Vuorte J, Lindsberg PJ, Kaste M, Meri S, Jansson SE, Rothlein R, et al. Anti-ICAM-1 mono-clonal antibody R6.5 (Enlimomab) promotes activation of neutrophils in whole blood. J Im-munol 1999;162:2353–7.

[95] Jasin HE, Lightfoot E, Davis LS, Rothlein R, Faanes RB, Lipsky PE. Amelioration of anti-gen-induced arthritis in rabbits treated with monoclonal antibodies to leukocyte adhesion mole-cules. Arthritis Rheum 1992;35:541–9.

[96] Barbadillo C, Arroyo A, Salas C, Mulero J, Sanchez-Madrid F, Andreu JL. Anti-integrin immunotherapy in rheumatoid arthritis: protective effect of anti-alpha 4 antibody in adjuvant arthritis. Springer Semin Immunopathol 1995;16:427–36.

[97] Iigo Y, Takashi T, Tamatani T, Miyasaka M, Higashida T, Yagita H, et al. ICAM-1-dependent pathway is critically involved in the pathogenesis of adjuvant arthritis in rats. J Immunol 1991; 147:4167–71.

[98] Sans M, Panes J, Ardite E, Elizalde JI, Arce Y, Elena M, et al. VCAM-1 and ICAM-1 mediate leukocyte-endothelial cell adhesion in rat experimental colitis. Gastroenterology 1999;116: 874–83.

[99] Orosz CG, Ohye RG, Pelletier RP, Van Buskirk AM, Huang E, Morgan C, et al. Treatment with anti-vascular cell adhesion molecule 1 monoclonal antibody induces long-term murine cardiac allograft acceptance. Transplantation 1993;56:453–60.

[100] Strand CV, Keystone E. Biologic agents for the treatment of rheumatoid arthritis. In: Ruddy S, Harris Jr ED, Sledge CB, Budd RC, Sergent JS, editors. Kelley's textbook of rheumatology. 6th edition. Philadelphia: WB Saunders; 2001. p. 899–912.

[101] Lin YS, Nguyen C, Mendoza JL, Escandon E, Fei D, Meng YG, et al. Preclinical pharmacokinetics, interspecies scaling, and tissue distribution of a humanized monoclonal antibody against vascular endothelial growth factor. J Pharmacol Exp Ther 1999;288:371–8.

[102] Skotnicki JS, Zask A, Nelson FC, Albright JD, Levin JI. Design and synthetic considerations of matrix metalloproteinase inhibitors. Ann N Y Acad Sci 1999;878:61–72.

ELSEVIER
SAUNDERS

RHEUMATIC
DISEASE CLINICS
OF NORTH AMERICA

Rheum Dis Clin N Am 30 (2004) 115–134

Dendritic cells: friend or foe in autoimmunity?

Frances Santiago-Schwarz, PhD[a,b,*]

[a]*Division of Rheumatology, State University of New York, Stony Brook, NY, USA*
[b]*Department of Biology, Farmingdale State University, 2350 Broadhollow Road,
Farmingdale, NY 11735, USA*

Historical overview on dendritic cell development and function

Dendritic cells (DCs) were described more than 30 years ago as potent activators of T-cell function in rodents [1]. Although their importance in human immunity was indicated not long thereafter [2–4], further understanding of normal and abnormal DC physiology was severely hampered by a lack of defined DC growth conditions and DC markers. Progress in overcoming these obstacles, together with studies of DC function, made it increasingly evident that DCs make up a complex lineage system that orchestrates immune responses. Aside from driving cell-mediated and humoral immunity that are meant to destroy "danger" in the form of infectious material, tumor cells, and so forth, there is ample evidence to support the idea that DCs are important in maintaining central and peripheral tolerance [5–7]. Thus, DCs may be viewed as double-edged swords of the immune system that promote stimulatory and inhibitory functions that are critical for host defenses and normal physiology.

DCs are well-equipped to present antigen to T cells by way of major histocompatibility complex (MHC) class I and II molecules and exhibit an abundance of coreceptors that are required for T-cell activation on their surface (eg, CD86, CD80.). They initiate a wide spectrum of antigen (Ag)-driven immune responses, including T-helper (TH1), TH2, CD8 and B-cell responses [5–7]. Their ability to stimulate naïve T-cell responses far surpasses that of other antigen presenting cells (APCs), including monocytes and B cells. The exceptional capacity of DCs to stimulate naïve T cells for active T-cell immunity initially was described convincingly in the allogeneic mixed leukocyte reaction (MLR); this assay remains the hallmark in vitro assay for assessing DC-mediated activation of naïve T cells.

This work was supported in part by a grant from the National Arthritis Foundation and by the Long Island Chapter of the Arthritis Foundation.

* Department of Biology, Farmingdale State University, 2350 Broadhollow Road, Farmingdale, NY 11735.

E-mail address: frances.santiago-schwarz@farmingdale.edu

An important recent realization is that DC-mediated functions, including those that occur in the MLR, may represent the induction of T regulatory cells with suppressive capacity and not necessarily active T-cell immunity [8–10]. The ability of DCs to interact with a wide variety of cellular and noncellular components of the innate immune system also establishes them as previously unrecognized liaisons between innate and acquired immunity [5,11,12].

Dendritic cell ontogeny and subtypes

Vital to progress in human DC biology was the description of a means for obtaining large numbers of this scarce cell type for further phenotypic and functional characterization. This was accomplished more than 10 years ago with the in vitro institution of the DC hematopoietic pathway from human cord blood or bone marrow–derived multipotent progenitors using defined growth factors [13–15]. The development of mature DCs from human peripheral blood precursors also was a milestone; it provided a ready source of DCs for use in clinical trials [16,17]. Notwithstanding the substantial progress that has been made in the areas of DC growth and development in recent years, opposing viewpoints have emerged about whether DC functional heterogeneity is appointed at the cellular level or is dictated by the environment [6]. This situation is complicated by phenotypic and functional differences between mouse and human subtypes [6]. Some investigators argue that functionally specialized DC subtypes arise from committed cells that represent specific DC lineages. Other investigators contend that there is no lineage compartmentalization of DCs and that they are highly plastic and acquire specific functions depending on the environment [18–20]. In both views, there is indication that mature DCs are more resistant to external influences than their precursors [21], a feature that is not uncommon in cells of hematopoietic origin.

The development and function of myeloid dendritic cells

Despite some controversy, the growing consensus concerning the DC lineage system is that distinct DC developmental pathways advance from unique progenitors, that particular cytokines drive development within each pathway, and that immature and mature DCs that arise from each pathway display specialized abilities to either stimulate or inhibit the immune response. At least three distinct DC developmental pathways that involve the myeloid and lymphoid lineages have been described (Fig. 1). Within the human myeloid DC lineage, two distinct pathways may develop from CD34$^+$ progenitor cells [22–24]. One pathway yields the monocyte (mono)-derived DC (also known as the CD14-derived DC and DC1). Intermediate developmental stages of this pathway include: myelodendritic progenitor cells that exhibit monocyte, granulocyte, and DC differentiating potential; CD14^{dim} precursors with either DC or monocyte differentiating potential; and CD14^{dim} CD1a$^+$ precursors which are DC committed and develop

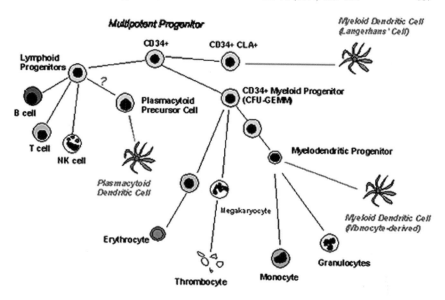

Fig. 1. The DC lineage system. Each lineage is driven by specific growth factors; phenotypic features can identify various stages within each line. Although myeloid DCs are clearly of myeloid origin, the exact branch-off point of plasmacytoid-derived DCs within the lymphoid pathway is still uncertain. Plasmacytoid precursor cells exhibit limited proliferative potential. CFU-GEMM, colony forming unit granulocyte–erythrocyte–macrophage–megakaryocyte; NK, natural killer.

from $CD14^{dim}$ precursors [22,23,25]. Monocyte-derived DCs also can be generated from peripheral blood monocytes. Granulocyte macrophage colony stimulating factor (GM-CSF) and interleukin (IL)-4 (or IL-13) are required for the initiation of DC maturation events from peripheral blood monocytes; terminal differentiation is accomplished in the presence of a "danger" signal, such as tumor necrosis factor (TNF) or lipopolysaccharide (LPS) [17,26–29]. Because of ready availability, peripheral blood monocytes are the most common source of DCs for in vitro studies and immunotherapy protocols that are directed against cancer and other diseases. Peripheral blood monocytes do not proliferate and are advanced in the DC hematopoietic pathway; therefore, limitations to this approach include restrictions in cell yield and bias toward a particular cell stage.

The second myeloid DC pathway produces the CD14-independent DC subtype (Langerhans cell [LC]) and includes $CD14^{neg}CD1a^{+}$ precursors [22,24,30]. A distinct $CD34^{+}CLA^{+}$ (cutaneous leukocyte antigen) progenitor was shown to preferentially yield CD14-independent DCs (LCs); this indicated that myeloid DC subtypes may be designated as a separate lineage during early stages of hematopoiesis [31]. In further support of the idea that discrete DC developmental pathways exist, highly proliferative myelodendritic progenitors that exhibit the capacity to yield monocytes, granulocytes, or DCs in the proper growth setting have been described in vitro and in vivo [25,32]. In vitro, the progenitors develop from $CD34^{+}$ cells after neutralization of TNF activity; in vivo, they are abundant in rheumatoid synovial fluid but not in osteoarthritis synovial fluid.

TNF/GM-CSF ± transforming growth factor β (TGFβ) seem to be primary growth factors for the CD14-independent (LC) pathway [33,34], whereas the monocyte-derived pathway is best established with TNF/GM-CSF + IL-4 or IL-13 [35–37]. Other cytokines that are important to the development of myeloid DCs include IL-1 and IL-6, which are accessory cytokines provoked by CD40 ligand (CD40L), TNF, GM-CSF [38–40], and interferon (IFN)-α, which favors the terminal maturation of monocyte-derived DCs.[41] Stem cell factor (SCF) is commonly used to increase DC yield from $CD34^+$ progenitors and acts by suppressing apoptosis and increasing the self-renewal potential of DC progenitors [42]. CD14-derived and CD14-independent myeloid DCs stimulate potent MLRs. In humans, CD14-derived DCs may preferentially activate TH1 cells that promote inflammatory-type responses (eg, IFNγ, IL-1, TNF) [36,43,44]. CD14-derived DCs also activate B cells to secrete IgM [22,45]. In psoriasis and atopic asthma, distinct DC subtypes activate either TH1 or TH2 responses [46,47]; this supports the existence of pathologic associations between DC subtypes and TH cell subsets and raises the prospect of redirecting pathogenic T-cell responses to nonpathogenic T-cell responses in these diseases.

Early control of myeloid dendritic cell hematopoiesis

The early regulatory mechanisms that control the in vitro development of myeloid DCs from multipotent progenitors involve a highly orchestrated series of proliferative, apoptotic, and developmental events (GM-CSF and TGFβ and the TNF, CD95, and bcl-2 protein families) [48–50]. Both myeloid DC pathways develop simultaneously from $CD34^+$ cord blood progenitors that are treated with GM-CSF/TNF ± SCF [22,23,50]. Although both pathways are produced, the CD-14 independent DC (Langerhens cell) pathway prevails in this model [22,23,50]. TNF must be present during the earliest phases of DC growth (within 48 hrs) for the institution of DC hematopoiesis from $CD34^+$ progenitors [25,51]. The mechanism of action that involves TNF at this level is a complex balance between its positive and negative effects. TNF facilitates the selection of myeloid DCs by upregulating GM-CSF receptors on DC progenitors, by promoting fas-mediated apoptosis of nonmyeloid and granulocytic progenitors, and by favoring the production of secondary cytokines, such as IL-6 [25,50,51]. If TNF activity is inhibited within 48 hours of cytokine exposure, DC growth is halted and granulocytopoiesis is favored [51].

A new role for tumor necrosis factor in myeloid dendritic cell development

Despite the absolute requirement for TNF during the earliest phases of DC growth from $CD34^+$ progenitors, neutralization of TNF activity at a later time point (Day 3) yields a distinct deviation in myeloid DC development [51]. Instead of downregulating the DC pathway and favoring granulocyte development, anti-TNF treatment provokes the selective expansion of the monocyte-derived DC pathway [25]. After an initial decrease in cell proliferation, a gradual rebound in cell growth yields a shift toward the monocyte-derived DC pathway, as judged by increases in $CD14^+CD1a^+$ DC precursors and the expansion of myelodendritic progenitors that express CD115 (macrophage colony stimulating factor [M-CSF] receptor), CD33, and class II major histocompatibility complex antigen (DR) [25]. The myelodendritic progenitors exhibit colony-forming unit potential in semisolid media and differentiate along the granulocytic, monocytic, and monocyte-derived DC lineages when cultured with the appropriate cytokine combinations. MLR stimulatory potential, however, is achieved only when myelodendritic cells are treated with cytokines that are known to produce mature DCs. The ability to generate monocyte-derived DCs from self-renewing myelodendritic progenitors provides a powerful means for studying the phenotypic and functional features of the monocyte-derived DC pathway. Because monocyte-derived DCs preferentially activate TH1 responses, this system is particularly useful for studying mechanisms of TH1 responses. These results also indicate that removal of danger signals (TNF) from the immediate environment can arrest the development of committed myeloid DC progenitors into mature DCs. The important implications of these observations for the treatment of autoimmune diseases, such as rheumatoid arthritis (RA), are discussed later.

The development and function of plasmacytoid dendritic cells

A third, less understood, DC subtype is the plasmacytoid cell–derived DC. The term "plasmacytoid cell" was originally used to describe an unusual cell that exhibited plasma cell-like morphology in lymphoid tissue. Because plasmacytoid cells lacked typical B-cell surface markers and exhibited a nonclassic distribution of molecules that are normally associated with T cells (CD4, CD38) and myeloid cells (CD123, CD68), they were designated as "plasmacytoid T-cells" or "plasmacytoid monocytes" [52]. Links to the DC pathway and acquired immunity were established with the ability to generate mature DCs with T-cell stimulatory capacity from plasmacytoid cells in vitro using IL-3 (the ligand for CD123) ± CD40L [36,52–54]. These mature DCs are commonly termed "plasmacytoid DCs" (also known as lymphoid-like DCs and DC2) to reflect their origin from the plasmacytoid precursors and are indistinguishable morphologically from mature myeloid DCs. The unique ability of plasmacytoid cells to secrete large amounts of type I IFN (α/β) in response to certain viruses and other microbial stimuli established these cells as the elusive IFN-producing cells in human blood and as having important functional links to innate immunity [55,56].

Plasmacytoid DCs may develop from thymic progenitors with IL-3, but not GM-CSF, and from lymphoid precursors in human tonsil with CD40L [6,52]. The advancement of plasmacytoid DCs from cord blood or bone marrow–derived progenitors that also have the potential to mature into T and natural killer cells with IL-3, CD40L, and fms-like tyrosine kinase 3 ligand (Flt-3 ligand), provides further evidence that plasmacytoid DCs are of lymphoid origin [18,57,58]. Other lines of evidence include the inhibition of plasmacytoid DC growth by transcription factors (id proteins) that are specifically known to suppress the differentiation of lymphoid cells [59] and the presence in plasmacytoid DCs of several gene products that are associated with lymphoid, and not myeloid, cell development [60–62]. The gene products include B-cell transcripts, such as immunoglobulin κ and λ chains, the lymphoid-restricted transcription factor Spi-B, and the pre-T antigen receptor α chain. Despite the well-documented generation of plasmacytoid DCs from lymphoid progenitors, the ability to generate these cells from certain myeloid progenitors [19] raises the possibility that, at least under certain conditions, they can be derived from nonlymphoid progenitors. In the mouse, in vivo administration of Flt-3 ligand resulted in the marked expansion of myeloid and plasmacytoid DCs; this indicated common regulatory mechanisms for the distinct phenotypes [63]. Further in vivo and clonal analysis should yield additional insight into the ontogeny and function of the DC lineage system.

Although initial studies in humans demonstrated that plasmacytoid DCs that were generated with IL-3 and CD40L preferentially activated TH2 type responses over TH1 type responses [36] and were costimulators of CD8$^+$ T cells [18], a recent study indicated that plasmacytoid DCs that are activated by influenza virus and CD40L selectively drive TH1 responses [53]. Thus, it is possible that, depending on the stimuli, plasmacytoid DCs can activate CD4$^+$ TH1 or TH2 cell subsets. In contrast with human peripheral blood, which contains an equal proportion of immature plasmacytoid and monocyte DCs, the principal DC component in the thymus is the plasmacytoid cell [64]. Within lymphoid tissue, such as the thymus, plasmacytoid DC-mediated activation of T regulatory cells was suggested as a principal mechanism in the prevention of autoreactive clones. Evolving ideas are that DC-activated T regulatory cells maintain central tolerance in the thymic medulla and peripheral tolerance in T-cell areas of lymphoid tissue [65].

The significance of pattern recognition receptors and receptors with inhibitory motifs on dendritic cells

The differential distribution of immunoglobulin-like transcript-like (ILT) receptors and pattern recognition molecules, such as toll-like receptors (TLRs), allows further functional and lineage distinction between plasmacytoid and myeloid DCs. The ILT family of cell receptors is made up of members that exhibit either inhibitory or activating motifs on the cytoplasmic side of the cell. The ultimate signaling outcome that is mediated by these opposing receptors is governed by a complex set of events that involve coligation of receptors and phosphorylation/dephosphorylation events that are involved in signal transduction [66]. Although ILT2 is expressed by all lymphoid and myelomonocytic cell types, including DCs, other ILTs display a more restricted cellular distribution. These include ILT3 and ILT4, which are expressed selectively in monocytes, macrophages, and DCs [67,68]. Recent studies indicate that the overexpression of inhibitory motif–bearing ILT3 and ILT4 receptors on monocyte-derived DCs might be associated with the induction of tolerance and the prevention of auto-immune diseases [68].

Toll-like receptors are an ancient family of receptors that recognize highly conserved molecular patterns on a wide spectrum of pathogens and are abundant on DCs [69]. The engagement of toll-like receptors by pathogenic material constitutes an early danger signal to the immune system and leads to the pro-duction of proinflammatory mediators. The differential expression of toll-like receptors on myeloid and plasmacytoid DCs indicates that these DC subtypes evolved to handle different pathogens [70–72]. For example, monocyte-derived DCs express toll-like receptors such as TLR2, TLR4, and TLR6 to interact with peptidoglycans and lipoproteins (including LPS) and respond to these danger signals by secreting large quantities of TNF and IL-6. Plasmacytoid DCs express TLR7 and TLR9 to interact with undermethylated bacterial cytosine guanine (CG) dinucleotide (CpG motifs) and secrete large quantities of IFNα [73].

Dendritic cell maturation stages and immunogenic dendritic cells

DC functions also are related to stages of maturity. Fully-matured DCs express high levels of class I/II MHC and T-cell costimulatory molecules and deliver antigenic signals to T cells in a MHC-restricted manner, but do not efficiently ingest or process Ag. Conversely, immature myeloid DCs, that do not have as much class I/II MHC and T-cell costimulatory molecules, present Ag poorly but avidly ingest and process Ag (Fig. 2) [5,6,12]. Besides capturing and processing foreign Ag that is acquired from pathogens by way of complement, Fc, and mannose receptors, immature myeloid DCs may acquire immunogens from autologous cells that are undergoing apoptotic death by way of receptors, such as CD36, CD91, and CD14 [74–82]. All of these molecules may associate with heat shock proteins (hsp), which are released from damaged or stressed cells. Hsps chaperone immunogens into the DC, and, once inside the antigen presenting cell, facilitate movement along the intracellular pathways that are associated with antigen presentation [83,84]. In this fashion, antigen that is acquired from infected apoptotic cells may be presented on the surface of mature DCs by way of class I or class II MHC molecules, even though the DCs were never infected with the pathogen. The process of acquiring antigen for representation in this manner is termed "cross-presentation." Cross-presentation may lead to either cross-priming or cross-tolerance, depending on factors, such as the number of cells that are undergoing apoptosis and the type of cytokines that are released into the microenvironment [5,6].

Unlike immature myeloid (monocyte-derived) DCs, monocyte macrophages (mΦs) do not process ingested antigen that is acquired from apoptotic cells for class I/II MHC presentation [77,78]. Instead, these cells completely degrade ingested apoptotic material and secrete high levels of IL-10. This limits antigen-presenting cell development and function and contributes to a state of tolerance. Immature monocyte-derived DCs that acquired antigen but have escaped matu-ration stimuli also contribute to immunosuppression by stimulating T regulatory

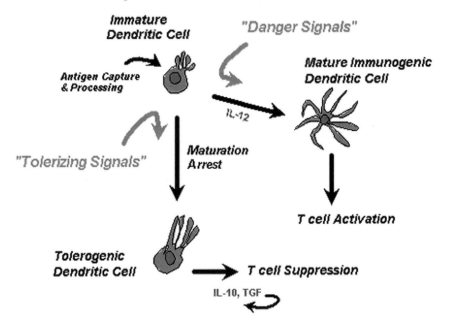

Fig. 2. The development of immunogenic versus tolerogenic dendritic cells. The type of dendritic cell response that is generated from immature myeloid DCs is highly regulated and is influenced greatly by external stimuli. The development of immunogenic DCs that express high levels of class I and II MHC molecules and T cell costimulatory receptors occurs when active immunity toward pathogens is required and is triggered by danger signals, such as TNF, LPS, dsRNA, and inflammatory cytokines. Tolerizing DCs that develop in the absence of such signals and in the presence of immunosuppressive signals, such as IL-10, are deficient in surface MHC and T-cell costimulatory molecules. The development of tolerizing DCs is believed to prevail during normal physiology as a means to guard against autoimmunity and during regulation of established immune reactions. Within the plasmacytoid DC subtype (not shown), IFNα seems to be the danger stimulus that directs immature plasmacytoid DCs toward an immunogenic phenotype.

cells that secrete IL-10 [5,89]. Of great physiologic importance, autoreactivity may develop when immature monocyte-derived DCs are exposed to high levels of apoptotic cells and proinflammatory cytokines, such as TNF, IL-1, and IFNγ [78].

Dendritic cell maturation stages and tolerogenic dendritic cells

The complexity of the DC lineage system is intensified by the ability of DCs to silence immune responses. Emerging concepts are that tolerogenic DCs normally make up a steady-state cell lineage that controls ongoing immune responses and prevents autoimmunity by repressing antigen-specific T-cell responsiveness. A tolerogenic DC phenotype can be displayed by immature monocyte–derived DCs that have escaped maturation stimuli (either partially or completely) (see Fig. 2) and immature or mature plasmacytoid cell–derived DCs [8,68, 85–91]. Although the exact process for promoting T-cell suppression is still unclear, various mechanisms may be involved, including the induction of T-cell anergy, T-cell apoptosis, T regulatory cells, and immunoregulatory cytokines by T cells. Immature myeloid DCs and immature and mature plasmacytoid DCs may activate $CD4^+$ and $CD8^+$ T regulatory cells [73]. Insight into the generation of tolerogenic DCs was acquired from animal models where repeated stimulation of immature DCs in the absence of "danger" signals, such as inflammatory cytokines, led to the development of regulatory T cells that suppress the formation of cytotoxic T cells [90]. In other instances, DCs that were propagated from mouse progenitors in the absence of TNF (with IL-3 and CD40L) promote regulatory T cells, that, when administered in vivo, prolong cardiac allografts [68]. In experimental animal models of type 1 diabetes or multiple sclerosis, suppression of disease after injection of tolerogenic DCs was associated with the induction of T regulatory cells and the ability of these T cells to produce IL-10 [68].

Evidence indicates that IL-10 and TGFβ production by T regulatory cells contributes to tolerance by limiting the distribution of MHC class II and costimulatory molecules on the DCs [85,91]. Other findings suggest CD40 as a key determinant on immunogenic DCs by showing that inhibition of the Rel B transcription factor produces $CD40^{neg}$ tolerogenic DCs that exhibit the capacity to generate IL-10–producing T regulatory cells [92]. In a recent human preclinical study, in vivo responses to recall antigens were greatly suppressed when normal volunteers were injected with in vitro antigen-primed immature DCs. [8] This effect was in marked contrast to the active immunity that was achieved with mature DCs and was linked to the generation of regulatory type $CD4^+$ and $CD8^+$ T cells and the production of IL-10. Although an important conclusion from this human study is that immature DCs must be avoided for vaccination with tumor antigens, it was instrumental in establishing the potential use of immature tolerogenic DCs as a powerful tool for the treatment of autoimmune and transplant-rejection diseases.

Abnormal expansion and function of monocyte-derived dendritic cells in rheumatoid arthritis

The idea that DCs play an important role in driving immunopathogenic responses that lead to the establishment of chronic proliferative synovitis and joint destruction in RA is not new [32,93–103]. Although much remains to be known about the mechanisms that regulate DC activity in RA, recent advances imply abnormal development and function within the monocyte-derived DC pathway. Consistent with the systemic nature of RA, abnormalities that are related to DC development and function in the periphery and the diseased joint exist. Distinct DC stages of myeloid DCs may be represented in different synovial microenvironments and in peripheral blood [93–96,98]. In the circulation, elevated levels of immature ($CD34^+CD33^+$) myeloid DC progenitors exist [96]. These cells develop in vitro into mature DCs with DC growth factors (GM-CSF/TNF/IL-1/SCF). In inflamed RA synovial tissue, most APCs exhibit the phenotype of fully matured DCs, with high levels of class I and II MHC Ag, T-cell costimulatory molecules, and nuclear versus cytoplasmic expression of the transcription factor RelB [95]. In contrast to RA synovial tissue, RA synovial fluid (RASF) may be enriched in immature DCs that express a phenotype similar to that exhibited by nonproliferating $CD14^{dim}CD33^+$ DC precursors of the myeloid lineage [101]. In another study, RA synovial fluid contained $CD34^{neg}$ $CD33^+CD115^+CD14^{\pm}$ myelodendritic progenitors that displayed extensive proliferative capacity and DC differentiating potential [32]. Thus, the rheumatoid synovial fluid space may be a reservoir for cells that represent multiple stages of the monocyte-derived DC lineage. Mature DCs, either present in RA synovial fluid initially or derived from the DC progenitors, elicit potent TH1 responses over TH2 responses. This suggests a primary mechanism for the generation of TH1 type responses, which are believed to be important to inflammation in RA [104–108].

The development and immunologic potential of DCs in RA seems to be dictated by ontogeny and the environment. Because $CD34^+CD33^+$ myeloid progenitors are lacking in the RA joint, circulating $CD34^+CD33^+$ progenitors may home to the RA joint where they are immediately subject to the differentiating effects of inflammatory cytokines [96]. Many of the proinflammatory cytokines that are highly expressed in the RA joint, including TNF, IL-6, IL-1, and GM-CSF, are myeloid DC growth factors [32]. SCF levels also are highly increased in RA synovial fluid versus normal peripheral blood and osteoarthritis synovial fluid [109]. Because SCF increases the yield of monocyte-derived DCs considerably when combined with GM-CSF and TNF by amplifying the self-renewal potential of DC progenitors [110,111], the presence of this factor in the RA joint may help to sustain progenitors that are advanced beyond the $CD34^+CD33^+$ stage.

IL-4 and IL-13 exhibit many overlapping functions and are powerful growth factors for monocyte-derived DCs [112]. Although IL-4 levels are not increased in RA [106,113], there is an abnormal increase in biologically-active IL-13, especially in the circulation [114], In patients who have RA, circulating levels of myeloid DC growth factors, including TNF, GM-CSF, IL-6, and IL-13, are reduced dramatically after short-term therapy with TNF antagonists [114,115]. This reduction occurs with a concomitant increase in M-CSF [114]. M-CSF is a cytokine that promotes the growth of nonantigen-presenting monocytes and does not sustain DC growth [25,32]. Biologic testing of sera after anti-TNF therapy in vitro revealed a lack of DC growth and the development of monocytes [114]. Thus, a mechanism for effective anti-TNF therapy in RA might include the development of monocytes (or immature DCs) that exhibit a suppressive, rather than an activating, phenotype.

Besides driving TH1 inflammatory responses, myeloid DCs may mediate other immune responses in RA, such as Ig (rheumatoid factor [RF]) synthesis by B cells and IFNγ synthesis by $CD8^+$ T cells [22,23,116]. Immature DCs also may contribute to autoimmunity by cross-presenting immunogens that are acquired from apoptotic cells. In support of DC-driven cross-priming events in the RASF space, dramatic increases in inducible hsp70 exist in RASF (Santiago-Schwarz

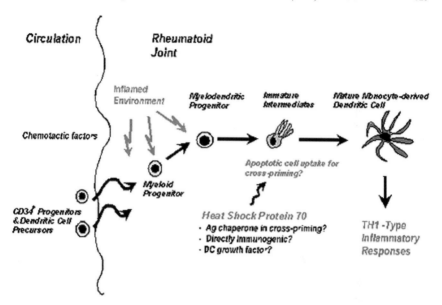

Fig. 3. The monocyte-derived dendritic cell pathway in RA. Immediately upon the DC's entry, the inflamed environment (containing several monocyte-derived DC growth factors) instructs differentiation toward the monocyte-derived DC pathway. As described for other autoimmune diseases, immature myeloid DCs ingesting and processing immunogens acquired from dying cells would develop in the context of inflammatory "danger" signals into mature immunogenic DCs. This representation does not take into account the possibility that other DC subtypes that have distinct effector/suppressor functions are amplified in RA and is not meant to diminish the importance of abnormalities that are related to nonimmune cells, such as fibroblasts in joint pathology.

et al, in press). A schematic representation of events that concern the myeloid-derived DC lineage is illustrated in Fig. 3. The final outcome of DC-driven events ultimately may be dictated by the proportion of factors that promote and inhibit the growth and function of particular members of the DC lineage system, and by the nature of factors that regulate the trafficking of DCs in the synovial space. Consistent with DC trafficking into the joint, studies of the chemokine/chemokine receptor system in RA indicate that there is selective recruitment of DC precursors that express receptors for inflammatory-type chemokines, such as CCR1, CCR2, CCR5, and CCR6, by inflammatory chemokines, such as macrophage inhibitory protein 3α (MIP-3α) [117,118].

Immunogenic dendritic cells and cross-priming in other autoimmune diseases

There is increasing evidence that cross-priming contributes to autoimmunity in systemic lupus erythematosus (SLE) and autoimmune type diabetes [75,82, 119,120]. In an evolving scenario that is supported by animal models of autoimmune diabetes and SLE, cross-priming of self antigens occurs when apoptotic/necrotic cell uptake is accompanied by "danger signals" that promote DC activation and maturation [121]. Thus, in the proper setting, self antigens that are present in damaged cells may be chaperoned by hsp into immature DCs for re-presentation by MHC molecules on mature DCs.

In humans who have SLE, there is strong evidence that abnormal clearance of apoptotic cells (because of defects in receptors that mediate apoptotic cell uptake, such as C1q) represents an important underlying abnormality that contributed to the development of autoimmunity [75,122]. A delay in apoptotic cell uptake would lead to the release of inflammatory mediators and intracellular antigens into the extracellular space [84]. Immature DCs that recognize these apoptotic cells (or necrotic cells produced by secondary necrosis) would process self antigens that were acquired from them for re-presentation to autologous T cells [83,84]. Unlike RA, which displays a predominant TH1 inflammatory cytokine profile that is provoked by monocyte-derived DCs, immune cell activity in SLE is linked with the overproduction of type I IFN, presumably by immature plasmacytoid DCs [123–125]. Thus, IFNα may be the primary danger signaling–molecule in this disease.

Interesting models that illustrate the complexity of cellular and noncellular interactions and the involvement of IFNα and plasmacytoid and monocyte-derived DCs in SLE have emerged (Fig. 4) [123–125]. In these models, initiating

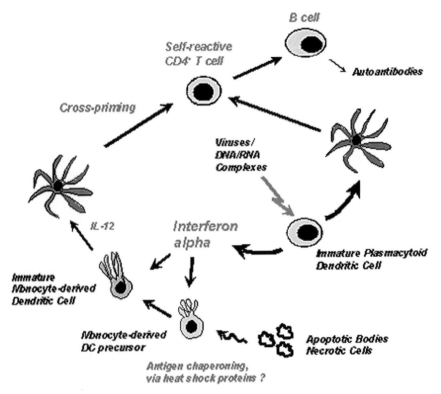

Fig. 4. Proposed DC-mediated events driving autoimmune responses in SLE. Triggering of IFNα may be prompted by DNA/RNA immune complexes or by viral stimuli.

events in genetically predisposed individuals include the induction of large amounts of IFNα (by viruses or apoptotic cell–derived nucleic acids?) from immature plasmacytoid DCs. IFNα drives the terminal maturation of monocyte-derived DCs that are primed with self antigens that were acquired from apoptotic cells [41,123]. The mature DCs activate self-reactive T-helper clones, which, in turn, sustain the maturation of B cells that secrete autoantibodies. Plasmacytoid DCs also activate T-helper cells to sustain B-cell development and autoantibody production. The idea that IFNα contributes to the development of other autoimmune diseases was substantiated by the induction of RA in patients who were undergoing IFNα therapy for malignancies [126].

Summary

The large amount of information that has been acquired from human and animal models substantiates that the DC lineage system represents a double-edged sword in the immune system. Presumably, in normal physiology, tolerizing DCs guard against autoimmunity and control established immune reactions, whereas immunogenic DCs provide active host defenses. In autoimmune diseases, there is strong evidence to support the idea that tolerance is overridden by the development of immunogenic DCs that favor cross-priming. Based on the wide range of possible clinical applications, it is not surprising that manipulation of DCs for clinical benefit is rampant. Indeed, multiple clinical strategies are currently underway, including the development of DC immunotherapy for cancer vaccines and graft survival. In cancer, DC-based vaccines for solid tumors, such as melanoma, were well-tolerated and produced beneficial antitumor responses, even in patients who had advanced disease [127,128]. Although initial trials such as these are highly promising, the ultimate goal is to develop DC-based strategies that will lead to highly specific, long-lasting immunity against the cancer cells. In autoimmune diseases and transplant settings, the goal is to devise strategies that will block the initiation and maintenance of autoreactive and antigraft responses, respectively. Specific strategies for autoimmune diseases might include interference with cross-priming events that activate autoreactive T cells and genetic engineering to introduce molecules that have immunosuppressive functions, such as IL-10, TGFβ, Fas ligand, ILT3, and ILT4. Successful application to these diseases will necessitate high specificity. In this regard, recent preliminary studies that described antigen-specific suppression of a primed immune response by tolerogenic DCs are especially informative [92].

Acknowledgments

The author is grateful to Michael Valentino for assistance in the preparation of the manuscript and to Drs. Carla A. Martin and Stanley Zucker for helpful discussions.

References

[1] Steinman RM, Cohn ZA. Identification of a novel cell type in peripheral lymphoid organs of mice. II. Functional properties in vitro. J Exp Med 1974;139:380–97.

[2] Santiago-Schwarz F, Bakke AC, Woodward JG, O'Brien RL, Horwitz DA. Further characterization of low density mononuclear cells: FACS-assisted analysis of human MLR stimulators. J Immunol 1985;134:779–85.

[3] Santiago-Schwarz F, Woodward JG, Dixon JF, Parker JW, Frelinger JA, O'Brien RL. Low-density mononuclear cells. Potent stimulators of the human MLR. Transplantation 1983;35: 463–9.

[4] Van Voorhis W, Hair LS, Steinman RM, Kaplan G. Human dendritic cells: enrichment and characterization from peripheral blood. J Exp Med 1982;115:1172–87.

[5] Savill J, Dransfield I, Gregory C, Haslett C. A blast from the past: clearance of apoptotic cells regulates immune responses. Nat Rev Immunol 2002;2:965–75.

[6] Shortman K, Liu YJ. Mouse and human dendritic cell subtypes. Nat Rev Immunol 2002;2: 151–61.

[7] Steinman RM, Nussenzweig MC. Avoiding horror autotoxicus: the importance of dendritic cells in peripheral T cell tolerance. Proc Natl Acad Sci USA 2002;99:351–8.

[8] Dhodapkar MV, Steinman RM, Krasovsky J, Munz C, Bhardwaj N. Antigen-specific inhibition of effector T cell function in humans after injection of immature dendritic cells. J Exp Med 2001;193:233–8.

[9] Jonuleit H, Schmitt E, Steinbrink K, Enk AH. Dendritic cells as a tool to induce anergic and regulatory T cells. Trends Immunol 2001;22:394–400.

[10] Khanna A, Morelli AE, Zhong C, Takayama T, Lu L, Thomson AW. Effects of liver-derived dendritic cell progenitors on Th1- and Th2-like cytokine responses in vitro and in vivo. J Immunol 2000;164:1346–54.

[11] Moretta A. Natural killer cells and dendritic cells: rendezvous in abused tissues. Nat Rev Immunol 2002;2:957–64.

[12] Palucka K, Banchereau J. Dendritic cells: a link between innate and adaptive immunity. J Clin Immunol 1999;19:12–25.

[13] Caux C, Dezutter-Dambuyant C, Schmitt D, Banchereau J. GM-CSF and TNF-α cooperate in the generation of dendritic langerhans cells. Nature 1992;360:258–61.

[14] Reid CD, Stackpoole A, Meager A, Tikerpae J. Interactions of tumor necrosis factor with granulocyte-macrophage colony-stimulating factor and other cytokines in the regulation of dendritic cell growth in vitro from early bipotent CD34 + progenitors in human bone marrow. J Immunol 1992;149:2681–8.

[15] Santiago-Schwarz F, Belilos E, Diamond B, Carsons SE. TNF in combination with GM-CSF enhances the differentiation of neonatal cord blood stem cells into dendritic cells and macrophages. J Leukoc Biol 1992;52:274–81.

[16] Romani N, Reider D, Heuer M, Ebner S, Kampgen E, Eibl B, et al. Generation of mature dendritic cells from human blood. An improved method with special regard to clinical applicability. J Immunol Methods 1996;196:137–51.

[17] Sallusto F, Lanzavecchia A. Efficient presentation of soluble antigen by cultured human dendritic cells is maintained by granulocyte/macrophage colony-stimulating factor plus interleukin 4 and downregulated by tumor necrosis factor alpha. J Exp Med 1994;179:1109–18.

[18] Galy A, Travis M, Cen D, Chen B. Human T, B, natural killer, and dendritic cells arise from a common bone marrow progenitor cell subset. Immunity 1995;3:459–73.

[19] Olweus J, BitMansour A, Warnke R, Thompson PA, Carballido J, Picker LJ, et al. Dendritic cell ontogeny: a human dendritic cell lineage of myeloid origin. Proc Natl Acad Sci USA 1997; 94:12551–6.

[20] Traver D, Akashi K, Manz M, Merad M, Miyamoto T, Engleman EG, et al. Development of CD8alpha-positive dendritic cells from a common myeloid progenitor. Science 2000;290: 2152–4.

[21] Pulendran B, Banchereau J, Maraskovsky E, Maliszewski C. Modulating the immune response with dendritic cells and their growth factors. Trends Immunol 2001;22:41–7.

[22] Caux C, Massacrier C, Vanbervliet B, Dubois B, Durand I, Cella M, et al. CD34+ hematopoietic progenitors from human cord blood differentiate along two independent dendritic cell pathways in response to granulocyte-macrophage colony-stimulating factor plus tumor necrosis factor: II Functional analysis. Blood 1997;90:1458–70.

[23] Caux C, Vanbervliet B, Massacrier C, Dezutter-Dambuyant C, de Saint-Vis B, Jacquet C, et al. CD34+ hematopoietic progenitors from human cord blood differentiate along two independent dendritic cell pathways in response to GM-CSF+ TNF. J Exp Med 1996;184:695–706.

[24] Santiago-Schwarz F. Positive and negative regulation of the myeloid dendritic cell lineage. J Leukoc Biol 1999;66:209–16.

[25] Santiago-Schwarz F, McCarthy M, Tucci J, Carsons SE. Neutralization of tumor necrosis factor activity shortly after the onset of dendritic cell hematopoiesis reveals a novel mechanism for the selective expansion of the CD14-dependent dendritic cell pathway. Blood 1998;92:745–55.

[26] Cao H, Verge V, Baron C, Martinache C, Leon A, Scholl S, et al. In vitro generation of dendritic cells from human blood monocytes in experimental conditions compatible for in vivo cell therapy. J Hematother Stem Cell Res 2000;9:183–94.

[27] Gallucci S, Matzinger P. Danger signals: SOS to the immune system. Curr Opin Immunol 2001; 13:114–9.

[28] Kiertscher SM, Roth MD. Human CD14+ leukocytes acquire the phenotype and function of antigen-presenting dendritic cells when cultured in GM-CSF and IL-4. J Leukoc Biol 1996;59: 208–18.

[29] Sato K, Nagayama H, Tadokoro K, Juji T, Takahashi TA. Interleukin-13 is involved in functional maturation of human peripheral blood monocyte-derived dendritic cells. Exp Hematol 1999;27:326–36.

[30] Reid CDL. The dendritic cell lineage in haemopoiesis. Br J Haematol 1997;96:217.

[31] Strunk D, Egger C, Leitner G, Hanau D, Stingl G. A skin homing molecule defines the langerhans cell progenitor in human peripheral blood. J Exp Med 1997;185:1131–6.

[32] Santiago-Schwarz F, Anand P, Liu S, Carsons SE. Dendritic cells (DCs) in rheumatoid arthritis (RA): progenitor cells and soluble factors contained in RA synovial fluid yield a subset of myeloid DCs that preferentially activate Th1 inflammatory-type responses. J Immunol 2001; 167:1758–68.

[33] Geissmann F, Prost C, Monnet JP, Dy M, Brousse N, Hermine O. Transforming growth factor 1, in the presence of granulocyte macrophage colony stimulating factor and interleukin 4, induces differentiation of human peripheral blood monocytes into dendritic Langerhans cells. J Exp Med 1998;187:961–6.

[34] Strobl H, Riedl E, Bello-Fernandez C, Knapp W. Epidermal Langerhans cell development and differentiation. Immunobiology 1998;198:588–605.

[35] Lopez M, Amorim L, Gane P, Cristoph A, Bardinet D, Abina AM, et al. IL-13 induces CD34+ cells from G-CSF mobilized blood to differentiate in vitro into potent antigen presenting cells. J Immunol Methods 1997;208:117.

[36] Rissoan MC, Soumelis V, Kadowaki N, Grouard G, Briere F, de Waal Malefyt R, et al. Reciprocal control of T helper cell and dendritic cell differentiation. Science 1999;283:1183–6.

[37] Rosenzwajg M, Camus S, Guigon M, Gluckman JC. The influence of interleukin (IL)-4, IL-13, and Flt3 ligand on human dendritic cell differentiation from cord blood CD34+ progenitor cells. Exp Hematol 1998;26:63–72.

[38] Companjen AR, van der Wel LI, Boon L, Prens EP, Laman JD. CD40 ligation-induced cytokine production in human skin explants is partly mediated via IL-1. Int Immunol 2002;14:669–76.

[39] Santiago-Schwarz F, Tucci J, Carsons SE. Endogenously produced interleukin 6 is an accessory cytokine for dendritic cell hematopoiesis. Stem Cells 1996;14:225–31.

[40] Vidalain PO, Azocar O, Servet-Delprat C, Rabourdin-Combe C, Gerlier D, Manie S. CD40 signaling in human dendritic cells is initiated within membrane rafts. EMBO J 2000;19: 3304–13.

[41] Luft T, Pang KC, Thomas E, Hertzog P, Hart DN, Trapani J, et al. Type I IFNs enhance the terminal differentiation of dendritic cells. J Immunol 1998;161:1947–53.

[42] Santiago-Schwarz F, Laky K, Carsons SE. Stem cell factor enhances dendritic cell development. Adv Exp Med Biol 1995;378:7–11.

[43] Hilkens CMU, Kalinski P, de Boer M, Kapsenberg ML. Human dendritic cells require exogenous interleukin-12-inducing factors to direct the development of naive T-helper cells toward the Th1 phenotype. Blood 1997;90:1920–6.

[44] McRae BL, Semnani RT, Hayes MP, van Seventer GA. Type 1 IFNs inhibit human dendritic cell IL-12 production and Th1 cell development. J Immunol 1998;160:4298–304.

[45] Fayette J, Durand I, Bridon JM, Arpin C, Dubois B, Caux C, et al. Dendritic cells enhance the differentiation of naive B cells into plasma cells in vitro. F Scand J Immunol 1998;48:563–70.

[46] Bellini A, Vittori E, Marini M, Ackerman V, Mattoli S. Intraepithelial dendritic cells and selective activation of Th2-like lymphocytes in patients with atopic asthma. Chest 1993;103:997–1005.

[47] Nestle FO, Turka LA, Nickloff BJ. Characterization of dermal dendritic cells in psoriasis: autostimulation of T lymphocytes and induction of Th1 type cytokines. J Clin Invest 1994;94:202.

[48] Canque B, Camus S, Yagello M, Gluckman JC. Special susceptibility to apoptosis of CD1a+ dendritic cell precursors differentiating from cord blood CD34+ progenitors. Stem Cells 1998;16:218–28.

[49] Riedl E, Strobl H, Majdic O, Knapp W. TGF-beta 1 promotes in vitro generation of dendritic cells by protecting progenitor cells from apoptosis. J Immunol 1997;158:1591–7.

[50] Santiago-Schwarz F, Borrero M, Tucci J, Palaia T, Carsons SE. In vitro expansion of CD13+CD33+ dendritic cell precursors from multipotent progenitors is regulated by a discrete fas-mediated apoptotic schedule. J Leukoc Biol 1997;62:493–502.

[51] Santiago-Schwarz F, Divaris N, Kay C, Carsons SE. Mechanisms of tumor necrosis factor-granulocyte-macrophage colony-stimulating factor-induced dendritic cell development. Blood 1993;82:3019–28.

[52] Galibert L, Maliszewski CR, Vandenabeele S. Plasmacytoid monocytes/T cells: a dendritic cell lineage? Semin Immunol 2001;13:283–9.

[53] Cella M, Facchetti F, Lanzavecchia A, Colonna M. Plasmacytoid dendritic cells activated by influenza virus and CD40L drive a potent TH1 polarization. Nat Immunol 2000;1:305–10.

[54] Grouard G, Rissoan MC, Filgueira L, Durand I, Banchereau J, Liu YJ. The enigmatic plasmacytoid T cells develop into dendritic cells with interleukin (IL)-3 and CD40 ligand. J Exp Med 1997;185:1101–11.

[55] Blom B, Ho S, Antonenko S, Liu YJ. Generation of interferon alpha-producing predendritic cell (pre-DC)2 from human CD34(+) hematopoietic stem cells. J Exp Med 2000;192:1785–96.

[56] Siegal FP, Kadowaki N, Shodell M, Fitzgerald-Bocarsly PA, Shah K, Ho S, et al. The nature of the principal type 1 interferon-producing cells in human blood. Science 1999;284:1835–7.

[57] Hao QL, Zhu J, Price MA, Payne KJ, Barsky LW, Crooks GM. Identification of a novel, human multilymphoid progenitor in cord blood. Blood 2001;97:3683–90.

[58] Pulendran B, Banchereau J, Burkeholder S, Kraus E, Guinet E, Chalouni C, et al. Flt3-ligand and granulocyte colony-stimulating factor mobilize distinct human dendritic cell subsets in vivo. J Immunol 2000;165:566–72.

[59] Spits H, Couwenberg F, Bakker AQ, Weijer K, Uittenbogaart CH. Id2 and Id3 inhibit development of CD34(+) stem cells into predendritic cell (pre-DC)2 but not into pre-DC1. Evidence for a lymphoid origin of pre-DC2. J Exp Med 2000;192:1775–84.

[60] Res PC, Couwenberg F, Vyth-Dreese FA, Spits H. Expression of pTalpha mRNA in a committed dendritic cell precursor in the human thymus. Blood 1999;94:2647–57.

[61] Rissoan MC, Duhen T, Bridon JM, Bendriss-Vermare N, Peronne C, de Saint Vis B, et al. Subtractive hybridization reveals the expression of immunoglobulin-like transcript 7, Eph-B1,

granzyme B, and 3 novel transcripts in human plasmacytoid dendritic cells. Blood 2002;100: 3295–303.

[62] Schotte R, Rissoan MC, Bendriss-Vermare N, Bridon JM, Duhen T, Weijer K, et al. The transcription factor Spi-B is expressed in plasmacytoid DC precursors and inhibits T-, B-, and NK-cell development. Blood 2003;101:1015–23.

[63] Maraskovsky E, Brasel K, Teepe M, Roux ER, Lyman SD, Shortman K, et al. Dramatic increase in the numbers of functionally mature dendritic cells in Flt3 ligand-treated mice: multiple dendritic cell subpopulations identified. J Exp Med 1996;184:1953–62.

[64] Briere F, Bendriss-Vermare N, Delale T, Burg S, Corbet C, Rissoan MC, et al. Origin and filiation of human plasmacytoid dendritic cells. Hum Immunol 2002;63:1081–93.

[65] Bendriss-Vermare N, Barthelemy C, Durand I, Bruand C, Dezutter-Dambuyant C, Moulian N, et al. Human thymus contains IFN-alpha-producing CD11c(−), myeloid CD11c(+), and mature interdigitating dendritic cells. J Clin Invest 2001;107:835–44.

[66] Thomas ML. Of ITAMs and ITIMs: turning on and off the B cell antigen receptor. J Exp Med 1995;181:1953–6.

[67] Cella M, Dohring C, Samaridis J, Dessing M, Brockhaus M, Lanzavecchia A, et al. A novel inhibitory receptor (ILT3) expressed on monocytes, macrophages, and dendritic cells involved in antigen processing. J Exp Med 1997;185:1743–51.

[68] Chang CC, Ciubotariu R, Manavalan JS, Yuan J, Colovai AI, Piazza F, et al. Tolerization of dendritic cells by T(S) cells: the crucial role of inhibitory receptors ILT3 and ILT4. Nat Immunol 2002;3:237–43.

[69] Aderem A, Ulevitch RJ. Toll-like receptors in the induction of the innate immune response. Nature 2000;406:782–7.

[70] Dabbagh K, Dahl ME, Stepick-Biek P, Lewis DB. Toll-like receptor 4 is required for optimal development of Th2 immune responses: role of dendritic cells. J Immunol 2002;168: 4524–30.

[71] Kadowaki N, Ho S, Antonenko S, Malefyt RW, Kastelein RA, Bazan F, et al. Subsets of human dendritic cell precursors express different toll-like receptors and respond to different microbial antigens. J Exp Med 2001;194:863–9.

[72] Pulendran B, Kumar P, Cutler CW, Mohamadzadeh M, Van Dyke T, Banchereau J. Lipopoly-saccharides from distinct pathogens induce different classes of immune responses in vivo. J Immunol 2001;167:5067–76.

[73] Gilliet M, Liu YJ. Human plasmacytoid-derived dendritic cells and the induction of T-regulatory cells. Hum Immunol 2002;63:1149–55.

[74] Albert Ml, Pearce SF, Francisco LM, Sauter B, Roy P, Silverstein RL, et al. Immature dendritic cells phagocytose apoptotic cells via alphavbeta5 and CD36, and cross-present antigens to cytotoxic T lymphocytes. J Exp Med 1998;188:1359–68.

[75] Andrade F, Casciola-Rosen L, Rosen A. Apoptosis in systemic lupus erythematosus. Clinical implications. Rheum Dis Clin North Am 2000;6:215–27.

[76] Hirao M, Onai N, Hiroishi K, Watkins SC, Matsushima K, Robbins PD, et al. CC chemokine receptor-7 on dendritic cells is induced after interaction with apoptotic tumor cells: critical role in migration from the tumor site to draining lymph nodes. Cancer Res 2000;60:2209.

[77] Matsue H, Takashima A. Apoptosis in dendritic cell biology. J Dermatol Sci 1999;20:159–71.

[78] Ronchetti A, Rovere P, Iezzi G, Galati G, Heltai S, Protti MP, et al. Immunogenicity of apoptotic cells in vivo: role of antigen load, antigen-presenting cells, and cytokines. J Immunol 1999;163:130.

[79] Rovere P, Sabbadini MG, Vallinoto C, Fascio U, Zimmermann VS, Bondanza A, et al. Delayed clearance of apoptotic lymphoma cells allows cross-presentation of intracellular antigens by mature dendritic cells. J Leuk Biol 1999;66:345–9.

[80] Rubartelli A, Poggi A, Zocchi MR. The selective engulfment of apoptotic bodies by dendritic cells is mediated by the alpha(v)beta3 integrin and requires intracellular and extracellular calcium. Eur J Immunol 1997;7:1893–900.

[81] Sauter B, Albert ML, Francisco L, Larsson M, Somersan S, Bhardwaj N. Consequences of cell

death: exposure to necrotic tumor cells, but not primary tissue cells or apoptotic cells, induces the maturation of immunostimulatory dendritic cells. J Exp Med 2000;191:423–34.

[82] Trudeau JD, Dutz JP, Arany E, Hill DJJ, Fieldus WE, Finegood DT. Neonatal beta-cell apoptosis: a trigger for autoimmune diabetes? Diabetes 2000;49:1–7.

[83] Srivastava P. Interaction of heat shock proteins with peptides and antigen presenting cells: chaperoning of the innate and adaptive immune responses. Annu Rev Immunol 2002;20: 395–425.

[84] Wallin RP, Lundqvist A, More SH, von Bonin A, Kiessling R, Ljunggren HG. Heat-shock proteins as activators of the innate immune system. Trends Immunol 2002;23:130–5.

[85] Jonuleit H, Schmitt E, Schuler G, Knop J, Enk AH. Induction of interleukin 10-producing, nonproliferating CD4(+) T cells with regulatory properties by repetitive stimulation with allogeneic immature human dendritic cells. J Exp Med 2000;192:1213–22.

[86] Feinberg MB, Silvestri G. T(S) cells and immune tolerance induction: a regulatory renaissance? Nat Immunol 2002;3:215–7.

[87] Figdor CG, van Kooyk Y, Adema GJ. C-type lectin receptors on dendritic cells and Langerhans cells. Nat Rev Immunol 2002;2:77–84.

[88] Kanazawa N, Okazaki T, Nishimura H, Tashiro K, Inaba K, Miyachi Y. DCIR acts as an inhibitory receptor depending on its immunoreceptor tyrosine-based inhibitory motif. J Invest Dermatol 2002;118:261–6.

[89] Lutz MB, Schuler G. Immature, semi-mature and fully mature dendritic cells: which signals induce tolerance or immunity? Trends Immunol 2002;23:445–9.

[90] Mahnke K, Schmitt E, Bonifaz L, Enk AH, Jonuleit H. Immature, but not inactive: the tolerogenic function of immature dendritic cells. Immunol Cell Biol 2002;80:477–83.

[91] Roncarolo MG, Levings MK, Traversari C. Differentiation of T regulatory cells by immature dendritic cells. J Exp Med 2001;193:F5–9.

[92] Martin E, O'Sullivan B, Low P, Thomas R. Antigen-specific suppression of a primed immune response by dendritic cells mediated by regulatory T cells secreting interleukin-10. Immunity 2003;18:155–67.

[93] Highton J, Kean A, Hessian PA, Thomson J, Rietveld J, Hart DN. Cells expressing dendritic cell markers are present in the rheumatoid nodule. J Rheumatol 2000;27:339–46.

[94] Kunkel HG, Crow M, Kunkel HG. Human dendritic cells: major stimulators of the autologous and allogeneic mixed leukocyte reactions. Clin Exp Immunol 1982;49:338–46.

[95] Pettit AR, MacDonald KP, O'Sullivan B, Thomas R. Differentiated dendritic cells expressing nuclear RelB are predominately located in rheumatoid synovial tissue perivascular mononuclear cell aggregates. Arthritis Rheum 2000;43:791–800.

[96] Santiago-Schwarz F, Sullivan C, Rappa D, Carsons SE. Distinct alterations in lineage committed progenitor cells exist in the peripheral blood of patients with rheumatoid arthritis and primary Sjogren's syndrome. J Rheumatol 1996;23:439–46.

[97] Summers K, O'Donnell JL, Heiser A, Highton J, Hart DN. Synovial fluid transforming growth factor beta inhibits dendritic cell-T lymphocyte interactions in patients with chronic arthritis. Arthritis Rheum 1999;42:507–18.

[98] Thomas R, Davis LS, Lipsky PE. Rheumatoid synovium is enriched in mature antigen-presenting dendritic cells. J Immunol 1994;152:2613–23.

[99] Thomas R, Lipsky PE. Could endogenous self-peptides presented by dendritic cells initiate rheumatoid arthritis? Immunol Today 1996;17:559.

[100] Thomas R, Lipsky PE. Presentation of self peptides by dendritic cells. Arthritis Rheum 1996;39:183–90.

[101] Thomas R, MacDonald KPA, Pettit AR, Cavanagh LL, Padmanabha J, Zehntner S. Dendritic cells and the pathogenesis of rheumatoid arthritis. J Leuk Biol 1999;66:286–92.

[102] Waalen K, Thoen J, Forre O, Hovig T, Teigland J, Natvig JB. Rheumatoid synovial dendritic cells as stimulators in allogeneic and autologous mixed leukocyte reactions-comparison with autologous monocytes as stimulator cells. Scand J Immunol 1986;23:233–41.

[103] Zvaifler NJ, Steinman RM, Kaplan G, Lau LL, Rivelis M. Identification of immunostimulatory

dendritic cells in the synovial effusions of patients with rheumatoid arthritis. J Clin Invest 1985; 76:789–800.

[104] Canete JD, Martinez SE, Farres J, Sanmarti R, Blay M, Gomez A, et al. Differential Th1/Th2 cytokine patterns in chronic arthritis: interferon gamma is highly expressed in synovium of rheumatoid arthritis compared with seronegative spondyloarthropathies. Ann Rheum Dis 2000;59:263–8.

[105] Del Prete G. The concept of type-1 and type-2 helper T cells and their cytokines in humans. Int Rev Immunol 1998;16:427–55.

[106] Dolhain RJ, van der Heiden AN, ter Haar NT, Breedveld FC, Miltenburg AM. Shift toward T lymphocytes with a T helper 1 cytokine-secretion profile in the joints of patients with rheumatoid arthritis. Arthritis Rheum 1996;39:1961–9.

[107] Rocken M, Racke M, Shevach EM. IL-4-induced immune deviation as antigen-specific therapy for inflammatory autoimmune disease. Immunol Today 1996;17:225–31.

[108] Skapenko A, Wendler J, Lipsky PE, Kalden JR, Schulze-Koops H. Altered memory T cell differentiation in patients with early rheumatoid arthritis. J Immunol 1999;163:491–9.

[109] Carsons SE, Santiago-Schwarz F, Diola C. Detection and quantitation of stem cell factor (kit ligand) in the synovial fluid of patients with rheumatic disease. J Rheumatol 2000;27:2798–800.

[110] Santiago-Schwarz F, Rappa DA, Laky K, Carsons SE. Stem cell factor augments tumor necrosis factor-granulocyte-macrophage colony-stimulating factor-mediated dendritic cell hematopoiesis. Stem Cells 1995;13:186–97.

[111] Saraya K, Reid CD. Stem cell factor and the regulation of dendritic cell production from CD34+ progenitors in bone marrow and cord blood. Br J Haematol 1996;93:258–64.

[112] Chomarat P, Banchereau J. Interleukin-4 and interleukin-13: their similarities and discrepancies. Int Rev Immunol 1998;17:1–52.

[113] Park SH, Min DJ, Cho ML, Kim WU, Youn J, Park W, et al. Shift toward T helper 1 cytokines by type II collagen-reactive T cells in patients with rheumatoid arthritis. Arthritis Rheum 2001; 44:561–9.

[114] Tokayer A, Carsons SE, Chokshi B, Santiago-Schwarz F. High levels of interleukin 13 in rheumatoid arthritis sera are modulated by tumor necrosis factor antagonist therapy: association with dendritic cell growth activity. J Rheumatol 2002;29:454–61.

[115] Charles P, Elliott MJ, Davis D, Potter A, Kalden JR, Antoni C, et al. Regulation of cytokines, cytokine inhibitors, and acute-phase proteins following anti-TNF-alpha therapy in rheumatoid arthritis. J Immunol 1999;163:1521–8.

[116] Berner B, Akca D, Jung T, Muller GA, Reuss-Borst MA. Analysis of Th1 and Th2 cytokines expressing CD4+ and CD8+ T cells in rheumatoid arthritis by flow cytometry. J Rheumatol 2000;27:1128–35.

[117] Katschke Jr KJ, Rottman JB, Ruth JH, Qin S, Wu L, LaRosa G, et al. Differential expression of chemokine receptors on peripheral blood, synovial fluid, and synovial tissue monocytes/macrophages in rheumatoid arthritis. Arthritis Rheum 2001;44:1022–32.

[118] Matsui T, Akahoshi T, Namai R, Hashimoto A, Kurihara Y, Rana M, et al. Selective recruitment of CCR6-expressing cells by increased production of MIP-3 alpha in rheumatoid arthritis. Clin Exp Immunol 2001;125:155–61.

[119] Rovere P, Vallinoto C, Bondanza A, Crosti MC, Rescigno M, Ricciardi-Castagnoli P, et al. Bystander apoptosis triggers dendritic cell maturation and antigen-presenting function. J Immunol 1998;161:4467–71.

[120] Steptoe RJ, Ritchie JM, Harrison LC. Increased generation of dendritic cells from myeloid progenitors in autoimmune-prone nonobese diabetic mice. J Immunol 2002;168:5032–41.

[121] Larsson M, Fonteneau JF, Bhardwaj N. Dendritic cells resurrect antigens from dead cells. Trends Immunol 2001;22:141–8.

[122] Pickering MC, Botto M, Taylor PR, Lachmann PJ, Walport MJ. Systemic lupus erythematosus, complement deficiency, and apoptosis. Adv Immunol 2000;76:227–324.

[123] Blanco P, Palucka AK, Gill M, Pascual V, Banchereau J. Induction of dendritic cell differentiation by IFN-alpha in systemic lupus erythematosus. Science 2001;294:1540–3.

[124] Gill MA, Blanco P, Arce E, Pascual V, Banchereau J, Palucka AK. Blood dendritic cells and DC-poietins in systemic lupus erythematosus. Hum Immunol 2002;63:1172–80.

[125] Ronnblom L, Alm GV. The natural interferon-alpha producing cells in systemic lupus erythematosus. Hum Immunol 2002;63:1181–93.

[126] Passos de Souza E, Evangelista Segundo PT, Jose FF, Lemaire D, Santiago M. Rheumatoid arthritis induced by alpha-interferon therapy. Clin Rheumatol 2001;20:297–9.

[127] Stift A, Friedl J, Dubsky P, Bachleitner-Hofmann T, Schueller G, Zontsich T, et al. Dendritic cell-based vaccination in solid cancer. J Clin Oncol 2003;21:135–42.

[128] Tatsumi T, Storkus WJ. Dendritic cell-based vaccines and therapies for cancer. Expert Opin Biol Ther 2002;2:919–28.

RHEUMATIC
DISEASE CLINICS
OF NORTH AMERICA

ELSEVIER
SAUNDERS

Rheum Dis Clin N Am 30 (2004) 135–157

Biology of T lymphocytes

Abbe N. Vallejo, PhD*, Eduardo Davila, PhD,
Cornelia M. Weyand, MD, Jörg J. Goronzy, MD*

*Departments of Medicine and Immunology, Guggenheim 401, Mayo Clinic, 200 First Street SW,
Rochester, MN 55905, USA*

T cells are mononuclear white blood cells that are derived from bone marrow stem cells that have undergone maturation in the thymus (hence the terms "thymus-derived" or "T cells") and are then seeded into the peripheral lymphoid tissues and the pool of circulating cells. Morphologically, T cells are indistinguishable from B cells, the other major class of lymphoid cells of the adaptive immune system. Historically, T cells were distinguished from other leukocytes by their avidity to sheep red blood cells through the CD2 molecule. The current definitive molecular marker of T cells is the T-cell receptor (TCR) complex, a disulfide-linked dimer of two polymorphic, membrane-bound polypeptide chains, which has specificity for an antigenic ligand and is associated with a collection of nonpolymorphic membrane-bound cytoplasmic proteins that are known collectively as CD3 [1]. Based on TCR expression, there are two types of T cells. Most T cells express TCR α- and β-chains; αβ T cells are derived chiefly from intrathymic precursors [2]. A small proportion of T cells (<15% of circulating T cells) expresses TCR δ- and γ-chains; γδ T cells are derived from intrathymic or extrathymic precursors [3]. αβ and γδ T cells differ significantly in the way that they recognize antigen and have different functions. αβ T cells are principally effectors and regulators of antigen-specific cell-mediated immune responses in

Supported by grants from the National Institutes of Health (R01 AG22379, R01 AG15043, R01 AR41974, R01 AI44142, R01 AR42527, R01 EY11916, and R01 HL63919) and by the Mayo Foundation.

* Corresponding authors.

E-mail addresses: jgoronz@emory.edu (J.J. Goronzy), vallejo.abbe@mayo.edu (A.N. Vallejo).

lymphoid and nonlymphoid tissues, whereas γδ T cells primarily seem to be sentinel cells that mediate local immunity within mucosal tissues [4,5].

The αβ T cells are further classified into two lineages by the expression of the coreceptor molecules CD4 or CD8 (ie, CD4$^+$ or CD8$^+$ T cells, respectively) [2]. Neither CD4 nor CD8 is expressed on γδ T cells [3]. CD4$^+$ T cells are the primary regulators of the immune response. Upon antigenic stimulation, they produce a variety of small bioactive molecules, generally termed "lymphokines," such as interleukin (IL)-2 and IL-4, which promote T-cell proliferation and differentiation, and interferon (IFN)-γ, which activates and enhances the microbicidal activity of monocytes and macrophages. CD4$^+$ T cells also can interact directly with B cells and help to promote B-cell differentiation into antibody-producing plasma cells. CD8$^+$ T cells are chiefly effector cells. Upon stimulation, CD8$^+$ T cells develop into cytotoxic cells that are capable of lysing target cells in an antigen-specific manner. In addition to lymphokines, activated CD4$^+$ and CD8$^+$ T cells can produce a wide variety of humoral factors.

T-cell antigen recognition

The antigen receptors on T cells and B cells have evolved to recognize pathogens in the extracellular milieu or endogenously-derived molecules, such as viral and tumor proteins, that pose a hazard to health and survival. These cells "see" antigen in different ways, however. The B-cell receptor recognizes and binds antigenic determinants (or epitopes) on soluble molecules or on particulate surfaces, whereas the TCR is essentially blind to antigenic substances in their native state. The TCR only recognizes epitopes that have been fragmented (or processed) from the native molecule and displayed (or presented) on the surfaces of nonlymphoid cells. The epitope usually is a peptide that is displayed on the surfaces of these antigen-presenting cells (APCs) that are bound to class I or class II major histocompatibility complex (MHC) molecules. Thus, the actual TCR ligand is a bimolecular complex of antigenic peptide and MHC that forms a unique conformation that is recognizable by a specific TCR. Presentation of the antigenic peptide that is bound to MHC molecules is the basis for the MHC restriction of T-cell–mediated immune responses.

CD4$^+$ T cells recognize antigenic peptides that are presented by class II MHC molecules, which are represented by human leukocyte antigen (HLA)-DP, DQ, and DR molecules, and by mouse H-2 I-A and I-E molecules. Class II MHC–bound antigenic peptides generally are derived from phagocytosis, pinocytosis, or receptor-mediated endocytosis of extracellular proteins or pathogens by APCs, such as dendritic cells (DCs) and monocytes/macrophages. Once internalized into lysosomal compartments, the proteins/pathogens are degraded into peptide fragments, among which are the relevant TCR epitopes. These lysosomes ultimately fuse with endoplasmic reticulum–derived vesicles that contain class II MHC molecules; this results in the formation of an acidic endosomal compartment that is conducive for peptide-loading of the class II molecules [6]. The peptide-binding cleft of newly-synthesized class II molecules is unoccupied because of protection that is conferred by the invariant chain (Ii or CD74). In the acidic endosomal compartment, the invariant chain is degraded, which renders class II molecules permissive to peptide-binding. Acquisition of antigenic peptide by class II molecules is a highly organized process that involves the proper trimming of peptide precursors and their subsequent loading into the peptide-binding cleft by accessory transporters and chaperone proteins. In humans, peptide-loading of antigen-presenting HLA-DR, -DP, and -DQ molecules is chaperoned by the class II molecules, HLA-DO and -DM [7]. Once loaded with peptides, class II molecules are transported to the cell surface, where they are accessible to antigen-specific $CD4^+$ T cells. Class II molecules on the surface of APCs also may be recycled by endocytosis and the peptide ligand can be exchanged for another in the acidic endosomal compartments.

By contrast, $CD8^+$ T cells recognize antigenic peptides that are presented by class I MHC molecules, represented by human HLA-A, -B, and -C molecules and by mouse H-2 K, D, and L molecules. Class I bound–peptides are derived from endogenously-synthesized proteins, such as viral and tumor proteins. Class I molecules acquire specific peptides at the endoplasmic reticulum such that actual peptide binding occurs cotranslationally with class I synthesis. Endogenously-synthesized proteins are degraded by proteosomes; this releases antigenic peptide precursors that are subject to further processing by a complex machinery of proteolytic enzymes and chaperones into short peptides that are eventually loaded into the class I peptide-binding cleft [8]. Antigen processing for class I–specific peptides invariably produces ligands that are 8 to 10 amino acid residues in length, whereas processing for class II–binding peptides results in longer ligands of 13 to 25 amino acid residues. Like peptide-loading of class II molecules, binding of specific peptides to class I molecules also requires chaperones, most notably the transporter of antigenic peptides (TAPs) and tapasin [7]. Subsequent to peptide-binding, class I molecules are transported to the surface of the APCs, where they are accessible to antigen-specific $CD8^+$ T cells.

Recognition of antigen by $CD4^{null}CD8^{null}$ $\gamma\delta$ T cells is fundamentally different from that of $CD4^+$ and $CD8^+$ $\alpha\beta$ T cells. $\alpha\beta$ T cells principally recognize peptide antigens that are presented by classic class I and class II MHC molecules, whereas $\gamma\delta$ T cells recognize peptide and nonpeptide antigens [2,4]. Among the nonpeptide antigens are alkylamines and pyrophosphates of varying lengths, many of which are of bacterial origin. How these nonconventional antigens are processed is not clear, but many of them are presented to $\gamma\delta$ T cells by the MHC class I–like (MIC) molecules, MIC-A and -B, and by CD1. MIC and CD1 are highly conserved antigen-presenting molecules. The structural requirements for recognition of MIC- or CD1-bound antigen by $\gamma\delta$ T cells are less stringent and more promiscuous than the MHC-bound peptides that are recognized by $\alpha\beta$ T cells [4]. Classic class I and class II MHC molecules are highly polymorphic molecules that impose structural constraints on the binding of the antigenic peptide [9]. Thus, TCR recognition of the MHC/peptide complex by $CD4^+$ and $CD8^+$ T cells is highly specific. The differences in antigen recognition between $\gamma\delta$ and $\alpha\beta$ T cells led to the suggestion that $\gamma\delta$ T cells are constituents of the innate immune system, whereas the CD4$^+$ and CD8$^+$ $\alpha\beta$ T cells are the mediators of adaptive immunity [3–5].

T-cell receptor structure and diversity

The TCR evolved to recognize an antigenic universe, estimated to be as large as 10^{15} to 10^{17} antigens, that humans encounter throughout life. The human genome is not nearly large enough to encode for such extreme genetic diversity. TCR genes make up less than 0.1% of the genome and are distributed in four loci TCRA, TCRB, TCRG, and TCRD, which encode for TCR α, β, γ, and δ chains, respectively. These loci contain approximately 250 TCR genes that exist as variable (V), diversity (D), joining (J), and constant (C) elements in the germline.

Multiple germline V, D, J, and C elements are key to generating a diverse TCR repertoire. These elements by themselves do not encode TCR diversity but are the building blocks to achieving it. Three complementary mechanisms contribute to the generation of TCR diversity. One mechanism is the combinatorial joining of V, D, J, and C elements, which results in a rearranged V(D)JC gene that encodes for a specific TCR α, β, γ, or δ polypeptide chain. A second mechanism involves nucleotide deletions by exonucleases or nucleotide additions by terminal deoxynucleotidyl transferase (TdT) during V(D)J rearrangement. The third mechanism is the pairing of α- and β-chains or of δ- and γ-chains in different combinations, a process called "combinatorial association." By these mechanisms, the immune system has an almost limitless capacity to generate a TCR repertoire that parallels, if not exceeds, the diversity of antigens that is encountered during life.

V(D)J somatic recombination is a developmentally regulated process that involves systematic excision and ligation events that are mediated by the recombination activation gene enzymes [10]. Recombination is a stepwise process during which a J gene-element fuses to a V gene-element in the case of TCRA and TCRG genes, generating a VJ segment. For the TCRB and TCRD genes, recombination brings about the initial fusion of a J gene-element to a D gene-element, forming a DJ segment; this is followed by DJ fusion to a V gene-element to generate a VDJ segment. Because of V(D)J recombination, the genome of each circulating mature T cell is different from that of other somatic cells. Nonlymphoid somatic cells have an intact germline, whereas T cells can have substantial deletions within the TCR regions of chromosomes 7 and 14 that result from recombination.

V(D)J combinatorial joining is inexact. The junctional regions between recombining V, D, and J elements are susceptible to modification [10]. There can be template-dependent additions of palindromic "P" nucleotides, or template-independent incorporation of "N" nucleotides by TdT. There also can be deletions of encoded nucleotides by exonucleases. These junctional regions of the rearranged VJ or VDJ genes encode the hypervariable complementarity-determining region 3 (CDR3). The CDRs (ie, the junctional CDR3 and the V-encoded CDR1 and CDR2), are regions of highest sequence variability that impart specificity and diversity of antigenic recognition by the TCR [11].

T-cell development and lineage commitment

T cells are descendants of hematopoietic stem cells (HSCs) in the bone marrow. Somewhere along the differentiation pathway of HSC, common lymphoid progenitors (CLPs) develop. CLPs are cells that have lost the capacity to generate myeloid and erythroid cells but retain the ability to generate T cells, B cells, and natural killer (NK) cells. It is believed that CLPs differentiate into the precursors of T cells and B cells/NK cells, namely pro-T and pro-B cells, respectively [12]. Pro-T cells in the bone marrow can initiate TCRD and TCRG gene rearrangement and develop into $\gamma\delta$ T cells, which eventually seed mucosal tissues [3,4] CLP or pro-T cells also migrate to the thymus where they develop into $\gamma\delta$ T cells or develop into pre-T cells, the immediate precursors of $\alpha\beta$ T cells [2,12].

Differentiation of CLP into either pro-T cells or pro-B cells is not well understood, but notch-1 signaling has been implicated in the commitment of HSC toward T-cell development [13]. Notch proteins are evolutionarily conserved receptors that regulate various cell fate decisions and differentiation during embryonic and postnatal development. Notch-1 normally is expressed on HSC and CLP; its triggering elicits the preferential development of pro-T cells. Introduction of the constitutively active form of notch-1 into bone marrow cells leads to the ectopic development of $CD4^+CD8^+$ T cells in the bone marrow and the simultaneous arrest of B-cell development at the pro-B stage. Additionally, targeted deletion of notch-1 leads to defective T-cell development in the thymus as well as the extrathymic development $\gamma\delta$ T cells in the mucosa and the maladaptive accumulation of pro-B cells in the thymus. Thus, notch-1 seems to be a critical regulator of early T-cell lineage commitment from CLP to pro-T development in the bone marrow.

Pro-T cells that enter the thymus are primitive $CD3^-TCR^-CD8^-CD4^-$ $cKit^+CD44^{hi}$ "triple-negative" cells, but they exit the thymus as mature "single-positive" (SP) $CD3^+\alpha\beta TCR^+CD8^-CD4^-$ or $CD3^+\alpha\beta TCR^+CD8^+CD4^-$ T cells (Fig. 1) [2]. In the thymic cortex, pro-T cells develop into pre-T cells as they undergo TCRB gene rearrangement and express the TCR β-chain; this dimerizes with the molecule $pT\alpha$, that is encoded on another chromosome, and leads to the assembly of the pre-TCR (ie, the $CD3/TCR\beta/pT\alpha$ complex). This gives rise to $CD3^+TCR\beta^+CD8^-CD4^\times$ "double-negative" (DN) T cells. Expression of the pre-TCR is a critical determinant for survival and the further development of DN thymocytes as they interact with thymic epithelial cells during their migration through the thymic microenvironment. Following TCRA gene rearrangements, the pre-TCR is replaced by an $\alpha\beta$-TCR, and DN T cells acquire expression of CD4 and CD8, giving rise to "double-positive" (DP) $\alpha\beta$ T cells. At the corticomedullary junction of the thymus, DP T cells eventually mature into SP $CD4^+$ or $CD8^+$ $\alpha\beta$ T cells that exit the thymus to seed peripheral lymphoid tissues and the circulating lymphocyte pool.

The transition from DP to SP $\alpha\beta$ T cells involves two complex biologic processes, T-cell selection [14] and CD4/CD8 differentiation [15], that may or

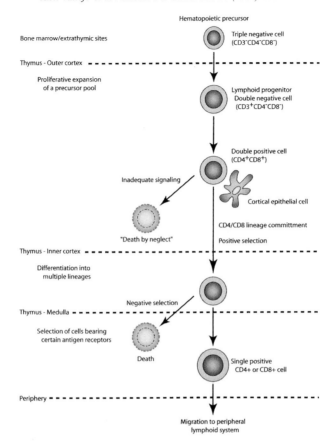

Fig. 1. T-cell development in the thymus. In the outer cortex, the early lymphoid progenitor cells assemble the pre-TCR and develop into $CD3^+CD4^{neg}CD8^{neg}$ (double negative) pre-T cells. Signaling from the pre-TCR/CD3 complex results in the generation of $CD4^+CD8^+$ (double positive) cells. In the inner cortex, the pre-TCR is replaced with an $\alpha\beta$-TCR, which enables double-positive cells to further sample MHC/peptide complexes on cortical epithelial cells and leads to further maturation and selection of $CD4^+CD8^+$ T cells. If the $\alpha\beta$-TCR recognizes a MHC/peptide ligand with high affinity, the T cell undergoes apoptosis, a process called "negative selection." Inadequate TCR signaling leads to passive apoptosis ("death by neglect"). It is believed that most double positive cells die by negative selection or lack of positive selection. Only a small proportion of the cells, those with intermediate affinity $\alpha\beta$ TCR-MHC/peptide interactions, survive and are "positively selected" to undergo further maturation into single positive $CD4^+$ or $CD8^+$ T cells.

may not be dependent on each other. In principle, T-cell selection is a means of testing the functionality of the newly-assembled $\alpha\beta$ TCR. As the cells move from the thymic cortex to the medulla, the $\alpha\beta$ TCR interacts with antigen-presenting class I and class II MHC molecules that are displayed on thymic epithelial cells. DP $\alpha\beta$ T cells that have low affinity interactions for MHC/peptide ligands are believed to undergo cell death because of insufficient signaling, a phenomenon that is vaguely referred to as "death by neglect." DP cells whose

TCR have sufficient ligand affinity continue to mature. Subsequent TCR-MHC/peptide interactions lead to another selection process whereby high-affinity T cells undergo apoptosis in a process called "negative selection," whereas T cells with intermediate affinity survive and mature as either SP CD4$^+$ or SP CD8$^+$ T cells in a process called "positive selection." TCR affinity as a determinant of thymic selection (or of DP to SP development) is measured qualitatively, such as the signaling competence of the TCR and the identification of selecting thymus-derived peptides that are bound to MHC molecules.

The relationship between selection and CD4/CD8 commitment comes from the designation of CD4 and CD8 molecules as coreceptors of TCR signaling. One paradigm, the so-called "instructive model" [15], is that CD4 or CD8 coordinate with the αβ TCR to generate a unique signal that leads to SP αβ T-cell development. As the αβ TCR samples the MHC/peptide ligands on thymic epithelial cells, CD4 or CD8 assists in establishing a correct fit for TCR-MHC/peptide interaction. CD4 molecules invariably impart a good fit for class II MHC TCR interaction, whereas CD8 molecules impart good fit for class I MHC TCR interaction. In doing so, these interactions lead to positive selection and SP T-cell development. An inappropriate fit of TCR-MHC/peptide interaction that is due to an ineffective CD4 or CD8 coreceptor leads to negative selection or apoptosis of that particular T cell. This instructive view of CD4/CD8 commitment is supported by studies that showed that CD4 and CD8 generated qualitatively different signals that profoundly influenced T-cell maturation [16,17].

An alternative paradigm is that CD4/CD8 commitment is stochastic [15]. In this view, the expression of CD4 and CD8 is unrelated to the specificity of the TCR. CD4 and CD8 molecules are more frequently inappropriate for the TCR and randomly interact with MHC molecules on the thymic epithelial cells. Only when the proper TCR-MHC/peptide-coreceptor interaction is achieved do the DP T cells enter the instructive phase of development that leads to SP T cells. A stochastic view of CD4/CD8 commitment is supported by studies that showed the lack of relationship between TCR specificity and SP T-cell development as well as lack of skewing of development of SP T cells in animals that overexpress CD4 or CD8 [18–20]. Even genetic lesions of CD4 gene regulatory elements are ineffective in shutting down CD4 expression; instead, they impair SP CD8$^+$ T-cell development [21]. Hence, silencing of CD4 or CD8 gene expression during DP to SP T-cell development could be completely random.

Innate and T-cell–mediated immunity

Inasmuch as T cells recognize processed, but not native, antigens that are bound to MHC molecules that are displayed on APCs, such as DCs and macrophages/monocytes, T-cell–mediated immune responses are linked inextricably to the induction of innate immunity (Fig. 2). DCs and macrophages are specialized phagocytes that are dispersed throughout the body, especially in mucosal areas and in the skin. They participate in the initial capture and

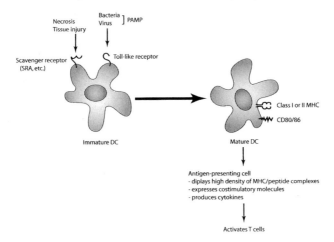

Fig. 2. APCs link innate and T-cell–mediated immunity. Pathogens or necrotic/damaged tissues are detected by APCs, such as dendritic cells (DCs) and resident tissue macrophages, through pattern recognition receptors (PRRs) such as toll-like and scavenger receptors. Signal transduction by way of these receptors leads to DC maturation and activates a wide array of interconnected and synergistic host defense mechanisms. DC maturation involves upregulation of class I and II MHC molecules and costimulatory molecules, such as CD80 and CD86, and, therefore, enables the DCs to present antigen to T cells. DC maturation also induces the production of various cytokines that influence T-cell differentiation (see Fig. 4). PAMP, pathogen-associated molecular patterns; SRA, scavenger receptor-A.

destruction of microorganisms, parasites, and other potentially immunogenic substances, as well as the clearance of apoptotic cells and cellular debris in developing, injured, and repairing tissues. In addition to their capability to process and present peptide antigens to T cells, activated DCs and macrophages cooperate and enhance the elimination of intracellular pathogens. They also secrete molecules that facilitate opsonization and phagocytosis of extracellular pathogens as well as humoral factors that induce and regulate local and systemic inflammatory responses.

DCs and macrophages express a variety of receptors that are referred to as pattern-recognition receptors (PRRs) because they are specific for discrete determinants on microorganisms, which are called collectively pathogen-associated molecular patterns (PAMPs). PRR specificity is broad and these receptors also can recognize endogenous determinants that mainly are derived from apoptotic and necrotic cells [22]. For instance, the mannose receptor recognizes PAMPs on various gram-negative bacteria, *Schistosoma*, and lysosomal hydrolases and mannosyl/fucosyl moieties of endogenous proteins. The scavenger receptors, SR-A and CD36, can recognize PAMPs on *Neisseria* and *Plasmodium*, respectively, and modified lipids and apoptotic cells. CD1 is also a PRR whose ligands include mycobacterial glycolipids and human ceramide sphingolipids.

The best-studied PRRs are the toll-like receptors (TLRs). Toll is a receptor that controls dorsoventral differentiation in *Drosophila* embryos and is involved in antifungal responses in adult *Drosophila*. In mammals, ten toll homologs are known [23]. Mammalian TLR ligands are invariably bacterial PAMPs, such as lipopolysaccharide (LPS), zymosan, outer membrane proteins, and flagellin. Some of the TLRs also recognize viral PAMPs, such as double-stranded RNA. Other TLRs recognize unmethylated CpG-DNA from invertebrate parasites and bacteria. Thus, TLR recognition of PAMPs is among the first lines of defense against infection.

Ligation of TLRs on DCs and macrophages induces activation and differentiation of function. Of the ten TLRs that have been identified, only TLR2 and TLR4 signaling and induction of effector functions are understood to some extent. TLR4 forms a complex with CD14 as the functional receptor for LPS [24]. Upon ligation by LPS, TLR4 induces activation of the transcription factors, NFκB and PU1, which are essential to survival, proliferation, and differentiation of DCs and macrophages. In injured tissues, TLR4/CD14 signaling in tissue macrophages induces oxidative burst and the production of macrophage migration inhibitory factor, which enhances phagocytic and microbicidal activity at the site of injury. TLR4 signaling also leads to the secretion of proinflammatory cytokines, such as IL-1, IL-6, and tumor necrosis factor (TNF)-α, thereby recruiting other cells to the site of injury to repair or contain the injury. For DCs, TLR4/CD14 signaling leads to their maturation and migration to lymphoid tissues where they elicit antigen-specific immune responses [22]. Among the key events in TLR-mediated maturation of DCs is the expression of costimulatory molecules, such as CD80 and CD86, and the upregulation of MHC molecules which imparts the antigen-presenting function of DCs in the induction of T-cell–mediated immune responses. TLR-mediated activation of DCs also leads to the production of IL-4, IL-10, and IL-12 [23], which regulate T-cell differentiation. Clearly, T-cell–mediated immunity is linked to the activation of cells of the innate immune system.

T-cell activation and regulation of proliferation

T-cell activation is triggered initially by the interaction of a few TCR and MHC/peptide ligands. This interaction progresses to the polarization of several receptor/counterreceptor interactions at the T-cell/APC contact (Fig. 3). Such receptor polarization triggers signaling, which leads to proliferation, protection from apoptosis, and eventually, the development of T-cell effector functions. When a T cell encounters an APC, it is believed that the TCR scans MHC/peptides ligands on the APC. Scanning is facilitated by integrin interaction, such as CD2-CD54, which bring about T-cell/APC contact. If the appropriate MHC/peptide ligand is recognized, low -level TCR signaling initiates cytoskeletal reorganization that brings about microclustering of the TCR and the corresponding MHC/peptide ligand on the APC. The TCR and MHC/peptide clusters eventually coalesce to form a single supramolecular structure, the immunologic synapse (IS), at the point of T-cell/APC contact [25]. On the T-cell surface, the IS consists

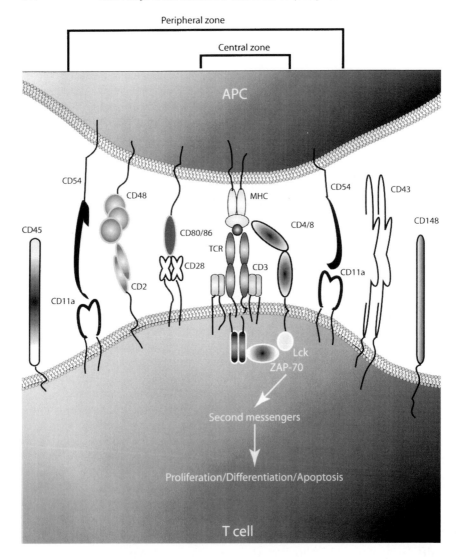

Fig. 3. The immunologic synapse is the platform for T-cell activation. The IS brings together receptors in an ordered fashion to achieve full control of signaling and cellular activation. The IS consists of two functionally distinct domains, the central supramolecular activation complex (cSMAC) and the peripheral supramolecular activation complex (pSMAC). The separation of receptor-ligand pairs between the two domains is based on size. The TCR-MHC/peptide interaction spans approximately 15 nm and the adhesion-associated interactions reach 30 to 40 nm between the T cell and APC. On the T-cell surface, the TCR, CD3, and CD4 (or CD8) constitute the core of the cSMAC. Costimulatory CD28 molecules are located immediately adjacent to this core. The pSMAC consists of larger adhesion molecules (eg, CD2, CD11a) that are held in a less rigid organization than the cSMAC. Together, the cSMAC and the pSMAC form the platform for efficient signal integration that ultimately results in T-cell proliferation, differentiation, or apoptosis.

of a central core of TCR and CD4 or CD8 coreceptors that is surrounded by a ring of CD2 and other adhesion molecules. On the surface of the APC, the IS consists of a central core of MHC/peptide and a ring of CD54 and the appropriate ligands/counterreceptors of other T-cell adhesion molecules.

Formation of the IS serves two functions. At the T-cell surface, the IS is a means to increase the avidity and ensure fidelity/specificity of TCR-MHC/peptide interaction. Because each TCR-MHC/peptide interaction generates only fairly transient low-level signaling, the IS integrates weak signals into one high amplitude signal above the threshold of activation so as to trigger a signaling cascade [26]. In the cytoplasm of the T cell, the IS is the platform whereby signal transduction molecules are brought into proximity and initiate the biochemical signaling cascade [27].

IS formation brings about the activation of the Lck kinase, which is the primary switch of TCR signaling (see Fig. 3). Lck, in turn, phosphorylates immunoreceptor tyrosine-based activation motifs (ITAM) on CD3ζ. The ITAM serves as a docking site for ZAP-70 which allows it to interact and become activated by Lck. This is followed by the activation of the membrane-bound linker for activation of T cells (LATs), SH2-containing leukocyte protein of 76kDa (SLP76), and other adapter proteins that results in downstream signaling events; these ultimately bring about the transcription of genes, proliferation, and differentiation [28].

Although the IS serves to integrate TCR signals into one signal, the TCR-derived signal alone generally is insufficient to sustain a signaling cascade. Hence, T-cell activation requires a costimulatory signal, which is principally provided by the interaction of CD28 on T cells and CD80 or CD86 on APCs [29]. The central role of CD28-mediated costimulation in T-cell activation is indicated by many studies in a variety of biologic systems which showed that perturbation of CD28-CD80/CD86 interaction leads to dysregulation of T-cell–dependent immune responses [30]. This is because CD28 is an integral component of the IS. Disruption of its interaction with CD80/CD86 leads to abortive signaling [31].

TCR signaling leads to the downstream expression of cytokines, such as IL-2, IFN-γ, and IL-4, and activation-induced membrane receptors, such as CD154, that enhance proliferation and regulate differentiation of T-cell effector function. The same activation signals also lead to expression of regulatory molecules that dampen the TCR-derived signal and ultimately downregulate immune responses. Among the key regulatory molecules is CD152, which is structurally homologous to CD28. Because CD152 has a higher affinity for CD80/86 [29], CD152 accumulation following activation blocks CD28-mediated costimulation by perturbing the IS and attenuating TCR signal transduction [32].

Inasmuch as proliferation is a direct consequence of TCR signaling, induction of apoptosis following clonal proliferation may be the most effective way to control immune responses [33]. Thus, the T-cell activation program includes the downstream upregulation of receptors that elicit apoptotic signals. The best studied of these receptors are CD95 and CD178, the predominant receptor-ligand pair that brings about activation-induced cell death (AICD) in T cells. An interesting aspect of CD95-mediated AICD is the proapoptotic effect of IL-2.

Although IL-2 is the quintessential T-cell growth factor that is induced by TCR-signaling itself, IL-2 also contributes to the induction of CD95 and CD178 and to the degradation of antiapoptotic molecules; this renders activated T cells responsive to death signals [34].

Helper T cells

T-helper (Th) cells originally were observed to cooperate or "help" in B-cell activation and proliferation and B-cell differentiation into immunoglobulin-secreting plasma cells. Th cells typically have a CD4$^+$ phenotype and they provide help through the interaction of CD154 on the T-cell surface and CD40 on B cells [35]. Th cell functions have expanded with the findings that activated CD4$^+$ T cells differentiate into Th1 or Th2 cells [36].

The types of lymphokines that activated CD4$^+$ T cells produce distinguish Th1 and Th2 phenotypes. Th1 cells produce an array of lymphokines that generally are associated with the induction of delayed-type hypersensitivity reactions and the activation of macrophages and other phagocytes. They predominantly produce IFN-γ, which is known to enhance the microbicidal activity of phagocytes and to increase MHC expression on APCs. Th1 cells also produce chemoattractants such as regulated upon activation normal T cell, expressed and secreted (RANTES) that facilitate recruitment of granulocytes and lymphocytes to sites of injury/inflammation. In contrast, Th2 cells have a lymphokine profile that is associated with immunoglobulin production and immunoglobulin-mediated responses. They predominantly produce IL-4, which is a B-cell growth factor and a regulator of immunoglobulin isotype switching in plasma cells. Th2 cells also produce IL-5 and IL-13, which are mediators of eosinophil activation and IgE synthesis, respectively.

Differentiation of activated CD4$^+$ T cells into Th1 or Th2 is controlled by at least two factors. First, the type of APCs with which CD4$^+$ T cells interact is key to Th1/Th2 development [37]. This is because APCs express a variety of inducible costimulatory molecules that differentially provide activation thresholds. Second, cytokines profoundly influence Th1/Th2 differentiation through feedback regulation of IFN-γ and IL-4 production (Fig. 4). IL-12, IL-18 and IFN-γ promote Th1 development, whereas IL-4 promotes Th2 development [38]. Th2 development is associated with the induction of the GATA-binding protein 3 (GATA-3) transcription factor. GATA-3 activates IL-5 production as well as IL-4 itself. It also contributes to the extinction of IFN-γ production, thereby committing CD4$^+$ T cells to Th2 development. In contrast, Th1 development is associated with the induction of the T-bet transcription factor by IFN-γ. T-bet synergizes with the IL-12–activated transcription factor, signal transducer and activator of transcript 4 (STAT4), in the induction of IFN-γ production itself. T-bet simultaneously inhibits IL-4 production, thereby promoting Th1 development.

The skewing of Th1 or Th2 development influences protection or susceptibility to disease. For instance, allergic diseases, such as asthma, are associated

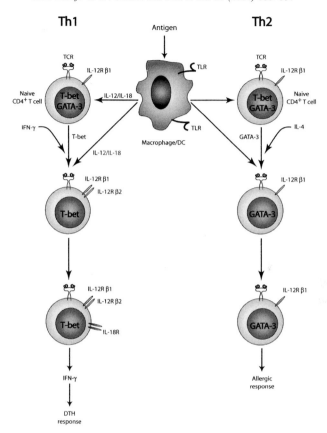

Fig. 4. Th1/Th2 differentiation is influenced by APCs and cytokines. Differentiation of naive Th cells to Th1 or Th2 cells requires that antigens be presented by APCs. It is believed that myeloid-derived APCs predominantly stimulate Th1 cell differentiation whereas lymphoid-derived APCs induce Th2 cell differentiation. Following antigen uptake and activation, APCs also produce a variety of cytokines that influences Th1/Th2 differentiation in concert with cytokines/humoral factors that are produced by other cells like activated natural killer cells. In a microenvironment with elevated levels of IFN-γ, activation of the T-bet transcription factor promotes Th1 development. In the presence of IL-12, the STAT4 transcription factor is activated and synergizes with T bet in the further production of IFN-γ and the simultaneous inhibition of IL-4 synthesis, thereby skewing development toward Th1 cells. An environment with elevated IL-4 and the absence of IL-12 results in a default track of differentiation toward IL-4-producers. This is because of the activation of the GATA-3 transcription factor, which promotes feedback upregulation of IL-4 production and the extinction of IFN-γ production that skews differentiation toward Th2 cells. DTH, delayed type hypersensitivity.

with Th2 dysregulation [37,38]. Patients who have asthma have elevated levels of IL-4, IL-9, and IL-13, which promote inflammation in the respiratory mucosa. In contrast, Crohn's disease is associated with Th1-dependent inflammatory processes [39]. Th1 effectors in the intestinal mucosa produce large amounts of IFN-γ to activate resident macrophages, which, in turn, produce other proinflammatory mediators, like IL-1 and TNF-α, that further amplify the inflammatory process. Thus, therapeutic interventions, such as allergen desensitization and anti–TNF-α therapy to attain the balance of Th1 and Th2 effectors, have become popular and effective means of managing certain immunologic disorders.

Cytotoxic T cells

Cytotoxic T lymphocytes (CTLs) are known for their role in the destruction of infected cells and tumors. CTLs are typically $CD8^+$ and express a variety of cytotoxic proteins, such as perforin, granzyme, and granulysin. They also express a variety of apoptosis-inducing membrane-bound proteins, such as CD178 and TNF-related apoptosis-inducing ligand [40]. Upon interaction with specific death receptors on target cells, these death-inducing ligands trigger an apoptosis-signaling pathway that involves the serial activation of caspases; this results in mitochondrial dysfunction and the cessation of oxidative respiration. Mitochondrial dysfunction is manifested by the release of cytochrome C and endonuclease G. The latter is a DNase that promotes DNA fragmentation, the hallmark of apoptosis.

Although the mechanism of caspase-mediated cell death is fairly well-defined [40], death mechanisms that are mediated by the cytotoxic proteins, perforin and granzyme, have been enigmatic [40,41]. Currently, there are three proposed pathways whereby these proteins might elicit cell death. The first and most popular pathway involves the pore-forming activity of perforin and the delivery of granzyme to the target cell through the perforin channel. This pathway is supported by the membranolytic property of perforin and electron microscopic studies that show the assembly of poly-perforin pores. The relevance of this pathway has been challenged by findings that granzymes A, B, and H can enter target cells and elicit death, even in the absence of perforin [42]. The subsequent finding of a granzyme receptor led to a second scenario that proposes an endocytic pathway of granzyme/perforin delivery to target cells [43]. In this pathway, granzyme and perforin are endocytosed into vesicles. Subsequently, perforin forms pores on the vesicle membrane through which granzyme is delivered to the cytoplasm. A third pathway was proposed based on observations that granzyme entry into the cell is autonomous and may not involve a perforin channel [44]. This pathway is similar to the second in so far as the receptor-mediated endocytosis of granzyme. It differs from the second pathway in that the release of granzyme into the cytoplasm does not involve perforin, but a yet undescribed endosomolytic agent.

Regardless of how granzyme and perforin are delivered to the target cell, there seems to be consensus that apoptosis is elicited by granzymes [40,41]. Granzyme B can activate caspase 8, which, in turn, activates caspase 3, the principal mediator of the caspase-dependent death pathway. Granzyme B also can activate a Bcl-related molecule, BH3-interacting domain death agonist (BID), which triggers mitochondrial dysfunction and leads to cell death in a caspase-independent fashion. Also, granzyme B activates DNA fragmentation factor 40 or caspase-activated deoxynuclease, which catalyzes DNA fragmentation.

Although CTLs are the key effectors in antipathogen and antitumor responses, they also are important effectors of autoimmune disorders [45]. For instance, CTLs that are reactive to endogenous antigens have been identified and are believed to elicit tissue damage in organ-specific autoimmune diseases, such as type I diabetes and Hashimoto's thyroiditis. CTL-induced damage is exacerbated by the dysregulation of proinflammatory cytokines, such as TNF-α in the CTLs themselves. Tissue damage can be amplified further by unique interactions of CTLs with resident cells. In rheumatoid arthritis, for example, interaction of receptor activator of NFkB (RANK) ligand (also known as TRANCE or osteoprotegerin ligand) on CTLs (in concert with TRANCE$^+$ Th cells) and osteoprotegerin on synovial fibroblasts can trigger osteoclastogenesis, which leads to bone resorption [46].

In contrast to autoimmune disease in which there is aggressive CTL activity, HIV/AIDS is associated with incompetent or anergic CTLs. Like any infectious disease, HIV infection elicits expansion of anti-HIV CTLs [47]. Such CTLs are ineffective killers because of their inability to generate an activating signal as a result of the downregulation of CD3ζ and the signaling molecules Lck, fyn, and ZAP-70. The CTLs also express a variety of class I MHC-recognizing inhibitory receptors, which dampen residual TCR/CD3-generated signals. Anti-HIV CTLs also produce large amounts of IL-10, which is immunosuppressive, but they produce extremely low levels of IFN-γ and IL-2. In the absence of CD4$^+$ T cells, which are normally the major source of IL-2 and IFN-γ, anti-HIV CTLs are anergic. Such anergic CTLs in HIV and the highly aggressive CTLs in autoimmune diseases illustrate the extremes of CTL function, which could provide insight into the development of efficacious CTL-based immunotherapy.

Memory T cells

Perhaps the single most important feature of adaptive immunity is memory, which is the ability of T cells and B cells to recall antigenic reactivity. Following the resolution of an immune response, most of the antigen-specific effector CD4$^+$ and CD8$^+$ T cells undergo AICD; a few survive and differentiate into memory T cells. During a subsequent encounter with the same antigen, these memory or "antigen-experienced" T cells are reactivated easily. They elicit an accelerated and more heightened immune response in comparison with the slow and low-amplitude responses that are generated by their naive or "antigen-inexperienced" precursors during the first antigenic encounter. Having survived the selective pressure of AICD and other death signals, memory T cells, are, in essence, the "fittest" lymphocytes that provide the basis for life-long immunity to certain infections and are the foundation for vaccine development [48].

The mechanisms for the generation of memory T cells is poorly understood. It was speculated that the strength of the signal that T cells receive from the interacting APC is a key determinant [49]. This concept of signal strength is essentially an extension of the principle that is applied to the mechanics of T-cell activation and differentiation. Just as there are hierarchical thresholds of activation to elicit T-cell proliferation, differentiation of effector function, and death [20], it is believed that a similar threshold determines memory cell development; the nature of such a threshold remains to be elucidated.

Although the selection process for effector T cells to become memory cells is unclear, memory phenotypes have been described. Based on homing behavior, central (T_{CM}) and effector (T_{EM}) memory T cells have been identified [49]. T_{CM} are CCR7$^+$CD62L$^+$ cells that preferentially home to lymphoid tissues, whereas T_{EM} are CCR7$^-$CD62L$^-$ cells that home to peripheral tissues. T_{EM} seem to maintain their activated phenotype and are believed to confer immediate local immune responses in the peripheral tissues. In contrast, T_{CM} are in a quiescent state but have a low activation threshold. Upon antigenic restimulation in the lymph nodes, T_{CM} proliferate and differentiate into effectors. The activated phenotype of T_{EM} is indicated by their selective responsiveness to IL-15 and IL-7, whereas T_{CM} require additional cytokines, including IL-6, IL-10, IL-12, and TNF-α. Such selective responsiveness to cytokines is largely antigen-independent, which brings about a low level of homeostatic proliferation that maintains a pool of T_{EM} in the peripheral tissues and a T_{CM} pool in the lymph nodes [49,50].

Although memory T cells are derived from antigen-specific effector T cells, the derivation of T_{EM} and T_{CM} is controversial. Some studies suggested that T_{EM} are descendants of T_{CM} that have emerged through homeostatic proliferation [51]. TCR repertoire studies, however, showed that T_{EM} and T_{CM} have distinct and autonomous repertoires [52], which indicates independent derivation of these memory T-cell subsets.

T-cell dependent tolerance and autoimmunity

Immunologic tolerance is a concept that takes its origins from the paradigm of self/nonself discrimination [53]. Immune responses are generated against foreign or nonself antigens, but not against one's own self-antigens. In this view, T-cell–mediated immunity is possible only because of the dominant selection of T cells with specificities that are directed against foreign substances. Self-reactive T cells, which have specificities for antigens or molecules that normally are expressed by one's own cells, break tolerance, and, therefore, are rare. It is believed that self-reactive T cells escape negative selection in the thymus or that particular autoantigens promoted their positive selection. In the periphery, a subsequent encounter of the same autoantigens drives the expansion of self-reactive T cells and contributes to the clinical manifestations of autoimmune disease. Evidence for this principle of self-reactivity comes primarily from transgenic animal models [54]. The role of autoantigens or selection of pathogenic self-reactive T cells in human disease is highly speculative, the exceptions may be type I diabetes and myasthenia gravis, in which expanded T-cell clones that are reactive to human proteins, such as glutamic acid decarboxylase and acetylcholine receptor, respectively, are pathognomonic.

In recent years, the self/nonself paradigm has been challenged by the "danger model" [55]. This model asserts that an immune response is initiated by conditions in which an antigenic substance causes damage regardless of its self-ness or foreign-ness. Therefore, initiation of an immune response depends on the recognition of danger signals. In this context, T-cell–mediated immunity is elicited only when an antigenic substance, whether it is a foreign pathogen or a self-derived protein, causes damage or stress such that APCs become activated [56] and trigger T-cell activation. Autoimmunity occurs because there is no absolute tolerance. Because T-cell maturation occurs in the thymus where the peripheral T-cell repertoire is selected/shaped by thymic antigens, self-reactive T cells do not exist because of positive selection but because they become activated by APCs that display their antigenic specificity. Antipancreas T cells, for instance, exist because pancreas-specific proteins are not expressed in the thymus. If pancreatic proteins were found in the thymus, antipancreas T cells would be eliminated by negative selection. Thus, in situations in which pancreatic injury does not get resolved/repaired but activates APCs like DC and tissue macrophages, antipancreas T cells would become activated and cause an autoimmune cascade. Such autoimmune cascades may cause disease or can be beneficial by facilitating tissue repair. The significance of danger signals in the induction of immunity and autoimmunity seems to be gaining momentum [57–59].

One of the concepts that was proposed to explain the breakdown of tolerance or incomplete tolerance is the phenomenon of molecular mimicry [60], which suggests that pathogens encode antigenic proteins that have identity or partial homology with proteins that are encoded by human cells. Thus, processing and presentation of these antigenic mimics (or "mimotopes") could activate self-reactive T cells. Molecular mimicry has been suggested to account, at least in part, for the development of autoimmunity in several inflammatory diseases, including Lyme disease and rheumatoid arthritis. Autoreactive T-cell clonotypes that also are reactive to bacterial peptides have been identified. The weakness of this concept, however, is that infections rarely include autoimmune manifestations.

Whether one espouses self/nonself recognition or the danger model, self-reactive T cells undoubtedly exist and are constituents of the normal T-cell repertoire. The question is how they are regulated such that they do not elicit unwanted pathologies. Several tolerance mechanisms in the periphery have been proposed and experimentally supported. Among these are clonal ignorance and anergy, phenotypic skewing or deviation, apoptosis, regulatory T cells, and the involvement of tolerogenic DCs [61].

Clonal ignorance and anergy refer to the absence of T-cell activation. Ignorance suggests that self-reactive or "autoreactive" T cells may never recognize the antigen for which they are specific. It is believed that the antigen could be inaccessible or that it is extremely infrequent. Considering that T cells undergo thymic selection and that peripheral T-cell homeostasis is an energy-consuming process, the idea of maintaining clonal T cells that never will be activated is tenuous, if not biologically unsound. Anergy, however, suggests that autoreactive T cells recognize antigen but that antigenic recognition does not activate the genetic program that is involved in TCR triggering. Anergic cells ultimately undergo apoptosis.

Because differentiation of T-cell effector function is influenced by cytokines, phenotypic deviation also could be an effective means of dampening the pathogenic effects of autoreactive T cells [62]. For example, autoreactive T cells in type I diabetes and psoriasis are predominantly of the Th1 type. The promotion of Th2 T-cell differentiation with cytokines, like IL-4, dramatically changes the clinical picture of the disease toward the dampening of the associated pathologies.

Apoptosis may be the most effective way to eliminate the ill effects of autoreactive T cells. TCR triggering at a certain threshold can induce AICD, mainly through the CD95 pathway. The importance of CD95 in controlling autoreactive T cells is illustrated by the autoimmune lymphoproliferative syndrome (ALPS). In ALPS, various components of the CD95-signaling pathway are mutated such that T cells become refractory to AICD which results in a lymphoproliferative disease [63]. Because apoptosis is a normal process in the self-renewal of tissues, mutated variants of proapoptotic molecules are important determinants of proliferative syndromes and malignancies.

A tolerance mechanism that has attracted renewed interest is the role of regulatory T cells. Regulatory T cells include $CD4^+CD25^+$ [64] and $CD8^+CD28^{null}$ suppressors [65]. The mechanisms through which they dampen T-cell responses is the focus of intensive research. Studies indicate that immunosuppression by $CD4^+CD25^+$ and by $CD8^+CD28^{null}$ T cells is achieved by inhibiting APC function, such as the downregulation of costimulatory molecules, class I and class II MHC molecules, and APC-derived cytokines. Consequently, the APC becomes an inefficient activator of a second T cell, be it an antigen-specific or autoreactive T cell. These suppressors also may produce cytokines, such as IL-10 and tumor growth factor TGF-β, which are known to inhibit T-cell proliferation. The suppressive activities of these regulatory T cells, at least in vitro, are overcome by IL-2. Thus, suppressor T cells are predicted to be inactive during an ongoing immune response or in an autoimmune setting in which there is increased IL-2 production. Inactivation of suppressor cells during an immune response is obviously beneficial. In autoimmune disease, a key question is how to maintain suppressive activity in an IL-2–rich environment.

The idea that DCs may serve as tolerogens comes from their APC function [66]. Because DC activation and maturation leads to the induction of immune responses [56], controlling DC activation, in theory, could be a means to induce tolerance. Immature DCs are clearly tolerogenic because they cannot activate T cells, whereas mature DCs are immunogenic because they provide the MHC/peptide ligand and costimulatory signal to T cells. "Semimature" DCs are tolerogenic, despite having APC capability. The lack of induction of DC-derived cytokines, such as TNF-α, IL-12, IL-6, and IL-1β, which profoundly influence T-cell effector differentiation seems to impart tolerogenecity. Instead, semimature DCs seem to preferentially induce the development of IL-10–secreting regulatory T cells. Thus, it was suggested that keeping DCs in the semimature state could be a means to induce tolerance in transplantation and autoimmune diseases [67]. Other studies showed that there is a distinct subset of DCs, referred to as plasmacytoid DCs, that are tolerogenic [56,66]. A current difficulty in the development of DCs as therapeutic agents is the heterogeneity of DC phenotypes and the limited understanding of DC ontogeny.

T-cell senescence

Inasmuch as TCR recognition of antigen generally leads to proliferation, repeated antigenic stimulation renders T cells susceptible to replicative senescence. T cells have a limited proliferative life span (referred to as the Hayflick limit). Hence, antigenic challenge throughout life or in an autoimmune setting where there is chronic immune activation could lead to accumulation of clonally-expanded senescent cells [68]. Because of rapid thymic involution after birth, the peripheral T-cell pool also is subject to senescence because of impaired production of new naive T cells [69]. Additionally, chronologic aging imparts epigenetic changes in the genome that contribute to alteration of T-cell function [70]. Consequently, aging is associated with immunoincompetence with the attendant increased morbidity and mortality from infections, malignancies, and autoimmune syndromes.

Although the program of T-cell senescence remains to be elucidated, a T cell that has features of advanced senescence has been identified, namely, CD28^{null} T cells in the CD8$^+$ and CD4$^+$ compartments [71,72]. Loss of CD28 expression on T cells is by far the single most consistent biologic indicator of aging in the immune system. Clinical studies showed that the frequency of CD28^{null} T cells correlates with the low rates of protective immune responses to influenza vaccination in elderly individuals [73,74]. CD28^{null} T cells also are found among patients who have chronic inflammatory conditions, regardless of age. They have been found in rheumatoid arthritis [75], Wegener's granulomatosis [76], ankylosing spondylitis [77], atherosclerotic coronary artery disease [78], and chronic infections, such as Chagas' disease [79]. In these pathologic states, CD28^{null} T cells were postulated to represent prematurely senescent T cells because of persistent activation [80,81].

Senescent cells, or cells in advanced senescence, generally are characterized by a limited or complete lack of proliferation, protection from apoptosis, and the development of new phenotypes [82]. Accordingly, CD28^{null} T cells are highly oligoclonal and have severely shortened telomeres when compared with their CD28$^+$ counterparts; this suggests that CD28 loss reflects a long replicative history [83]. CD28^{null} T cells also are highly resistant to apoptosis, which may explain their persistence for many years in the circulation [84]. In the CD4$^+$ compartment, CD28^{null} T cells have lost their Th function [85]; however, they produce high levels of IFN-γ and have gained expression of molecules, such as killer cell immunoglobulin-like receptors, perforin, and granzyme. Acquisition of these molecules makes $CD4^+CD28^{null}$ T cells functionally distinct from the typical $CD4^+$ Th1 or Th2 cells [86].

Because of the altered functions of senescent or presenescent $CD4^+CD28^{null}$ T cells, the mechanism of CD28 regulation is viewed as fundamental to understanding the pathway of T-cell senescence [87]. Molecular studies showed that CD28 expression is controlled at the level of transcriptional initiation [80,88]. Because CD28 is central to induction and maintenance of T-cell–mediated immunity [29], such studies are valuable because they provide insights into possibilities for functional reconstitution of senescent T cells [89].

Summary

T cells constitute one arm of the adaptive immune system. The accumulating information on various aspects of T-cell biology shows the intricacies in the regulation of immune responses. How we translate the cellular and molecular details of this regulation into innovation and development of therapies for disease management remains a fundamental, but exciting, challenge.

Acknowledgments

We thank James W. Fulbright for creating the figures and assistance in the preparation of the manuscript and Linda H. Arneson for secretarial support.

References

[1] Clevers H, Alarcon B, Wileman T, et al. The T cell receptor/CD3 complex: a dynamic protein ensemble. Annu Rev Immunol 1988;6:629–62.
[2] Spits H. Development of alphabeta T cells in the human thymus. Nat Rev Immunol 2002;2: 760–72.
[3] Haas W, Pereira P, Tonegawa S. Gamma/delta cells. Annu Rev Immunol 1993;11:637–85.
[4] Carding SR, Egan PJ. Gammadelta T cells: functional plasticity and heterogeneity. Nat Rev Immunol 2002;2:336–45.
[5] Lefrancois L, Masopust D. T cell immunity in lymphoid and non-lymphoid tissues. Curr Opin Immunol 2002;14:503–8.
[6] Hiltbold EM, Roche PA. Trafficking of MHC class II molecules in the late secretory pathway. Curr Opin Immunol 2002;14:30–5.
[7] Brocke P, Garbi N, Momburg F, et al. HLA-DM, HLA-DO and tapasin: functional similarities and differences. Curr Opin Immunol 2002;14:22–9.
[8] Pamer E, Cresswell P. Mechanisms of MHC class I–restricted antigen processing. Annu Rev Immunol 1998;16:323–58.
[9] Bjorkman PJ. MHC restriction in three dimensions: a view of T cell receptor/ligand interactions. Cell 1997;89:167–70.
[10] Gellert M. V(D)J recombination: RAG proteins, repair factors, and regulation. Annu Rev Biochem 2002;71:101–32.
[11] Jorgensen JL, Reay PA, Ehrich EW, et al. Molecular components of T-cell recognition. Annu Rev Immunol 1992;10:835–73.

[12] Hirose J, Kouro T, Igarashi H, et al. A developing picture of lymphopoiesis in bone marrow. Immunol Rev 2002;189:28–40.

[13] Radtke F, Wilson A, Ernst B, et al. The role of notch signaling during hematopoietic lineage commitment. Immunol Rev 2002;187:65–74.

[14] Starr TK, Jameson SC, Hogquist KA. Positive and negative selection of T cells. Annu Rev Immunol 2003;21:139–76.

[15] Germain RN. T-cell development and the CD4–CD8 lineage decision. Nat Rev Immunol 2002; 2:309–22.

[16] Legname G, Seddon B, Lovatt M, et al. Inducible expression of a p56Lck transgene reveals a central role for Lck in the differentiation of CD4 SP thymocytes. Immunity 2000;12:537–46.

[17] Hernandez-Hoyos G, Sohn SJ, Rothenberg EV, et al. Lck activity controls CD4/CD8 T-cell lineage commitment. Immunity 2000;12:313–22.

[18] Corbella P, Moskophidis D, Spanopoulou E, et al. Functional commitment to helper T-cell lineage precedes positive selection and is independent of T-cell receptor MHC specificity. Immunity 1994;1:269–76.

[19] Robey E, Itano E, Fanslow WC, et al. Constitutive CD8 expression allows inefficient maturation of CD4+ helper T cells in class II major histocompatibility complex mutant mice. J Exp Med 1994;179:1997–2004.

[20] Paterson RK, Burkly LC, Kurahara DK, et al. Thymic development in human CD4 transgenic mice. Positive selection occurs after commitment to the CD8 lineage. J Immunol 1994;153: 3491–503.

[21] Leung RK, Thomson K, Gallimore A, et al. Deletion of the CD4 silencer element supports a stochastic mechanism of thymocyte lineage commitment. Nat Immunol 2001;2:1167–73.

[22] Gordon S. Pattern recognition receptors: doubling up for the innate immune response. Cell 2002; 111:927–30.

[23] Barton GM, Medzhitov R. Toll-like receptors and their ligands. Curr Top Microbiol Immunol 2002;270:81–92.

[24] Schmitz G, Orso E. CD14 signalling in lipid rafts: new ligands and co-receptors. Curr Opin Lipidol 2002;13:513–21.

[25] Krummel MF, Davis MM. Dynamics of the immunological synapse: finding, establishing and solidifying a connection. Curr Opin Immunol 2002;14:66–74.

[26] Rachmilewitz J, Lanzavecchia A. A temporal and spatial summation model for T-cell activation: signal integration and antigen decoding. Trends Immunol 2002;23:592–5.

[27] Kane LP, Lin J, Weiss A. Signal transduction by the TCR for antigen. Curr Opin Immunol 2000;12:242–9.

[28] Clements JL, Boerth NJ, Lee JR, et al. Integration of T cell receptor-dependent signaling pathways by adapter proteins. Annu Rev Immunol 1999;17:89–108.

[29] Alegre ML, Frauwirth KA, Thompson CB. T-cell regulation by CD28 and CTLA-4. Nat Rev Immunol 2001;1:220–8.

[30] Saloman B, Bluestone JA. Complexities of CD28/B7: CTLA-4 costimulatory pathways in autoimmunity and transplantation. Annu Rev Immunol 2001;19:225–52.

[31] Bromley SK, Iaboni A, Davis SJ, et al. The immunological synapse and CD28–CD80 interactions. Nat Immunol 2001;2:1159–66.

[32] Egen JG, Allison JP. Cytotoxic T lymphocyte antigen-4 accumulation in the immunological synapse is regulated by TCR signal strength. Immunity 2002;16:23–35.

[33] Baumann S, Krueger A, Kirchhoff S, et al. Regulation of T cell apoptosis during the immune response. Curr Mol Med 2002;2:257–72.

[34] Van Parijs L, Refaeli Y, Lord JD, et al. Uncoupling IL-2 signals that regulate T cell proliferation, survival, and Fas-mediated activation-induced cell death. Immunity 1999;11:281–8.

[35] van Kooten C, Banchereau J. CD40–CD40 ligand. J Leukoc Biol 2000;67:2–17.

[36] Romagnani S. The Th1/Th2 paradigm. Immunol Today 1997;18:263–6.

[37] Moser M, Murphy KM. Dendritic cell regulation of TH1–TH2 development. Nat Immunol 2000;1:199–205.

[38] Murphy KM, Reiner SL. The lineage decisions of helper T cells. Nat Rev Immunol 2002;2: 933–44.

[39] Neurath MF, Finotto S, Glimcher LH. The role of Th1/Th2 polarization in mucosal immunity. Nat Med 2002;8:567–73.

[40] Barry M, Bleackley RC. Cytotoxic T lymphocytes: all roads lead to death. Nat Rev Immunol 2002;2:401–9.

[41] Trapani JA, Smyth MJ. Functional significance of the perforin/granzyme cell death pathway. Nat Rev Immunol 2002;2:735–47.

[42] Shresta S, Graubert TA, Thomas DA, et al. Granzyme A initiates an alternative pathway for granule-mediated apoptosis. Immunity 1999;10:595–605.

[43] Motyka B, Korbutt G, Pinkoski MJ, et al. Mannose-6-phosphate/insulin-like growth factor II receptor is a death receptor for granzyme B during cytotoxic T-cell induced apoptosis. Cell 2000; 103:491–500.

[44] Browne KA, Blink E, Sutton VR, et al. Cytosolic delivery of granzyme B by bacterial toxins: evidence that endosomal disruption in addition to transmembrane pore formation, is an important function of perforin. Mol Cell Biol 1999;19:8604–15.

[45] Liblau RS, Wong FS, Mars LT, et al. Autoreactive CD8 T cells in organ-specific autoimmunity: emerging targets for therapeutic intervention. Immunity 2002;17:1–6.

[46] Jones DH, Kong YY, Penninger JM. Role of RANKL and RANK in bone loss and arthritis. Ann Rheum Dis 2002;61(Suppl 2):32–9.

[47] Lieberman J, Shankar P, Manjunath N, et al. Dressed to kill? A review of why antiviral CD8 T lymphocytes fail to prevent progressive immunodeficiency in HIV-1 infection. Blood 2001;98: 1667–77.

[48] Kaech SM, Wherry EJ, Ahmed R. Effector and memory T-cell differentiation: implications for vaccine development. Nat Rev Immunol 2002;2:251–62.

[49] Sprent J, Surh CD. T cell memory. Annu Rev Immunol 2002;20:551–79.

[50] Jameson SC. Maintaining the norm: T-cell homeostasis. Nat Rev Immunol 2002;2:547–56.

[51] Geginat J, Lanzavecchia A, Sallusto F. Proliferation and differentiation potential of human CD8 + memory T-cell subsets in response to antigen or homeostatic cytokines. Blood 2003;101:4620–6.

[52] Baron V, Bouneaud C, Cumano A, et al. The repertoires of circulating human CD8(+) central and effector memory T cell subsets are largely distinct. Immunity 2003;18:193–204.

[53] Burnet FM. The clonal selection theory of acquired immunity. Nashville (TN): Vanderbilt University Press; 1959.

[54] Anderton SM, Wraith DC. Selection and fine-tuning of the autoimmune T-cell repertoire. Nat Rev Immunol 2002;2:487–98.

[55] Matzinger P. The danger model: a renewed sense of self. Science 2002;296:301–5.

[56] Lipscomb MF, Masten BJ. Dendritic cells: immune regulators in health and disease. Physiol Rev 2002;82:97–130.

[57] Moseley P. Stress proteins and the immune response. Immunopharmacology 2000;48:299–302.

[58] Stuart LM, Lucas M, Simpson C, et al. Inhibitory effects of apoptotic cell ingestion upon endotoxin-driven myeloid dendritic cell maturation. J Immunol 2002;168:1627–35.

[59] Ren Y, Savill J. Apoptosis: the importance of being eaten. Cell Death Differ 1998;5:563–8.

[60] Wucherpfennig KW. Mechanisms for the induction of autoimmunity by infectious agents. J Clin Invest 2001;108:1097–104.

[61] Walker LS, Abbas AK. The enemy within: keeping self-reactive T cells at bay in the periphery. Nat Rev Immunol 2002;2:11–9.

[62] Lafaille JJ. The role of helper T cell subsets in autoimmune diseases. Cytokine Growth Factor Rev 1998;9:139–51.

[63] Fischer A, Rieux-Laucat F, Le Deist F. Autoimmune lymphoproliferative syndromes (ALPS): models for the study of peripheral tolerance. Rev Immunogenet 2000;2:52–60.

[64] Shevach EM. CD4+CD25+ suppressor T cells: more questions than answers. Nat Rev Immunol 2002;2:389–400.

[65] Cortesini R, LeMaoult J, Ciubotariu R, et al. CD8+. Immunol Rev 2001;182:201–6.

[66] Steinman RM, Hawiger D, Nussenzweig MC. Tolerogenic dendritic cells. Annu Rev Immunol 2003;21:685–711.

[67] Hackstein H, Morelli AE, Thomson AW. Designer dendritic cells for tolerance induction: guided not misguided missiles. Trends Immunol 2001;22:437–42.

[68] Effros RB, Pawelec G. Replicative senescence of T cells: does the Hayflick Limit lead to immune exhaustion? Immunol Today 1997;18:450–4.

[69] Fry TJ, Mackall CL. Current concepts of thymic aging. Springer Semin Immunopathol 2002; 24:7–22.

[70] Richardson BC. Role of DNA methylation in the regulation of cell function: autoimmunity, aging and cancer. J Nutr 2002;132:2401S–5S.

[71] Posnett DN, Sinha R, Kabak S, et al. Clonal populations of T cells in normal elderly humans: the T cell equivalent to "benign monoclonal gammapathy. J Exp Med 1994;179:609–18.

[72] Vallejo AN, Nestel AR, Schirmer M, et al. Aging-related deficiency of CD28 expression in CD4 + T cells is associated with the loss of gene-specific nuclear factor binding activity. J Biol Chem 1998;273:8119–29.

[73] Goronzy JJ, Fulbright JW, Crowson CS, et al. Value of immunological markers in predicting responsiveness to influenza vaccination in elderly individuals. J Virol 2001;75:12182–7.

[74] Saurwein-Teissl M, Lung TL, Marx F, et al. Lack of antibody production following immunization in old age: association with CD8(+)CD28(−) T cell clonal expansions and an imbalance in the production of Th1 and Th2 cytokines. J Immunol 2002;168:5893–9.

[75] Martens PB, Goronzy JJ, Schaid D, et al. Expansion of unusual CD4 + T cells in severe rheumatoid arthritis. Arthritis Rheum 1997;40:1106–14.

[76] Moosig F, Csernok E, Wang G, et al. Costimulatory molecules in Wegener's granulomatosis (WG): lack of expression of CD28 and preferential up-regulation of its ligands B7–1 (CD80) and B7–2 (CD86) on T cells. Clin Exp Immunol 1998;114:113–8.

[77] Schirmer M, Goldberger C, Wurzner R, et al. Circulating cytotoxic CD8(+) CD28(−) T cells in ankylosing spondylitis. Arthritis Res 2002;4:71–6.

[78] Liuzzo G, Kopecky SL, Frye RL, et al. Perturbation of the T-cell repertoire in patients with unstable angina. Circulation 1999;100:2135–9.

[79] Dutra WO, Martins-Filho OA, Cancado JR, et al. Chagasic patients lack CD28 expression on many of their circulating T lymphocytes. Scand J Immunol 1996;43:88–93.

[80] Vallejo AN, Weyand CM, Goronzy JJ. Functional disruption of the CD28 gene transcriptional initiator in senescent T cells. J Biol Chem 2001;276:2565–70.

[81] Bryl E, Vallejo AN, Weyand CM, et al. Down-regulation of CD28 expression by TNF-alpha. J Immunol 2001;167:3231–8.

[82] Campisi J. Cancer, aging and cellular senescence. In Vivo 2000;14:183–8.

[83] Monteiro J, Batliwalla F, Ostrer H, et al. Shortened telomeres in clonally expanded CD28–CD8+ T cells imply a replicative history that is distinct from their CD28+CD8+ counterparts. J Immunol 1996;156:3587–90.

[84] Vallejo AN, Schirmer M, Weyand CM, et al. Clonality and longevity of CD4 + CD28[null] T cells are associated with defects in apoptotic pathways. J Immunol 2000;165:6301–7.

[85] Weyand CM, Brandes JC, Schmidt D, et al. Functional properties of CD4 +. Mech Ageing Dev 1998;102:131–47.

[86] Snyder MR, Lucas M, Vivier E, et al. Selective activation of the c-Jun NH2-terminal protein kinase signaling pathway by stimulatory KIR in the absence of KARAP/DAP12 in CD4 + T cells. J Exp Med 2003;197:437–49.

[87] Vallejo AN, Brandes JC, Weyand CM, et al. Modulation of CD28 expression: distinct regulatory pathways during activation and replicative senescence. J Immunol 1999;162:6572–9.

[88] Vallejo AN, Bryl E, Klarskov K, et al. Molecular basis for the loss of CD28 expression in senescent T cells. J Biol Chem 2002;277:46940–9.

[89] Warrington KJ, Vallejo AN, Weyand CM, et al. CD28 loss in senescent CD4 + T cells: reversal by interleukin-12 stimulation. Blood 2002;101:3543–9.

ELSEVIER
SAUNDERS

RHEUMATIC
DISEASE CLINICS
OF NORTH AMERICA

Rheum Dis Clin N Am 30 (2004) 159–174

B-cell biology

Elena Weinstein, MD[a], Elena Peeva, MD[a,b],
Chaim Putterman, MD[a,b], Betty Diamond, MD[a,b],*

[a]Division of Rheumatology, Department of Medicine, Albert Einstein College of Medicine,
1300 Morris Park Avenue, Bronx, NY 10461, USA
[b]Department of Microbiology and Immunology, Albert Einstein College of Medicine,
1300 Morris Park Avenue, Bronx, NY 10461, USA

Twice in the life of a B cell, autoreactive specificities are generated. The first time occurs during bone marrow development when the naïve or immature B-cell repertoire is generated. The second occurs in the germinal center reaction when an antigen-specific B-cell population is diversified to generate high affinity antibodies that are the hallmark of the memory response. Generation of autoreactive B cells does not necessarily lead to disease. In fact, all persons consistently generate autoreactive B cells. Most of these cells are eliminated so that they do not contribute to the memory cell or plasma cell repertoire. The mechanisms by which these cells are targeted for elimination constitute the process of negative selection. Whether an autoreactive B cell is prompted to undergo negative selection is based on: (1) the strength of signaling at the B-cell receptor (BCR); (2) the intrinsic resistance to apoptosis; and (3) the influence of a variety of cytokines and costimulatory molecules that can rescue B cells from negative selection. A defect or lack of stringency in negative selection of B cells is critical to all diseases that are characterized by the presence of autoantibodies. Autoantibodies are secreted by autoreactive B cells that escape negative selection and mature to immunocompetence due to intrinsic B cell defects or by normal B cells that experience excessive costimulation from T cells and dendritic cells which leads to their rescue from negative selection. Thus, defects in multiple cells in the immune system may lead to impaired negative selection of autoreactive B cells.

Determining the mechanisms that underlie incomplete or ineffective negative selection is critical for developing an understanding of autoimmunity. This is an evolving area of research and knowledge. We appreciate now that the predisposition to autoimmunity represents a continuum. At one end of the spectrum is the

* Corresponding author. Department of Medicine, Forscheimer 405, Albert Einstein College of Medicine, 1300 Morris Park Avenue, Bronx, NY 10461.
  E-mail address: diamond@aecom.yu.edu (B. Diamond).

0889-857X/04/$ – see front matter © 2004 Elsevier Inc. All rights reserved.
doi:10.1016/S0889-857X(03)00109-1

"normal" individual who is resistant to the development of autoantibodies. Although "normal" individuals produce autoreactive B cells, most of the autoreactive B cells are negatively selected. At the other end of the continuum are those individuals who have frank autoimmune disease. What lies between these two extremes of immune function is a fascinating spectrum that may hold many clues to the cause, pathogenesis, and treatment of autoimmune disease. In this "middle ground" between strong resistance to autoimmunity and overt disease are individuals who have a known genetic predisposition to autoimmune disease, such as first degree relatives of patients who have systemic lupus erythematosus (SLE) and other autoimmune diseases. Also in this "middle ground" are individuals who express antinuclear antibodies, but have no disease. Finally, in this "middle ground" are individuals who develop autoantibodies secondary to an environmental stimulus, such as infection or medication.

The fundamentals of B-cell development, activation, and regulation and the ways in which they may go awry are considered here. We discuss some of the pathways by which autoimmunity is believed to be generated in SLE and rheumatoid arthritis (RA). Finally, we highlight important developments in B-cell–directed therapeutics.

Immunoglobulin structure and function

Immunoglobulins, described in 1962 by Rodney Porter, are tetrameric molecules that are composed of two pairs of polypeptide chains. Immunoglobulin has two identical light chains, each with a molecular weight of 25 kD, and two identical heavy chains, each with a molecular weight of 50 kD to 75 kD. Each light chain is linked to a heavy chain by a disulfide bond; the two heavy chains are linked to each other by a variable number of disulfide bonds. The tertiary structure is determined by covalent and noncovalent forces [1].

The light and heavy chains contain a variable region and a constant region. The variable regions are responsible for the great diversity of antigens that are recognized by the immunoglobulin. The constant regions of the heavy chains determine the immunoglobulin class or isotype. Principal effector functions of the immunoglobulin molecule include complement activation, binding to Fc receptors on phagocytic cells, and placental transfer. These functions vary significantly with antibody class. There are five known isotypes in mice and humans: IgM, IgG, IgA, IgE, and IgD.

IgM is the first isotype that is generated in developing B cells, the first antibody generated during the primary immune response, and makes up about 10% of the serum Ig pool. It usually is secreted as a pentamer linked by a peptide known as the J or joining chain. Monomeric IgM has a low affinity for antigen; however, polymerization greatly enhances its avidity for antigen and allows for binding of multimeric antigen. IgM is a potent activator of complement through the classical pathway [1]. A critical feature of IgM antibodies is that they do not have a mechanism to leave the bloodstream and penetrate tissue. Thus, IgM autoantibodies are of pathogenic consequence only if they are directed against antigens that are present on blood cells or in plasma or if they are produced by B cells that are present in nonlymphoid tissue. For example, in hemolytic anemia, IgM antibodies can bind to red blood cells in the circulation and cause hemolysis. In RA, in contrast, plasma cells that make IgM rheumatoid factor are present in the inflamed synovium.

IgG is the most common Ig isotype and accounts for about 75% of the Ig pool. There are four known subclasses of IgG in humans, IgG1 through IgG4, which differ in their functional characteristics. IgG is the predominant isotype of the secondary immune response and the only isotype that can leave the bloodstream and penetrate tissues. Thus, IgG autoantibodies that are produced by plasma cells in lymphoid tissue or in the bone marrow can cause pathology in any organ that expresses the target antigen. All IgG subclasses activate the classical pathway of complement. IgG1 also is capable of initiating complement activation through the alternative pathway. All four subclasses are capable of binding to Fc receptors on T and B lymphocytes and platelets. IgG1 and IgG3 also can bind to mononuclear cells and neutrophils. IgG4 binds to mast cells and basophils. All subclasses cross the placenta; maternal IgG is believed to be the principal source of passive, protective immunity and the principal potential source of autoreactivity in the neonate [2].

IgA is the predominant isotype at mucosal surfaces. It makes up about 15% of the serum Ig pool. IgA exists as two subclasses, IgA1 and IgA2. IgA1 exists mainly as a monomer in serum. IgA2 is a dimer linked by a J chain and linked to a peptide known as secretory component. Secretory component is added to IgA as IgA binds to pIgR and transits through secretory epithelium. This component renders polymeric IgA resistant to enzymatic degradation. IgA activates complement through the alternative pathway. It binds to effector cells through a specific FcαR; however, the physiologic role of this binding is not well understood [2].

IgE, as a monomer, is found in trace amounts in serum. It binds in the monomeric form to the high affinity FcεR on basophils and mast cells. When antigen binds to cell-bound IgE, degranulation and release of mediators causes immediate hypersensitivity reactions [2].

Soluble IgD also is found in trace amounts in serum. It is typically membrane-bound in association with membrane-bound IgM and its expression is a marker for immunocompetent B cells [3]. Its physiologic function is not well understood.

Two light chains exist in most vertebrates, κ and λ. During immunoglobulin assembly, a heavy chain associates with either a κ or a λ light chain. There is no known physiologic function for the constant region of the light chain. κ chains are more common than λ chains in humans (60%) and mice (95%) [2].

The antigen binding region of the immunoglobulin molecule is composed of the variable domains of the light and heavy chains. The heavy chain variable region is encoded by three distinct gene segments: the variable (V), diversity (D), and joining (J) segments. The light chain variable region is encoded by V and J segments only. Within the variable regions of the heavy and light chains are three hypervariable regions, also known as complementarity determining regions

(CDRs). Abutting the CDRs are four segments that are known as framework regions that have more highly conserved amino acid sequences and are believed to provide the scaffolding for the antigen-binding site [2].

Anti-idiotypic antibodies are formed normally in individuals and recognize antigenic epitopes on immunoglobulin variable regions. These antibodies can function like antigen to activate or inactivate B cells that express particular variable region genes. Because autoantibodies of a particular antigenic specificity often share idiotypic determinants, there has been interest in developing anti-idiotypes to target drugs to particular B cells.

The primary means of generating the diversity in the antibody repertoire of immature B cells is rearrangement of the V(D)J segments of the light and heavy chains. This occurs in immature B cells in primary lymphoid tissue that is naïve to antigen. Proteins, known as recombination activating gene (RAG)-1 and RAG2, initiate rearrangement of V(D)J genes at the heavy and light chain loci by causing breaks in double-stranded DNA at specific recombination signal sites. The resulting cleaved segments are joined by a complex of molecules that constitutes the recombination machinery and includes Ku70, Ku80, and DNA-dependent protein kinase [4]. Further diversity is generated by the addition of nontemplate encoded nucleotides, at VD and DJ junctions in the heavy chain, by the enzyme terminal deoxynucleotidyl transferase [5].

Somatic point mutations that occur in the variable regions of the heavy and light chains of antigen-activated B cells that mature in germinal centers of secondary lymphoid tissue, further increase variable region diversity. These mutations may alter affinity of the immunoglobulin molecule for an antigen or change its specificity altogether [6–8]. It is clear that somatic mutation generates autoreactive B cells routinely during the course of a response to foreign antigen.

The critical feature of V(D)J rearrangement and of somatic hypermutation is that a vast repertoire of antigenic specificities is generated by each mechanism, which includes autoantigenic specificities. Thus, when the naïve B-cell repertoire is generated and when the antigen-activated repertoire is further diversified, there needs to be a selection against autoreactive B cells.

For more detail on immunoglobulin structure and assembly, the interested reader is referred to several excellent and comprehensive reviews [1–3].

Tolerance

Central to the appropriate functioning of the immune system is the establishment of tolerance (ie, the ability to eliminate antiself reactivity). This occurs at critical checkpoints along the pathway of B-cell development and can be divided broadly into central and peripheral tolerance. Central tolerance is established in the immature B cells in the bone marrow and spleen. Peripheral tolerance involves regulation of antigen-activated B cells that mature in the germinal centers. A malfunction in either of these populations can result in autoimmunity and rheumatologic disease.

Because V(D)J rearrangement is a random process, autoreactive B cells are generated in the course of normal B cell development. These cells may become immunocompetent, and, therefore, potentially pathogenic if they are not subject to negative selection. There are three well-documented pathways of negative selection: receptor editing, anergy, and deletion [9–11]. All of these processes are initiated by the ligation of the BCR by antigen. Autoreactive B cells that experience little cross-linking of the BCR because of low concentration of, or low affinity for, antigen, will not undergo negative selection and will mature to immunocompetence. If the antigen concentration or the affinity of the BCR for antigen increases at a later stage in B-cell development, the B cell may be activated.

It now is believed that if a naïve B cell is engaged while the cell is still present in primary lymphoid tissue, the first option for negative selection is a process that is known as "receptor editing." During receptor editing, RAG1 and RAG2 are re-expressed and a new light chain rearrangement occurs. Receptor editing also may occur at the heavy chain locus; this event seems to be much less common. If the process leads to a nonautoreactive B cell receptor, B cell maturation continues. If this process is not successful and the BCR remains autoreactive, the B cell undergoes anergy or deletion [10–12].

Anergy is a state of functional hyporeactivity. An anergic B cell can no longer be activated through its BCR. Anergy is believed to occur when an immature B cell experiences a moderate degree of engagement of the BCR. Anergic B cells have shortened life spans and undergo apoptosis and death if anergy is not reversed. How rescue from anergy occurs is an area of active investigation. It seems that there is a limited window of time during which the B cell can be rescued; rescue can be mediated by engagement of costimulatory molecules or toll-like receptors on the B cell. Anergic B cells do not enter lymphoid follicles; this trafficking pattern is termed "follicular exclusion" [12].

Deletion occurs through programmed cell death when there is extensive cross-linking of the BCR of an immature B cell. If an immature autoreactive B cell escapes negative selection in primary lymphoid tissue, it still may undergo negative selection after it emigrates to the spleen. The B cell enters the spleen as a transitional B cell and remains subject to tolerance induction through receptor editing, anergy, or deletion. Like anergic B cells, immature or transitional B cells that encounter antigen can be rescued from deletion by a variety of costimulatory molecules or cytokines [13]. Tolerance induction is, therefore, a dynamic process that is influenced by a variety of modulators, including antigen concentration, hormones, and other factors that regulate the strength of the BCR signal, co-stimulatory pathways, and cytokines [14]. Thus, stringency of negative selection may differ at different times and B cells that normally are eliminated may survive to maturity in certain environments. Furthermore, it is apparent that the threshold for negative selection differs among individuals and that the degree of auto-reactivity present in the repertoire of immunocompetent B cells varies. Finally, this model may help to explain the spectrum of autoantibodies that is seen in SLE. It was postulated that an overabundance of apoptotic bodies may be present in individuals who have defects in clearance of apoptotic cells [15]. B cells with

BCRs that bind to the nuclear antigens in apoptotic bodies may be rescued from negative selection by the engagement of toll-like receptors that have specificity for DNA or RNA [16]. Thus, B cells that produce antinuclear antibodies escape negative selection.

B-cell activation and B-cell subsets

Mature B lymphocytes may be divided into subsets that differ in their location, cell surface phenotype, antigenic specificity, and threshold for activation. B1 B cells are the first B cells to be formed during fetal development and are made in the fetal liver. They are divided into B1a and B1b cells. B1a cells express the transmembrane glycoprotein CD5; B1b cells do not. Both express the surface markers CD9 and CD45RA [17]. The functional distinction between these two subsets remains unclear. B1a and B1b cells are involved in T-cell independent responses. B1 cells are unique in their ability to self renew. They accumulate in the pleural and peritoneal cavities and may have specialized functions there. B1 B cells secrete low affinity, polyreactive IgM antibodies. It has been suggested that the ability of these antibodies to bind autoantigen and potentially shield autoantigen from recognition by other B cells may contribute to self tolerance [18]. Whether B1 cells are a distinct B cell lineage is an unresolved question. It is possible that differentiation of B cells into B1 cells is favored by low-strength BCR signaling [19]. This would account for the skewing of the B1-cell repertoire to low-affinity autoreactivity.

B1 cells interact with large multivalent antigens, such as bacterial polysaccharide. These antigens can directly cross-link the BCR on B1 cells, which initiates activation of the B cell and secretion of immunoglobulin. Although T-cell help is not required for B1-cell activation, T cells that express CD4 affect isotype switching and enhance BCR activation of B1 cells. Increased numbers of B1 cells were found in animal and human studies of autoimmune disease [20–22] and elimination of B1 cells was shown to diminish autoantibody titers in some mouse models [23]. Taken together, these data suggest a potential role for B1 cells in the pathogenesis of autoimmune disease.

B2 cells are generated in the bone marrow. They may become marginal zone B cells in the spleen and tonsil or follicular B cells in the spleen, tonsil, and lymph nodes. This differentiation is believed to be influenced by a variety of factors, including chemokines, strength of BCR signaling, and type of antigen. These mechanisms are not fully understood [24].

Marginal zone B2 cells are found in the marginal zone of the spleen and tonsil and are involved in T-cell independent responses [25]. They have a low threshold for activation and respond quickly to blood borne pathogens. In animal studies, antigens that are injected into the bloodstream rapidly localize to the marginal zone [26]. Activated marginal zone B cells organize into primary foci and differentiate into short-lived antibody-secreting plasma cells that are known as "plasmacytes." This subgroup of plasma cells secretes low-affinity IgM and does not undergo somatic mutation [27]. The role of marginal zone B cells in auto-immunity is an active area of research. The marginal zone B-cell compartment is expanded in NZB/NZW F1 lupus-prone mice and is associated with nephri-tis [28,29]. This B-cell subset also is expanded in many genetically-engineered models of autoimmunity.

Follicular B cells are involved in T-cell dependent immune responses. These B cells are activated when they encounter antigen-specific T helper cells and anti-gen. The B cells can use the BCR to engulf the antigen, process it, and present it to the T cell. Subsequent T-cell activation involves engagement of the T-cell recep-tor with the major histocompatibility complex–associated processed antigen and the complex interactions of a variety of costimulatory molecules on the sur-faces of the T helper cell and the B cell [30]. Thus, there is a cascade of B- and T-cell activation that leads to an expansion of the number of epitopes that are seen by B and T cells on an inciting antigen. This process is believed to be critical to protection from microbial antigens, but may lead to an expansion of autoreactive responses as well.

Once activated, follicular B cells form germinal centers and participate in setting up the memory immune response and the population of long-lived plasma cells. Germinal centers represent a specialized microenvironment that forms within lymphoid tissue. Within the germinal center, follicular dendritic cells present antigen on their surface which excites the proliferation of antigen-specific B cells. Few B cells survive the journey through the germinal center. B cells that undergo somatic mutations that result in production of antibodies with a higher affinity for antigen are positively selected, expanded, and continue to mature, whereas B cells with somatic mutations that result in antibodies with a decreased affinity for antigen or autoreactivity undergo negative selection. It remains a matter of debate whether secondary immunoglobulin gene rearrangements occur in germinal centers [31].

Memory B cells are the foundation of the secondary immune response—the immunologic response to a previously recognized antigen. These cells cir-culate throughout the body in a resting state until a specific antigen is encountered again. The resulting secondary immune response occurs much faster, is more efficient than the primary response, requires significantly less antigenic stimulus, and gives rise to high-affinity antibodies [32].

The primary function of plasma cells is antibody secretion. Long-lived plasma cells arise in the germinal center and migrate to the bone marrow where they may persist for many years. Studies of autoantibodies in RA and SLE suggest that follicular B cells are a major source of autoreactivity; many of the autoantibodies display extensive somatic maturation and evidence of affinity maturation against self-antigenis [33,34].

Regulation of B-cell activation

The BCR is a six-chain complex that consists of the four chains of the mem-brane-bound immunoglobulin in association with a single chain of each of the accessory molecules Iga and Igb (CD79a and CD79b). These accessory molecules are involved in signal transduction. Both contain amino acid sequences that are known as ITAMs (immunoreceptor tyrosine-based activation motifs) that are essential to transmembrane signaling pathways. When a B cell encounters antigen, BCR-associated tyrosine kinases such as Lyn, Fyn, and Lyk phospho-rylate tyrosine residues in the ITAMs. Phosphorylated ITAMs then interact with protein tyrosine kinases, such as Syk and Btk, which further phosphorylate the ITAMs, as well as other signaling molecules [35]. Subsequent pathways involve activation of phospholipase C, phosphatidylinositol 3-kinase, and Ras [2]. The outcome of these complex and interconnected signaling pathways is B-cell acti-vation and proliferation.

All of these events may be modulated by several molecules that are included in the B-cell coreceptor complex. This complex is composed of several molecules that can enhance BCR signaling, including CD19, CD21, CD45, CD38, CD81, and Leu-13. CD19 is associated on the B-cell membrane with CD21, which binds to cleavage fragments of the C3 component of complement that are formed when complement is activated. When CD19, CD21, and C3b associate, the positive signaling that is associated with the BCR increases [36,37]. CD19 and CD21 are essential for T-cell dependent B-cell activation and germinal center formation. The functions of CD81 and Leu-13 have not been demonstrated clearly. CD45 is a positive regulator of BCR signaling. CD38 is a membrane-associated enzyme that may increase BCR signaling by its interaction with CD19 [38]. The importance of a properly functioning B-cell coreceptor complex was demonstrated in animal studies. In transgenic mice that overexpress CD19, for example, anergic B cells are activated and spontaneously produce autoantibodies [39].

Coreceptors that inhibit BCR activation are SHP-1, CD22, CD5, and FcγRIIb1. Lyn, the tyrosine kinase that is associated with ITAM phosphorylation, also phosphorylates and activates CD22 and FcγRIIb1, which then diminish the BCR-mediated signal. Thus, one regulatory molecule can play multiple roles in governing B-cell activation [35]. Agents that alter the strength of BCR signaling, when developed, could potentially alter the B-cell repertoire, and move indi-viduals closer to, or further from, autoimmunity.

Another important pathway that is involved in regulating B-cell activation involves a group of molecules on the surfaces of B and T cells that are collectively known as "costimulatory molecules." The interactions between these molecules are critical to many of the steps in B-cell development, proliferation, and acti-vation. Specific interactions may either suppress or stimulate the B cell. Defective negative costimulation or excessive positive costimulation may predispose to autoimmunity. A discussion of some of the most important of these cellular interactions, many of which are still being characterized fully, appears below.

B-cell activating factor (BAFF) is a member of the tumor necrosis factor family of molecules. It was identified recently and seems to be critical for B-cell survival. It is essential for the progression of transitional T1 cells to T2 cells in the spleen [40]. It is also an important stimulator of B-cell proliferation and differentiation [41]. There are three known receptors for BAFF: B cell maturation antigen, transmembrane activator and calcium-modulator and cyclophilin ligand interactor (TACI), and BAFF receptor (BAFF-R). All are expressed on B cells, but BAFF-R is most critical for B-cell maturation [42].

Mice that are transgenic for BAFF demonstrate increased B-cell numbers, produce autoantibodies, and develop lupuslike and Sjögren's-like pathology [43,44]. Further evidence of BAFF's role in autoimmunity is the observation of an elevated level of BAFF in serum of patients who have SLE, RA, or Sjögren's disease [44–46]. Like other costimulatory molecules, BAFF is a potential therapeutic target.

CD40 is expressed by B cells at all stages of development. It also is found on monocytes, dendritic cells, and a wide variety of other cell types throughout the body, including epithelial cells, fibroblasts, and endothelial cells. CD40 ligand (CD40L), also known as CD154, is expressed primarily on activated CD4 T cells [47]; however, it also may be expressed by small numbers of CD8 T cells, mast cells, basophils, eosinophils, B cells, monocytes, dendritic cells, and platelets [48–50]. The engagement of CD40 by CD40L promotes B-cell activation, maturation, differentiation, and immunoglobulin production [51–54]. It is critical to germinal center formation and promotes the development of memory B cells and prevents differentiation into plasma cells [55–57]. CD40/CD40L interactions are important in rescuing immature B cells from negative selection and germinal center B cells from apoptosis [58,59].

Another costimulatory interaction that is required for T-cell activation is the engagement of CD28 on a T cell by B7 molecules (CD80 and CD86) on an antigen-presenting cell. Because antigen-specific T-cell activation is critical to T-dependent B cell responses, interfering with the B7-CD28 interaction can prevent B-cell activation [60].

Recently, it was discovered that costimulation also may be mediated by molecules that are known as "toll-like receptors." These receptors are molecules on the surface of B cells that recognize microbial compounds or apoptotic particles [61–63]. This type of costimulation is generally less potent than that achieved through interactions with T cells and does not result in a high-affinity immunoglobulin response [24].

A major consequence of costimulation, in general, is to rescue cells from negative selection. Thus, increasing costimulatory engagement increases the degree of autoreactivity in the repertoire.

B cells and autoimmunity

The production of autoantibodies is a clearly established mechanism of B-cell induced autoimmunity. For example, autoantibodies are a hallmark of SLE and are known to cause tissue damage by a variety of mechanisms, including interference with cellular physiology, immune complex formation, and cytolysis or phagocytosis of target cells [64]. It is now clear, however, that B cells contribute more than autoantibody production to the development of autoimmune disease.

B cells play a critical role in amplifying an immune response through their function as antigen-presenting cells. Epitope spreading, or the recognition of an increasing number of antigenic determinants on a molecule or molecular complex, is an important mechanism in autoimmunity [64]. This process involves B cells and T cells. Epitope spreading occurs when antigen A is recognized by the BCR, internalized, processed, and presented to T cells. The B cell may present "cryptic" antigens of antigen A, self peptides which under normal conditions are not presented to T cells for induction of tolerance. When activated B cells present cryptic peptides, they activate naïve autoreactive T cells [65]. Furthermore, antigen A may be associated physically with antigen B [65]. Because of this association, when antigen A is internalized, antigen B also is internalized, processed, and presented to T cells. The mechanism of epitope spreading may have evolved to provide an enhanced response to pathogens [66]. In SLE, the phenomenon of epitope spreading offers an explanation for the development of autoantibody specificities to antigens that are part of the same molecular complex, such as the close association of anti-Ro and anti-La antibodies.

The critical function of B cells as antigen-presenting cells in autoimmune disease is demonstrated most convincingly in autoimmune-prone mice with an induced genetic lesion such that their B cells do not secrete immunoglobulin. These mice display T-cell activation and develop nephritis [67]. This model suggests that B cells are critical to the activation of the autoreactive T cells. It also was speculated that B cells may contribute directly to organ pathology by production and local secretion of cytokines in the target tissue [68].

In patients who have SLE, B cells seem to be hyperreactive, but it is not known if this is an intrinsic B-cell abnormality or if it is related to abnormal interactions between B cells and T cells [69]. In murine models of SLE, it is clear that all mature B-cell subsets can produce anti-DNA antibodies. In human SLE, it is not clear which B-cell subset is critical for anti-DNA antibody production. Because B-cell activation differs for each subset, different therapeutic interventions may be necessary, depending on the B-cell subset that contributes to autoantibody production.

RA has long been considered to be a T-cell mediated disease. In rheumatoid synovium, T cells predominate over B cells and T-cell–induced inflammatory cytokines are prominent [70,71]. More recent studies, however, are focusing attention on the role of B cells in this disease. Rituximab is a chimeric monoclonal antibody that binds CD20 on B cells and leads to their depletion [72]. It has been used successfully in the treatment of B-cell malignancies and recently was shown to be beneficial in a group of patients who had RA [73]. The therapeutic success of rituximab in RA supports an important role for B cells in this disease. Rheumatoid factors are immunoglobulins (usually IgM) that are directed against the Fc portion of IgG. Rheumatoid factor–producing B cells, however, are found in high concentrations in rheumatoid synovium where they may internalize immune complexes that contain diverse autoantigens and promote T-cell activation and T-cell dependent inflammation [74]. Thus, rheumatoid factor–producing B cells may be important antigen-presenting cells in RA.

Implications for therapy

Autoimmune diseases are a heterogeneous and complex group of disorders. A variety of genetic and environmental factors contribute to the development and natural history of these diseases. Many of our current therapies for rheumatic disease are nonspecific and broadly suppress multiple components of the immune system, and, therefore, are associated with significant toxicities. As our under-standing of the cellular and molecular basis for autoimmune disease advances, so do opportunities for intervention and treatment.

In all diseases with autoreactive B cells, there is necessarily a defect in B-cell negative selection. This may reflect a genetic predisposition to B-cell survival (either through diminished BCR signaling or resistance to apoptosis) or enhanced sensitivity to costimulation or cytokines that are rescue factors for B cells that are destined for negative selection. Alternatively, there may be a genetic alteration in T-cell or dendritic cell activation, such that they overproduce rescue factors for autoreactive B cells. Finally, there may be environmental factors that alter B-cell selection. The potential causes of B-cell autoreactivity are, therefore, multiple and complex and include genetic and environmental factors. A focus on altering BCR signaling or on blocking costimulation or cytokines that protect against negative selection, can, however, help prevent autoreactivity, whatever the causative al-teration of the immune system.

In SLE and RA, pathogenic B cells have been targeted by interrupting cos-timulatory pathways. Recent studies in lupus mice, using anti-CD40L anti-bodies, demonstrated a decrease in anti-DNA antibodies and diminished renal disease [75]. Although the clinical trial with this agent had to be discontinued because of thrombotic complications, the promise of therapy through costimula-tory blockade remains. Inhibition of the B7-CD28 pathway with CTLA4 Ig, which blocks T-cell activation by antigen-presenting cells, suppressed or blocked autoantibody production and improved survival in murine lupus [76,77] and prevented development of collagen-induced arthritis [78,79]. In addition, a pilot clinical trial demonstrated that CTLA4 Ig is a well-tolerated and effective thera-peutic agent for RA [80]. TACI-Ig, a soluble receptor for BAFF that interferes with BAFF function, can diminish or prevent disease in animal models of lupus and RA [43,81].

Another potential approach to the elimination of autoreactive B cells is the use of antigen conjugates to induce tolerance by cross-linking B-cell receptors in the absence of costimulation. When tetrameric nucleotides conjugated with polyeth-ylene glycol are given to lupus-prone mice, the mice display a decrease in renal disease and autoantibody production and improved survival. A similar compound, LJP 394, recently was studied in patients who had SLE and renal disease [82]. Although this particular compound was not particularly efficacious, the approach still may have merit, especially if the antigen is given in conjunction with an agent to block costimulatory molecules or toll-like receptors. The development of specific kinase or phosphatase inhibitors that alter BCR signaling also may be efficacious [24].

B-cell depletion with rituximab was demonstrated to have clinical efficacy in a small-scale study of RA [73]. In open trials of patients who had lupus who were refractory to other therapies, rituximab was beneficial [83]. The role of B-cell depletion in the treatment of other autoimmune diseases is being studied, but it is difficult to imagine that it will be possible to treat disease in this manner without some compromise of immunocompetence.

Summary

In recent years, our understanding of B-cell biology and the roles of B cells in normal immune responses and autoimmunity has increased dramatically. We no longer think of B cells simply as antibody factories. It is clear that these diverse and exquisitely regulated cells may contribute in a multitude of ways to immune responses. Animal models, clinical trials of biologic agents, and the ever expanding field of molecular biology have made great contributions to our current knowledge. With this improved understanding, we are afforded the opportunity to consider numerous potential therapeutic targets for treating autoimmune disease. As this growing science evolves, we can expect to see the advent of new therapies and new hope for patients who are afflicted with these disorders.

References

[1] Tuner M. Antibody structure and function. In: Roitt I, Brostoff J, Male D, editors. Immunology. 4th edition. London: Mosby; 1996. p. 5.1–5.8.
[2] Diamond B, Grimaldi C. B cells. In: Kelley WN, Ruddy S, Harris E, Sledge C, editors. Textbook of rheumatology. 6th edition. Philadelphia: WB Saunders; 2000. p. 131–49.
[3] Janeway CA, Travers P, Walport M, Sholmchick M. Structural variation in immunoglobulin constant regions. In: Janeway CA, Travers P, Walport M, Sholmchik M, editors. Immunolobiology. 5th edition. New York: Garland Pub.; 2001. p. 142–3.
[4] Chu G. Role of the Ku autoantigen in V(D)J recombination and double-strand break repair. Curr Top Microbiol Immunol 1996;217:113–32.
[5] Desiderio SV, Yancopoulos GD, Paskind M, Thomas E, Boss MA, Landau N, et al. Insertion of N regions into heavy-chain genes is correlated with expression of terminal deoxytransferase in B cells. Nature 1984;311(5988):752–5.
[6] Clarke SH, Rudikoff S. Evidence for gene conversion among immunoglobulin heavy chain variable region genes. J Exp Med 1984;159(3):773–82.
[7] Clarke SH, Huppi K, Ruezinsky D, Staudt L, Gerhard W, Weigert M. Inter- and intraclonal diversity in the antibody response to influenza hemagglutinin. J Exp Med 1985;161(4):687–704.
[8] Reynaud CA, Anquez V, Dahan A, Weill JC. A single rearrangement event generates most of the chicken immunoglobulin light chain diversity. Cell 1985;40(2):283–91.
[9] Meffre E, Casellas R, Nussenzweig MC. Antibody regulation of B cell development. Nat Immunol 2000;1(5):379–85.
[10] Goodnow CC, Cyster JG, Hartley SB, Bell SE, Cooke MP, Healey JI, et al. Self-tolerance checkpoints in B lymphocyte development. Adv Immunol 1995;59:279–368.
[11] Tiegs SL, Russell DM, Nemazee D. Receptor editing in self-reactive bone marrow B cells. J Exp Med 1993;177(4):1009–20.
[12] Cyster JG, Goodnow CC. Antigen-induced exclusion from follicles and anergy are separate and complementary processes that influence peripheral B cell fate. Immunity 1995;3(6):691–701.

[13] Diamond B. Speculations on the immunogenicity of self proteins. In: Brown F, Mire-Sluis AR, editors. Immunogenicity of therapeutic biological products. Developments in Biologicals. Basel: Karger; 2003. p. 29–34.

[14] Peeva E, Diamond B, Putterman C. The structure and derivation of antibodies and autoanti-bodies. In: Wallace DJ, Hahn BH, editors. Duboios systemic lupus erythematosus. 6th edition. Philadelphia: Lippincott, Williams and Wilkins; 2001. p. 391–413.

[15] Napirei M, Karsunksky H, Zevnik B, Stephan H, Mannherz HG, Moroy T. Features of sys-temic lupus erythematosus in Dnase1-deficient mice. Nat Genet 2000;25(2):177–81.

[16] Leadbetter EA, Rifkin IR, Hohlbaum AM, Beaudette BC, Shlomchik MJ, Marshak-Rothstein A. Chromatin-IgG complexes activate B cells by dual engagement of IgM and toll-like receptors. Nature 2002;416:603–7.

[17] Paloczi K, Batai A, Gopcsa L, Ezsi R, Petranyi GG. Immunophenotypic characterisation of cord blood B-lymphocytes. Bone Marrow Transplant 1998;22(Suppl 4):S89–91.

[18] Stall AM, Wells SM, Lam KP. B-1 cells: unique origins and functions. Semin Immunol 1996; 8(1):45–59.

[19] Rothstein TL. Cutting edge commentary: two B-1 or not to be one. J Immunol 2002;168(9): 4257–61.

[20] Burastero SE, Casali P, Wilder RL, Notkins AL. Monoreactive high affinity and polyreactive low affinity rheumatoid factors are produced by CD5+ B cells from patients with rheumatoid arthri-tis. J Exp Med 1988;168(6):1979–92.

[21] Dauphinee M, Tovar Z, Talal N. B cells expressing CD5 are increased in Sjogren's syndrome. Arthritis Rheum 1988;31(5):642–7.

[22] Hayakawa K, Hardy RR, Herzenberg LA. Peritoneal Ly-1 B cells: genetic control, autoantibody production, increased lambda light chain expression. Eur J Immunol 1986;16(4):450–6.

[23] Murakami M, Yoshioka H, Shirai T, Tsubata T, Honjo T. Prevention of autoimmune symptoms in autoimmune-prone mice by elimination of B-1 cells. Int Immunol 1995;7(5):877–82.

[24] Davidson A, Konstantinov K, Diamond B. Targeting B cells. In: Smolen J, Lipsky P, editors. Targeted therapies in rheumatology: biological therapy in rheumatology. London: Martin Dunitz Publishers; 2002. p. 23–42.

[25] Martin F, Kearney JF. B-cell subsets and the mature preimmune repertoire. Marginal zone and B1 B cells as part of a 'natural immune memory'. Immunol Rev 2000;175:70–9.

[26] Zandvoort A, Timens W. The dual function of the splenic marginal zone: essential for initiation of anti-TI-2 responses but also vital in the general first-line defense against blood-borne antigens. Clin Exp Immunol 2002;130(1):4–11.

[27] Smith KG, Hewitson TD, Nossal GJ, Tarlinton DM. The phenotype and fate of the antibody-forming cells of the splenic foci. Eur J Immunol 1996;26(2):444–8.

[28] Wither JE, Paterson AD, Vukusic B. Genetic dissection of B cell traits in New Zealand black mice. The expanded population of B cells expressing up-regulated costimulatory molecules shows linkage to Nba2. Eur J Immunol 2000;30(2):356–65.

[29] Zeng D, Lee MK, Tung J, Brendolan A, Strober S. Cutting edge: a role for CD1 in the patho-genesis of lupus in NZB/NZW mice. J Immunol 2000;164(10):5000–4.

[30] Reif K, Ekland EH, Ohl L, Nakano H, Lipp M, Forster R, et al. Balanced responsiveness to chemoattractants from adjacent zone determine B-cell position. Nature 2002;416:94–9.

[31] Guzman-Rojas L, Sims-Mourtada JC, Martinez-Valdes H. Life and death within germinal cen-ters: a double edged sword. Immunology 2002;107(2):167–75.

[32] Sprent J. Immunological memory. Curr Opin Immunol 1997;9:371–9.

[33] Manheimer-Lory AJ, Zandman-Goddard G, Davidson A, Aranow C, Diamond B. Lupus specific antibodies reveal an altered pattern of somatic mutation. J Clin Invest 1997;100(10):2538–46.

[34] Williams DG, Moyes SP, Mageed RA. Rheumatoid factor isotype switch and somatic mutation variants within rheumatoid arthritis synovium. Immunology 1999;98(1):123–6.

[35] Tsubata T. Co-receptors on B lymphocytes. Curr Opin Immunol 1999;11(3):249–55.

[36] Tedder TF, Inaoki M, Sato S. The CD19–CD21 complex regulates signal transduction thresh-olds governing humoral immunity and autoimmunity. Immunity 1997;6(2):107–18.

[37] O'Rourke L, Tooze R, Fearon DT. Co-receptors of B lymphocytes. Curr Opin Immunol 1997; 9(3):324–9.

[38] Venkataraman C, Lu PJ, Buhl AM, Chen CS, Cambier JC, Ondada S. CD72-mediated B cell activation involves recruitment of CD19 and activation of phosphatidylinositol 3-kinase. Eur J Immunol 1998;28(10):3003–16.

[39] Inaoki M, Sato S, Weintraub BC, Goodnow CC, Tedder TF. CD19-regulated signaling thresholds control peripheral tolerance and autoantibody production in B lymphocytes. J Exp Med 1997; 186(11):1923–31.

[40] Schneider P, Takatsuka H, Wilson A, Mackay F, Tardivel A, Lens S, et al. Maturation of marginal zone and follicular B cells requires B cell activating factor of the tumor necrosis factor family and is independent of B cell maturation antigen. J Exp Med 2001;194(11):1691–7.

[41] Huard B, Schneider P, Mauri D, Tschopp J, French LE. T cell costimulation by the TNF ligand BAFF. J Immunol 2001;167(11):6225–31.

[42] Mackay F, Mackay CR. The role of BAFF in B-cell maturation, T-cell activation and auto-immunity. Trends Immunol 2002;23(3):113–5.

[43] Gross JA, Johnston J, Mudri S, Enselman R, Dillon SR, Madden K, et al. TACI and BCMA are receptors for a TNF homologue implicated in B-cell autoimmune disease. Nature 2000;404: 995–9.

[44] Groom J, Kalled SL, Cutler AH, Olsen C, Woodcock SA, Schneider P, et al. Association of BAFF/Blys overexpression and altered B-cell differentiation with Sjogren's syndrome. J Clin Invest 2002;109:59–68.

[45] Zhang J, Roschke V, Baker KP, Wang Z, Alarcon GS, Fessler BJ, et al. A role for B-lymphocyte stimulator in systemic lupus erythematosus. J Immunol 2001;166:6–10.

[46] Cheema GS, Roschke V, Hilbert DM, Stohl W. Elevated serum B-lymphocyte stimulator levels in patients with systemic immune-based rheumatic diseases. Arthritis Rheum 2001;44:1313–9.

[47] van Kooten C, Bancherau J. Functions of CD40 on B cells, dendritic cells and other cells. Curr Opin Immunol 1997;9:325–30.

[48] Mach F, Schonbeck U, Sukhova GK, Bourcier T, Bonnefoy JY, Pober JS, et al. Functional CD40 ligand is expressed on human vascular endothelial cells, smooth muscle cells, and macrophages: implications for CD40–CD40 ligand signaling in atherosclerosis. Proc Natl Acad Sci USA 1997;94(5):1931–6.

[49] Henn V, Slupsky JR, Grafe M, Anagnostopoulos I, Forster R, Muller-Berghaus G, et al. CD40 ligand on activated platelets triggers an inflammatory reaction of endothelial cells. Nature 1998; 391(6667):591–4.

[50] Pinchuk LM, Klaus SJ, Magaletti DM, Pinchuk GV, Norsen JP, Clark EA. Functional CD40 ligand expressed by human blood dendritic cells is up-regulated by CD40 ligation. J Immunol 1996;157(10):4363–70.

[51] Grammer AC, Bergman MC, Miura Y, Fujita K, Davis LS, Lipsky PE. The CD40 ligand expressed by human B cells costimulates B cell responses. J Immunol 1995;154(10):4996–5010.

[52] Bancherau J, Bazan F, Blanchard D, Briere F, Galizzi JP, van Kooten C, et al. The CD40 antigen and its ligand. Annu Rev Immunol 1994;12:881–922.

[53] Foy TM, Aruffo A, Bajorath J, Buhlmann J, Noelle RJ. Immune regulation by CD40 and its ligand gp39. Annu Rev Immunol 1996;14:591–617.

[54] van Kooten C, Bancherau J. CD40–CD49 ligand: a multifunction receptor-ligand pair. Adv Immunol 1996;61:1–77.

[55] Hu BT, Lee SC, Marin E, Ryan DH, Insel RA. Telomerase is up-regulated in human germinal center B cells in vivo and can be re-expressed in memory B cells activated in vitro. J Immunol 1997;159(3):1068–71.

[56] Arpin C, Dechanet J, van Kooten C, Merville P, Grouard G, Briere F, et al. Generation of memory B cells and plasma cells in vitro. Science 1995;268(5211):720–2.

[57] Randall TD, Heath AW, Santos-Argumedo L, Howard MC, Weissman IL, Lund FE. Arrest of B lymphocyte terminal differentiation by CD40 signaling: mechanism for lack of antibody-secreting cells in germinal centers. Immunity 1998;8(6):733–42.

[58] Rothstein T, Wang JKM, Panka DJ, Foote LC, Wang Z, Stanger B, et al. Protection against Fas-dependent Th1-mediated apoptosis by antigen receptor engagement in B cells. Nature 1995; 374:163–5.

[59] Galibert L, Burdin N, Barthelemy C, Meffre G, Durand I, Garcia E, et al. Negative selection of human germinal center B cells by prolonged BCR crosslinking. J Exp Med 1996;183:2075–85.

[60] Bour-Jordan H, Bluestone J. CD28 function: a balance of costimulatory and regulatory signals. J Clin Immunol 2002;22(1):1–7.

[61] Hoshino K, Takeuchi O, Kawai T, Sanjo H, Ogawa T, Takeda Y, et al. Cutting edge: toll-like receptor 4 (TLR4)-deficient mice are hyporesponsive to lipopolysaccharide: evidence for TLR4 as the Lps gene product. J Immunol 1999;162:3749–52.

[62] Takeuchi O, Hoshino K, Kawai T, Sanjo H, Takada H, Ogawa T, et al. Differential roles of TLR2 and TLR4 in recognition of gram-negative and gram-positive bacterial cell wall components. Immunity 1999;11:443–51.

[63] Krieg AM. CpG motifs in bacterial DNA and their immune effects. Annu Rev Immunol 2002; 20:709–60.

[64] Davidson A, Diamond B. Autoimmune diseases. N Engl J Med 2001;345(5):340–50.

[65] Craft J, Fatenejad S. Self antigens and epitope spreading in systemic autoimmunity. Arthritis Rheum 1997;40(8):1374–82.

[66] James JA, Harley JB. B-cell epitope spreading in autoimmunity. Immunol Rev 1998;164: 185–200.

[67] Chan OT, Madaio MP, Shlomchik MJ. B cells are required for lupus nephritis in the polygenic, Fas-intact MRL model of systemic autoimmunity. J Immunol 1999;163(7):3592–6.

[68] Youinou P, Lydyard PM, Mageed RA. B cells underpin lupus immunopathology. Lupus 2002; 11(1):1–3.

[69] Zubler RH, Huang YP, Miescher PA. Mechanisms of physiologic B cell responses and B cell hyperactivity in systemic lupus erythematosus. Springer Semin Immunopathol 1986;9(2–3): 195–218.

[70] Janossy G, Panayi G, Duke O, Befill M, Poulter LW, Goldstein G. Rheumatoid arthritis: a disease of T lymphocyte-macrophage immunoregulation. Lancet 1981;2(8251):839–42.

[71] Simon AK, Seipelt E, Sieper J. Divergent T-cell cytokine patterns in inflammatory arthritis. Proc Natl Acad Sci USA 1994;91:8562–6.

[72] Gopal AK, Press OW. Clinical applications of anti-CD20 antibodies. J Lab Clin Med 1999;134: 445–50.

[73] Leandro MJ, Edwards JCW, Cambridge G. Clinical outcome in 22 patients with rheumatoid arthritis treated with B lymphocyte depletion. Ann Rheum Dis 2002;61:883–8.

[74] Newkirk MM. Rheumatoid factors: host resistance or autoimmunity? Clin Immunol 2002;104: 1–13.

[75] Mohan C, Shi Y, Laman JD, Datta SK. Interaction between CD40 and its ligand gp39 in the development of murine lupus nephritis. J Immunol 1995;154:1470–80.

[76] Finck BK, Linsley PS, Wofsy D. Treatment of murine lupus with CTLA4Ig. Science 1994;265: 1225–7.

[77] Mihara M, Tan I, Chuzin Y, Reddy B, Budhai L, Holzer A, et al. CTLA4Ig inhibits T cell-dependent B-cell maturation in murine SLE. J Clin Invest 2000;106:91–101.

[78] Knoerzer DB, Karr RW, Schwartz BD, Mengle-Gaw LJ. Collagen-induced arthritis in the BB rat. Prevention of disease by treatment with CTLA-4-Ig. J Clin Invest 1995;96(2):987–93.

[79] Quattrocchi E, Dallman MJ, Feldmann M. Adenovirus-mediated gene transfer of CTLA-4Ig fusion protein in the suppression of experimental autoimmune arthritis. Arthritis Rheum 2000; 43(8):1688–97.

[80] Moreland LW, Alten R, Van den Bosch F, Appleboom T, Leon M, Emery P, et al. Costimulatory blockade in patients with rheumatoid arthritis: a pilot, dose-finding, double-blind, placebo-controlled clinical trial evaluating CTLA-Ig and LEA29Y eighty-five days after the first infusion. Ann Rheum 2002;46(6):1470–9.

[81] Gross JA, Dillon SR, Mudri S, Johnston J, Littau A, Roque R, et al. TACI-Ig neutralizes

molecules critical for B-cell development and autoimmune disease: impaired B-cell maturation in mice lacking BlyS. Immunity 2001;15:289–302.

[82] Alarcon-Segovia D, Tumlin JA, Furie RA, McKay JD, Cardiel MH, Strand V, et al. LJP 394 for the prevention of renal flare in patients with systemic lupus erythematosus: results from a randomized, double-blind, placebo-controlled study. Arthritis Rheum 2003;48(2):442–54.

[83] Leandro MJ, Edwards JC, Cambridge G, Ehrenstein MR, Isenberg DA. An open study of B lymphocyte depletion in systemic lupus erythematosus. Arthritis Rheum 2002;46(10):2673–7.

ELSEVIER
SAUNDERS

RHEUMATIC
DISEASE CLINICS
OF NORTH AMERICA

Rheum Dis Clin N Am 30 (2004) 175–191

Costimulatory molecules and T-cell–B-cell interactions

Mary K. Crow, MD

Mary Kirkland Center for Lupus Research, Hospital for Special Surgery, 535 East 70th Street, New York, NY 10021, USA

The immune system has evolved to recognize invasive pathogenic microbes and to eliminate them efficiently and with minimal collateral damage to host tissue. The response to microbes is implemented by components of the immune system that act sequentially in a highly coordinated manner. First, the innate immune response recognizes the presence of a foreign invader by using cells and molecules that are present at sites that form a barrier between environment and host. Second, the adaptive immune response, which is characterized by activation of lymphocytes and generation of antibodies that are highly specific for the invading microbe, efficiently targets the microbe for clearance from the body. Although the immune system includes innumerable mechanisms to assure selective recognition of foreign antigens, rather than self-antigens, and to limit tissue damage while destroying invaders, there are many potential points at which regulation may fail. The result is recognition by the immune system of self, rather than non-self, and damage to self-tissue, which results in disease. The cells and molecules that so effectively detect and eliminate pathogens can turn against the body and mediate autoimmunity and inflammation.

Because the same molecules that mediate host defense also can mediate disease, studies of normal immune function have contributed to identification of new targets for therapies for inflammatory diseases, including many of the rheumatic diseases. Knowledge of the role of tumor necrosis factor (TNF) and other cytokines in innate immune responses has complemented studies in rheumatoid arthritis (RA) synovial tissue and fluid. Together, these investigations led to the development of highly effective inhibitors of proinflammatory cytokines

E-mail address: crowm@hss.edu

0889-857X/04/$ – see front matter © 2004 Elsevier Inc. All rights reserved.
doi:10.1016/S0889-857X(03)00111-X

and a major advance in the care of patients who have RA or related diseases. Not all patients respond to cytokine-blockade; most who do respond do not experience a full remission of disease. Cell surface molecules that mediate cell–cell interactions and generate intracellular biochemical signals in the interacting cells may be as important as soluble cytokines in the regulation of protective and pathogenic immune responses. These molecules, termed "costimulatory molecules," based on the synergistic cell signals that they provide with antigen-specific signals, are key regulators of the immune response and are promising targets for a distinct class of therapeutics.

Families of costimulatory molecules

As animal hosts and pathogenic microbes have coevolved, each in response to the other, families of immune system molecules have been generated whose members have common structural features. The costimulatory signals that serve to regulate the magnitude and duration of adaptive immune responses are mediated by members of two major gene families: the immunoglobulin superfamily and the TNF family. Members of the immunoglobulin superfamily are characterized by a structure that is composed of layers of β-sheets and include molecules that mediate cell–cell interaction in the immune and nervous systems. Presumably, these interactions were initially adhesive and later developed signaling properties through association of immunoglobulin superfamily molecules with intracellular adaptor molecules and kinases [1]. In the adaptive immune system, the T-cell antigen receptor (TCR) and immunoglobulins that serve as recognition receptors are highly sophisticated members of the immunoglobulin superfamily. A growing group of costimulatory molecules, including CD28, are immunoglobulin superfamily members and generate or modulate intracellular signaling pathways when ligated [2–5].

A second large superfamily, the TNF and TNF receptor family, may have evolved from primitive microbial recognition molecules of the innate immune system, such as C1q [6]. Its members include numerous receptor-ligand pairs that mediate innate and adaptive immune responses and bridge immunity with other organ systems, including skeletal and reproductive systems. Among the members of the TNF family, CD40 and its ligand (CD40L;CD154), are central to regulation of the immune response [7].

This article focuses on activating and inhibiting costimulatory signals that are delivered to the T cell from antigen-presenting cells (APCs), mediating and modulating T-cell clonal expansion and development of effector functions, as well as costimulatory signals that are delivered by activated T cells to interacting target cells. The coordinated expression and interaction of these molecules regulates responses to foreign antigens and avoidance of response to self-antigens. Knowledge of the structure and function of these costimulatory molecules can be used to manipulate immune function and inhibit autoimmunity and inflammation in the setting of disease.

The two-signal model

Most CD4$^+$ T cells express the α and β chains of the TCR that confer responsiveness to peptides that are 9 to 12 amino acids in length and are bound in a groove in major histocompatibility class (MHC) II molecules on the APC surface. TCRs that make a good fit with self-antigenic peptides during T-cell repertoire selection in the thymus are deleted using apoptotic mechanisms. It is likely that many T cells that bear receptors with some avidity for a self-antigen–MHC complex persist in the peripheral immune system. A central task of the immune system is to discriminate what is self, and therefore, harmless, from what is a dangerous pathogenic microbe.

The classic paper that proposed a model that might account for self–nonself discrimination was presented by Bretscher and Cohn in 1970 [8]. The concept was that in addition to the recognition of antigen by antigen receptor (signal 1), a second signal would be required by a T or B cell before productive lymphocyte activation could take place. Signal 2 is now known to be provided by the co-stimulatory molecules [9]. Studies in the late 1970s and early 1980s, including some from our laboratory, defined the nature of the APC that could effectively activate T cells [10,11]. Dendritic cells (DCs) were the most efficient APCs. B cells could also serve as APCs, but only after they were activated by cell surface–mediated signals [12]. Monoclonal antibodies that were reactive with activated B cells and B-lymphoma cells were used to identify and characterize B-cell surface molecules that were present on activated cells but rare on resting B cells. These so-called "B7 molecules" turned out to be the ligands for the most important costimulatory receptor on T cells, CD28 [3,5]. This line of investigation then incorporated the concept of "anergy"; if T cells received only signal 1, the antigen signal, they would fail to respond to the antigen when triggered subsequently [13]. If the T cells received signal 1, antigen, and signal 2, CD28 ligation, productive T-cell activation occurred, followed by proliferation, secretion of interleukin (IL)-2, and generation of effector functions. The two-signal hypothesis suggested that both signals would be present in the setting of microbial invasion but would not be encountered during interactions among host cells (Fig. 1). Thus, the two-signal system provides a mechanism for self-non-self discrimination.

The issue of how costimulatory molecule expression on APCs comes about in the setting of infection was addressed recently, but many details still need to be elucidated. The pattern recognition receptors, particularly the toll-like receptors (TLR), recognize lipopolysaccharide, double-stranded RNA, CpG DNA, and other structures that are common to bacterial and viral microbes but rarely are encountered in host tissue. TLR ligation induces expression of costimulatory molecules on APCs that will activate the T cells of the adaptive immune response [14]. A second set of costimulatory molecules that are expressed on the T cells after full activation further increases the B7 family of molecules on APCs, including activated B cells, and can contribute to the expansion and perpetuation of the immune response through the process of determinant spreading to a broader

A   **Anergic or Weakly Active**   **B**   **Activated**
                    T Cell   **T Cell**

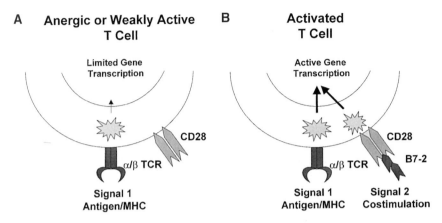

Fig. 1. The two-signal model of T-cell activation. (*A*) T cells that are stimulated through the TCR, after specifically binding to the antigenic peptide-MHC complex, and through CD28, after binding to B7 molecules on APC, generate multiple biochemical signals that result in new gene transcription and augmented stability of mRNAs that encode T-cell cytokines and cell surface molecules. T cells that receive two signals differentiate into helper or effector T cells. (*B*) T cells that are stimulated through the TCR in the absence of a second signal through CD28 or other cell surface costimulatory molecules generate more limited biochemical signals and low-level transcription of genes that encode T-cell cytokines and cell surface molecules. Some mRNAs are less stable in T cells that receive one signal compared with those that receive two signals. T cells that receive only one signal may be anergic or ineffective in differentiating into helper or effector T cells.

spectrum of antigenic epitopes on an immunizing particle [15]. Costimulatory molecule expression on APCs is essential for full activation of the adaptive immune response and costimulatory molecule expression on activated T cells is important for expansion of that response.

Afferent signals to T cells

Positive regulators

The B7 family of molecules is expressed mainly on APCs. The efficacy of an APC in mediating T-cell activation is, in good part, attributable to the level of B7 molecules on its surface. The "professional" APCs, such as DCs, have some B7-2 (CD86) on their surface, but further APC activation is required for expression of B7-1 (CD80) [2–5]. The prototype T-cell counterpart of the B7 family is CD28. In the initial interaction between APCs and T cells, peptide-MHC binds TCR and B7-2 binds CD28 which provides important biochemical signals that strengthen and prolong those transduced by the TCR and its CD3 signaling complex. In addition to promoting adaptive immune responses through costimulatory effects on resting T cells, CD28 ligation is required for development, although not the effector function of, T regulatory cells that can inhibit adaptive immune responses [16]. In aging and in autoimmune conditions, including RA, a population of CD28$^-$ T cells develops that may represent chronically activated cells and that may use alternative pathways to mediate effector functions [17].

Inducible costimulator (ICOS) is a T-cell surface molecule that is related to CD28; its ligand (ICOSL; also called LICOS or B7-H2) is expressed on APCs and peripheral tissues [18–20]. Although CD28 is important for activation of naïve or resting T cells, ICOS performs a parallel function on activated T cells [21]. This distinction is reflected in the differential expression of CD28, which is constitutively present on T cells, compared with ICOS, which is only expressed several days after T-cell activation. Two other TNF receptor family members, OX40 (CD134) and 4-1BB (CD137), are expressed on activated T cells and when engaged by their respective ligands on APCs, also provide positive signals to T cells [22,23]. OX40 seems to be important for expansion of the population of memory cells after immunization; OX40$^+$ cells may be enriched in autoantigen-specific T cells. 4-1BB may be particularly responsive to stimulation by DCs and may protect T cells from activation-induced cell death.

CD28 and ICOS trigger as yet incompletely defined biochemical pathways that converge on the signals derived from TCR ligation [24–26]. CD28 bears an amino acid motif in its intracytoplasmic domain, YMNM (amino acid code), that binds phosphatidylinositol 3-kinase (PI3K), an enzyme that has been implicated in its signaling in some studies. CD28 also has an SH3 motif that is important for IL-2 production. The intracytoplasmic tail of ICOS has a distinct amino acid motif, YMFM, that binds a subunit of PI3K; ICOS does not bear the SH3 kinase binding site. CD28 and ICOS signals act at the level of transcription to increase the generation of mRNA for important cytokines, cytokine receptors, and other costimulatory molecules. CD28 signals also increase the stability and prolong the half-life of some of those mRNAs [27]. CD28 ligation is required for IL-2 production as well as expression of CD40L and other T-cell costimulatory molecules [28]. ICOS ligation stimulates production of T helper (Th)-1 and Th2 cytokines, with some preference for Th2 cytokines, particularly IL-4, IL-10, and IL-13 [29].

Negative regulators

The Fc receptor (FcR) family, also members of the immunoglobulin superfamily, includes paired receptor systems, one with activating potential and the other with inhibitory potential, that act in a coordinated manner to regulate immune responses. Amino acid sequences in the intracytoplasmic region of the receptors have characteristic features that either mediate positive generation of biochemical signals or recruit molecules, including phosphatases, that inhibit the amplification of the biochemical signal [30]. Some of the sequence motifs used in the FcR are also used by members of the costimulatory molecule family, whereas other costimulatory molecules use distinct sequence motifs. Cytotoxic T lymphocyte antigen 4 (CTLA-4;CD152) and programmed cell death 1 (PD-1) are two family members that balance the activating T-cell signals derived from CD28 and ICOS and are important for toning down and turning off the immune system after it has orchestrated successfully a full adaptive response [31–33]. CTLA-4 is related to CD28, but in contrast to CD28, it is not present on resting T cells but is expressed several days after T-cell activation. Even when the protein has been produced, CTLA-4 is maintained in intracellular vesicles and expression on the cell surface is difficult to detect. CTLA-4 bears a YVKM sequence that transduces the inhibitory signal by binding to PI3K and the phosphatase, SHP-2. The ligands for CTLA-4 are shared with CD28, so the expression of CTLA-4 presents a competitor for CD28 and modulates further T-cell activation (Fig. 2). The precise mechanisms of inhibition that follow CTLA-4 ligation are not clear, but they include promotion of negative signals that involve the phosphatases, SHP-2 and PP2A. An important functional outcome of CTLA-4 signaling is the inhibition of cell cycle progression, possibly by preventing degradation of the cell cycle inhibitor $p27^{kip1}$ [33]. In addition to these direct inhibitory effects on T-cell activation, recent data indicate that CTLA-4 can indirectly inhibit T-cell function. Ligation of B7 on DC induces an enzyme (indoleamine 2,3-dioxygenase) that mediates tryptophan catabolism, contributing to decreased T-cell viability or function [34].

PD-1 is the second inhibitory receptor that is expressed on T cells, as well as B cells and monocytes [19,31,33]. Like CTLA-4, PD-1 is not present on resting T cells but is induced several days following T-cell activation. Its ligands in-

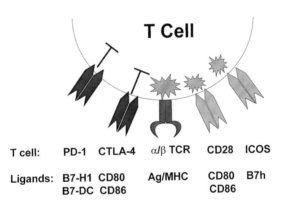

Fig. 2. Afferent costimulatory molecule pairs. T-cell surface receptors of the immunoglobulin superfamily include CD28, ICOS, CTLA-4, and PD-1. CD28 and ICOS transduce positive costimulatory signals, whereas CTLA-4 and PD-1 transduce negative signals to the T cell. CD28 is expressed constitutively, whereas ICOS, CTLA-4, and PD-1 are expressed after T-cell activation. CD28 and CTLA-4 share at least two ligands, CD80 (B7-1) and CD86 (B7-2). In the early phase of a T-cell–mediated immune response, CD28 will bind preferentially to B7-2 and mediate positive costimulatory signals. Later in a T-cell–mediated response, when CTLA-4 is expressed on the cell surface, CTLA-4 will compete with CD28 for binding B7-1 and B7-2, and T-cell activation will be modulated negatively. Ag, antigen; MHC, major histocompatibility complex.

clude PD-L1 and PD-L2 (also called B7-H1 and B7-DC, respectively). They are expressed constitutively on APCs and parenchymal cells, are related to the other B7 family members, and require cell activation for their expression. Like the FcγRIIb member of the FcR family, PD-1 has an immunoreceptor tyrosine-based inhibition motif in its intracytoplasmic tail that recruits SH2-containing phosphatases. Recent data suggest that additional, unidentified T-cell receptors may interact with B7-H1 and B7-DC to provide positive, rather than negative, stimulatory signals to T cells which further complicates this complex system [35].

Coordination of positive and negative afferent signals

New data from Collins et al [36] provided important information elucidating the differential binding properties of CD28, CTLA-4, and ICOS with their ligands. These investigators produced recombinant proteins and performed careful binding studies using the technology of surface plasmon resonance with the BIAcore instrument (BIAcore, Piscataway, NJ). Fig. 3, modeled on the data from Collins et al [36] demonstrates that although CD28 and CTL4-4 share the same ligands, the stoichiometry of interaction is different and the affinity of interaction with those ligands differs. Briefly, B7-2 and ICOSL are expressed on the APC surface as monomers, whereas B7-1 can self-associate with other B7-1 molecules. On the T cell, CD28 mediates monovalent binding, whereas CTLA-4 and ICOS mediate divalent binding to their ligands. Moreover, B7-2 binds 13-fold more weakly to CTLA-4 than does B7-1; B7-2 binds two to three times better to CD28 than to CTLA-4. Taken together, these properties support the initial binding of B7-2 to CD28, and even after CTLA-4 is induced on the T-cell surface, B7-2 will

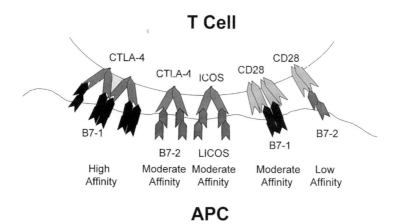

Fig. 3. Stoichiometry of T-cell–APC molecular interactions. CD28 has a monovalent interaction with B7-1 and B7-2, whereas CTLA-4 has a bivalent interaction with B7-1 and B7-2. The ICOS–LICOS interaction is also bivalent.

favor interaction with CD28. When B7-1 is expressed on the APC, however, its interactions with CTLA-4 will be favored over interaction with CD28, because of its increased affinity for CTLA-4 and its bivalent binding thereto. The structural features of the afferent costimulation system defined by Collins et al [36], along with the kinetics of expression of the members of positive and negative signaling molecules, promote T-cell activation before B7-1 expression but favor turning off the immune response after B7-1 is expressed. That is, CD28 constitutively expressed on the T cell initially binds B7-2 on the APC. After the T cell is activated, CTLA-4 is expressed on its surface which indicates the readiness of the T cell to be turned off. Only after B7-1 is expressed on the APC, following either strong signals through the B-cell antigen receptor or more likely through T-cell–mediated efferent signals, does CTLA-4 finds its most effective ligand and T-cell activation is abrogated.

ICOS and its ligands provide a mechanism to maintain T-cell activation and assure that even if CD28 is lost from the cell surface, as sometimes happens after chronic T-cell activation, the important functions of Th cells can be maintained, including induction of B cell immunoglobulin class switching to produce mature antibodies [37]. It is not clear how intracellular positive activating signals through CD28 or ICOS and inhibitory signals through CTLA-4 or PD-1 are coordinated. It was suggested that the late expression of PD-1 on effector T cells and the expression of its ligand, PD-L1 or PD-L2, on parenchymal cells might be a mechanism to inhibit damage to self tissue by activated T cells with reactivity to self-antigens. In analogy to the complement inhibitory protein system that protects cells from inadvertent damage by complement that is activated in the setting of innate immunity, parenchymal expression of ligand for the negative costimulatory molecules may protect tissue from damage by cells of the adaptive immune response [38].

Efferent signals to targets of T cells

Positive regulators

After T cells have been activated, T-cell surface costimulatory molecules are expressed and play central roles in mediating effector functions that determine the overall activity of the immune response. Among the most important mediators of efferent signals that come from Th cells and regulate the function of target cells are members of the TNF family and its receptors [39]. CD40L is arguably the most important; mutations in CD40L result in hyper IgM syndrome, an immunodeficiency disease in which B cells fail to "class switch" from producing IgM to producing more mature IgG, IgA, and IgE [7,40–47]. TNF family members, including CD40L, are expressed on the cell surface as homotrimers and interact with homotrimers of the TNF receptor family on their target cells. CD40L is expressed briefly on CD4 T cells after they are activated through the TCR, but T cells require concomitant triggering through CD28 for high level and more prolonged expression [28]. Recent data suggest that signaling through ICOS also is important in activating T-cell targets. Whether the role of ICOS in supporting immunoglobulin class switching, like CD28, is based on increasing expression of CD40L or another TNF family member has not been clarified [37]. In addition to inducing immunoglobulin class switching, CD40L promotes the formation of germinal centers and memory B cells; induces increased expression of costimulatory molecules, including B7-1 and B7-2 on target cells; and contributes to B-cell proliferation [48–53]. CD40 ligation by CD40L also inhibits the induction of B-cell apoptosis through the Fas receptor pathway [54]. Because CD40L gene transcription and mRNA stability are particularly responsive to CD28 costimulatory signals transduced on naïve or resting cells, CD40L expression is an important component of the early stage of an immune response to either foreign or self proteins. To the extent that ICOS also regulates CD40L expression, CD40L also mediates the activation of target cells by activated memory and effector T cells.

Ligation of target cell CD40 by T-cell CD40L has important consequences for regulation of the immune response (Fig. 4). Immunoglobulin class switching and increased expression of B-cell surface costimulatory molecules are regulated by

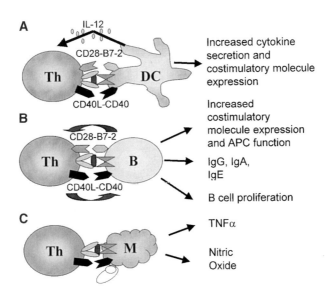

Fig. 4. Effector functions mediated by CD40 ligand-CD40 interactions. (*A*) Interaction between CD40L on Th cells and DCs results in expression of cytokines, including IL-12, and costimulatory molecules, including B7-1 and B7-2. (*B*) Interaction between CD40L on Th cells and CD40 on B cells results in B-cell proliferation; increased expression of costimulatory molecules, including B7-1 and B7-2; and augmented capacity for antigen presentation; and immunoglobulin class switching to mature isotypes. (*C*) Interaction between CD40L on Th cells and CD40 on monocytes (M) results in expression of proinflammatory molecules, including TNF-α and nitric oxide.

CD40 ligation. In addition, DCs receive CD40 signals which lead to further maturation of the DCs and production of IL-12, a cytokine that promotes Th1 immune responses [55]. Ligation of CD40 on macrophages also results in cell activation, including production of TNF and other cytokines [56]. In addition to CD40L, another TNF family member, CD70, is expressed on T cells after induction of primary immune responses and binds CD27 on memory B cells, which contributes to their differentiation to plasma cells [57].

Because of the important role of CD40L in orchestrating the immune response, the regulation of its expression operates at many levels. The extent of costimulatory signals that are delivered to the T cell, along with the TCR-mediated signals, determines the level and duration of transcription of the CD40L gene. In addition, the half-life of CD40L mRNA is correlated with cell surface protein expression and also is regulated by costimulation. Other members of the TNF family, although not as well-studied as CD40L, also contribute to positive regulation of the immune response. Thus, the afferent costimulatory signals that are delivered to the T cell determine the availability of efferent molecules that drive effector function, and, consequently, regulate many aspects of immune function.

Negative regulators

The strong positive effects of CD40L on target cells are partially balanced by negative ligand-receptor pairs. After T-cell activation, Fas ligand, another member of the TNF family, is expressed on the T-cell surface and has the potential to bind its receptor, Fas, on target cells [54]. TNF also can be expressed in a cell membrane form on activated T cells, which has the potential to induce apoptosis or activation of TNF-receptor–bearing target cells. Other TNF family members have been less well-studied but also are expressed on activated T cells and give negative or death signals through their respective receptors on target cells. TNF-related apoptosis-inducing ligand (TRAIL) expression, like the other TNF family members that are synthesized by T cells, depends on TCR ligation but is augmented by interferon-α and binds to its receptors, DR4 and DR5, which are expressed widely on various cell types [58]. CD30 ligand on T cells binds to CD30, also a TNF receptor family member, on activated B cells and inhibits the positive B-cell signals that are delivered by CD40, possibly by competing for limiting quantities of intracellular adaptor molecules that are used by both receptors [59].

Lessons from knock-out mice

Mice that are genetically manipulated to produce a deficiency in a specific gene can be useful in understanding the contribution of that gene to normal biology [60]. In the case of the immunoglobulin superfamily and TNF family costimulatory molecules that mediate T-cell activation and function, knock-out mice have suggested potential mechanisms of promoting or mediating autoimmune and inflammatory diseases.

CD40-deficient B cells do not produce IgG1 or IgE antibodies; ICOS-deficient mice are impaired in their capacity to produce class switched IgG1 and IgG2a antibodies to T dependent antigens [61–63]. Deficiency of CTLA-4, which normally provides inhibitory signals to activated T cells, resulted in a phenotype that is characterized by extensive inflammation in many organ systems [64,65]. Deficiency of PD-1 in otherwise normal C57BL/6 mice resulted in a phenotype with many similarities to systemic lupus erythematosus (SLE), including auto-antibody production and glomerulonephritis [66]. Deficiency of PD-1 in another normal strain, BALB/c, resulted in antibody-mediated cardiomyopathy [67]. These phenotypes demonstrate the important role of PD-1 in inhibiting the development of autoimmunity, as well as the important contribution of background genes to the type of autoimmunity that is manifested.

In contrast to these situations of afferent costimulatory molecule deficiency, transgenic mice that overexpress CD40L demonstrate immune system activation, immunoglobulin isotype switching, and nephritis [68]. When pathways that mediate activation-induced cell death through the process of apoptosis are impaired, as in the MRL/lpr mice that demonstrate a mutation in the Fas gene, autoreactive cells may not be controlled effectively and lymphoproliferation and some autoimmunity result [69]. Animal studies also support a role for TRAIL in controlling some forms of organ-specific autoimmunity [70].

Taken together, the data from mice that are deficient in inhibitory costimulatory molecules or overexpress activating costimulatory molecules confirm the in vitro analysis of their effects on T-cell activation and function and suggest that defects in these molecules may be present in patients who have autoimmune and inflammatory diseases. In addition, these studies indicate that pathways that are mediated by costimulatory molecules may be appropriate targets for therapeutic intervention.

Alterations in costimulatory molecule expression in rheumatic diseases

It is not surprising that some alterations in costimulatory molecule expression have been observed in patients who have autoimmune disease. Abundant data demonstrated prolonged expression of CD40L in human SLE and murine lupus models [71–73]. In addition, elevated circulating levels of the soluble form of CD40L have been observed [74,75]. Although the soluble CD40L is unlikely to be the physiologic form of the molecule, our earlier work showed that sCD40L can have agonistic functional effects on CD40 target cells, such as induction of increased B7-2 expression [74]. B7-2 also was reported to be increased on lupus APCs [76]. Increased expression of at least some of the activating costimulatory molecules on SLE mononuclear cells likely reflects the chronic immune system activation of SLE and suggests that interruption of the costimulatory pathways might be efficacious in breaking the cycle of immune activity.

Of great interest, a polymorphism in PD-1, the costimulatory molecule that normally delivers inhibitory signals to T cells, was reported to be increased in frequency in a population of European patients who had lupus; it is predicted that the polymorphism could contribute to impaired negative signaling [77]. In addition, altered distribution of polymorphisms in the promoter and exon 1 of the CTLA-4 gene were associated with SLE, but their functional significance is not clear [78,79].

Potential therapeutic applications

The current understanding of the contribution of afferent and efferent T-cell costimulatory molecular pairs, data from knock-out and transgenic mouse models, and data that demonstrated altered expression or polymorphisms in costimulatory molecules in patients who had SLE support a rationale for therapeutically targeting the costimulatory pathways in rheumatic diseases. The pathogenic autoantibodies that develop in SLE are dependent on cognate, cell membrane–mediated signals from $CD4^+$ Th cells. T cells also play a prominent role in the RA synovium, likely contributing to macrophage production of TNF and other proinflammatory cytokines, as well as B-cell and DC activation.

Inhibition of the CD28 pathway now is being approached with recombinant CTLA-4 that is engineered to include the Fc fragment of IgG [80,81]. This CTLA-4Ig reagent will bind directly to B7-1 and B7-2 costimulatory ligands on APCs and inhibit access of those molecules to their natural receptor, CD28. Data in animal models of spontaneous SLE and in collagen-induced arthritis support the efficacy of blocking CD28 with CTLA-4Ig [80,82,83]. Suppression of T-cell function through modulation of tryptophan metabolism may be a distinct mechanism of CTLA-4Ig action [34]. Given the presence of a partially-overlapping afferent costimulatory pathway mediated by ICOS and ICOS ligand, inhibiting CD28 might permit activation of memory cells specific for previously experienced antigens derived from microbes while inhibiting activation of resting T cells by self-antigens. The consequence of blockade of CD28 signals would not be limited to the T cell, because efficient expression of CD40L and other efferent costimulatory molecules depends on adequate CD28 signals. One of the commonly-used therapeutics for active SLE and RA, azathioprine, recently was demonstrated to specifically inhibit CD28-dependent activation of the small GTPase Rac1, which resulted in reduced expression of NF-κB and bcl-x_L and induction of T-cell apoptosis [84]. These interesting observations indicate that rheumatologists are already targeting the CD28 costimulatory pathway through their use of azathioprine in current therapeutic protocols.

Although not as far along in development, inhibition of the other afferent signals to T cells, through ICOS and 4-1BB, also hold promise of modulating immune function in autoimmune and inflammatory diseases. Therapeutic inhibition of ICOS costimulation was shown to prevent transplant-associated atherosclerosis, a T-cell–dependent disease [85]. A recent and impressive study in the (NZB x NZW)F1 model of spontaneous murine lupus demonstrated prolonged survival up to 2 years (comparable with healthy mice) after treatment with monoclonal antibody to 4-1BB [86]. These results were observed after lupus disease was far along and suggested that the treatment could be efficacious in clinical lupus after disease onset.

Similarly, CD40L–CD40 interactions have been approached using mono-clonal antibodies to CD40L [87]. This pathway holds great promise for thera-peutic inhibition because it represents the central point of regulation of delivery of T-cell help to multiple target cells. In addition, blockade of CD40 activation limits expression of increased levels of B7-1 and B7-2 on those $CD40^+$ cells, which reduces their capacity to act as effective APCs. Unfortunately, trials of two blocking agents in SLE have not been successful, either because of thrombotic complications, perhaps due to expression of CD40L on activated platelets as well as activated T cells, or prominent placebo effect [88,89]. Given the strong rationale for targeting the pathway, it is hoped that alternative or modified ap-proaches to CD40L inhibition can be developed.

Manipulation of PD-1 and other negative costimulatory pathways may repre-sent additional approaches to limiting the excessive Th cell activity that character-izes several rheumatic diseases. Finally, the inhibition of immune system activity through concurrent blockade of afferent (CD28) and efferent (CD40L) costimu-latory pathways, as well as costimulatory blockade in conjunction with existing, but distinct, approaches, such as TNF blockade in RA, could be considered for more powerful therapeutic effect.

References

[1] Edelman GM. CAMs and Igs: cell adhesion and the evolutionary origins of immunity. Immunol Rev 1987;100:11–45.

[2] Gonzalo JA, Delaney T, Corcoran J, Goodearl A, Gutierrez-Ramos JC, Coyle AJ. Cutting edge: the related molecules CD28 and inducible costimulator deliver both unique and complementary signals required for optimal T cell activation. J Immunol 2001;166:1–5.

[3] Coyle AJ, Gutierrez-Ramos JC. The expanding B7 superfamily: increasing complexity in co-stimulatory signals regulating T cell function. Nat Immunol 2001;2:203–9.

[4] Frauwirth KA, Thompson CB. Activation and inhibition of lymphocytes by costimulation. J Clin Invest 2002;109:295–9.

[5] Sharpe AH, Freeman GJ. The B7–CD28 family. Nat Rev Immunol 2002;2:116–26.

[6] Shapiro L, Scherer PE. The crystal structure of a complement-1q family protein suggests an evolutionary link to tumor necrosis factor. Curr Biol 1998;8(6):335–8.

[7] Banchereau J, Bazan F, Blanchard D, Briere F, Galizzi JP, van Kooten C, et al. The CD40 antigen and its ligand. Annu Rev Immunol 1994;12:881–922.

[8] Bretscher P, Cohn M. A theory of self-nonself discrimination. Science 1970;169:1042–9.

[9] Bretscher P. The two-signal model of lymphocyte activation twenty-one years later. Immunol Today 1992;13:74–6.

[10] Crow MK, Kunkel HG. Human dendritic cells: major stimulators of the autologous and alloge-neic mixed leucocyte reactions. Clin Exp Immunol 1982;49(2):338–46.

[11] Van Voorhis WC, Valinsky J, Hoffman E, Luban J, Hair LS, Steinman RM. Relative efficacy of human monocytes and dendritic cells as accessory cells for T cell replication. J Exp Med 1983;158(1):174–91.

[12] Crow MK, Kunkel HG. Activated B lymphocytes: stimulators of an augmented autologous mixed leukocyte reaction. Cell Immunol 1985;90(2):555–68.

[13] Schwartz RH. T cell anergy. Annu Rev Immunol 2003;21:305–34.

[14] Dabbagh K, Dahl ME, Stepick-Biek P, Lewis DB. Toll-like receptor 4 is required for optimal development of Th2 immune responses: role of dendritic cells. J Immunol 2002;168(9): 4524–30.

[15] Shlomchik MJ, Craft JE, Mamula MJ. From T to B and back again: positive feedback in systemic autoimmune disease. Nat Rev Immunol 2001;1(2):147–53.

[16] Salomon B, Lenschow DJ, Thee L, Ashourian N, Singh B, Sharpe A, et al. B7/CD28 costimulation is essential for the homeostasis of the CD4+CD25+ immunoregulatory T cells that control autoimmune diabetes. Immunity 2000;12:431–40.

[17] Martens PB, Goronzy JJ, Schaid D, Weyand CM. Expansion of unusual CD4+ T cells in severe rheumatoid arthritis. Arthritis Rheum 1997;40(6):1106–14.

[18] Hutloff A, Dittrich AM, Beier KC, Eljaschewitsch B, Kraft R, Anagnostopoulos I, et al. ICOS is an inducible T-cell co-stimulator structurally and functionally related to CD28. Nature 1999; 397:263–6.

[19] Coyle AJ, Lehar S, Lloyd C, Tian J, Delaney T, Manning S, et al. The CD28-related molecule ICOS is required for effective T cell-dependent immune responses. Immunity 2000;13:95–105.

[20] Okazaki T, Iwai Y, Honjo T. New regulatory co-receptors: inducible co-stimulator and PD-1. Curr Opin Immunol 2002;14:779–82.

[21] Wallin JJ, Liang L, Bakardjiev A, Sha WC. Enhancement of CD8+ T cell responses by ICOS/ B7h costimulation. J Immunol 2001;167:132–9.

[22] Linton P-J, Bautista B, Biederman E, Bradley ES, Harbertson J, Kondrack RM, et al. Costimulation via OX40L expressed by B cells is sufficient to determine the extent of primary CD4 cell expansion and Th2 cytokine secretion in vivo. J Exp Med 2003;197:875–83.

[23] Futagawa T, Akiba H, Kodama T, Takeda K, Hosoda Y, Yagita H, et al. Expression and function of 4-1BB and 4-1BB ligand on murine dendritic cells. Int Immunol 2002;14(3):275–86.

[24] Feito MJ, Vaschetto R, Criado G, Sanchez A, Chiocchetti A, Jimenez-Perianez A, et al. Mechanisms of H4/ICOS costimulation: effects on proximal TCR signals and MAP kinase pathways. Eur J Immunol 2003;3:204–14.

[25] Acuto O, Mise-Omata S, Mangino G, Michel F. Molecular modifiers of T cell antigen receptor triggering threshold: the mechanism of CD28 costimulatory receptor. Immunol Rev 2003; 192:21–31.

[26] Rudd CE, Raab M. Independent CD28 signaling via VAV and SLP-76: a model for in trans costimulation. Immunol Rev 2003;192:32–41.

[27] Lindstein T, June CH, Ledbetter JA, Stella G, Thompson CB. Regulation of lymphokine messenger RNA stability by a surface-mediated T cell activation pathway. Science 1989;244(4902): 339–43.

[28] de Boer M, Kasran A, Kwekkeboom J, Walter H, Vandenberghe P, Ceuppens JL. Ligation of B7 with CD28/CTLA-4 on T cells results in CD40 ligand expression, interleukin-4 secretion and efficient help for antibody production by B cells. Eur J Immunol 1993;23(12):3120–5.

[29] Smith KM, Brewer JM, Webb P, Coyle AJ, Gutierrez-Ramos C, Garside P. Inducible costimulatory molecule-B7-related protein 1 interactions are important for the clonal expansion and B cell helper functions of naïve, Th1, and Th2 T cells. J Immunol 2003;170:2310–5.

[30] Pricop L, Redecha P, Teillaud JL, Frey J, Fridman WH, Sautes-Fridman C, et al. Differential modulation of stimulatory and inhibitory Fc gamma receptors on human monocytes by Th1 and Th2 cytokines. J Immunol 2001;166(1):531–7.

[31] Freeman GJ, Long AJ, Iwai Y, Bourque K, Chernova T, Nishimura H, et al. Engagement of the PD-1 immunoinhibitory receptor by a novel B7 family member leads to negative regulation of lymphocyte activation. J Exp Med 2000;192:1027–34.

[32] Greenwald RJ, Oosterwegel MA, van Der Woude D, Kubal A, Mandelbrot DA, Boussiotis VA, et al. CTLA-4 regulates cell cycle progression during a primary immune response. Eur J Immunol 2002;32:366–73.

[33] Greenwald RJ, Latchman YE, Sharpe AH. Negative co-receptors on lymphocytes. Curr Opin Immunol 2002;14:391–6.

[34] Fallarino F, Grohmann U, Hwang KW, Orabona C, Vacca C, Bianchi R, et al. Modulation of tryptophan catabolism by regulatory T cells. Nat Immunol 2003;4:1206–12.

[35] Wang S, Bajorath J, Flies DB, Dong H, Honjo T, Chen L. Molecular modeling and functional mapping of B7–H1 and B7-DC uncouple costimulatory function from PD-1 interaction. J Exp Med 2003;197:1083–91.

[36] Collins AV, Brodie DW, Gilbert RJ, Iaboni A, Manso-Sancho R, Walse B, et al. The interaction properties of costimulatory molecules revisited. Immunity 2002;17(2):201–10.

[37] McAdam AJ, Greenwald RJ, Levin MA, Chernova T, Malenkovich N, Ling V, et al. ICOS is critical for CD40-mediated antibody class switching. Nature 2001;409:102–5.

[38] Liszewski MK, Farries TC, Lublin DM, Rooney IA, Atkinson JP. Control of the complement system. Adv Immunol 1996;61:201–83.

[39] Mackay F, Kalled SL. TNF ligands and receptors in autoimmunity: an update. Curr Opin Immunol 2002;14(6):783–90.

[40] Lederman S, Yellin MJ, Krichevsky A, Belko J, Lee JJ, Chess L. Identification of a novel surface protein on activated CD4$^+$ T cells that induces contact dependent B cell differentiation. J Exp Med 1992;175:1091–101.

[41] Hollenbaugh D, Grosmire I, Kullas C, Chalupny N, Braesch-Andersen S, Noelle R, et al. The human T cell antigen gp39, a member of the TNF gene family, is a ligand for the CD40 receptor: expression of a soluble form of gp39 with B cell costimulatory activity. EMBO J 1992;11: 4314–21.

[42] Spriggs MK, Armitage RJ, Strockbine L, Clifford KN, Macduff BM, Sato TA, et al. Recombinant human CD40 ligand stimulates B cell proliferation and immunoglobulin E secretion. J Exp Med 1992;176:1543–50.

[43] Allen RC, Armitage RJ, Conley ME, Rosenblatt H, Jenkins NA, Copeland NG, et al. CD40 ligand gene defects responsible for X-linked hyper-IgM syndrome. Science 1993;259:990–3.

[44] Korthauer U, Graf D, Mages HW, Briere F, Padayachee M, Malcolm S, et al. Defective expression of T-cell CD40 ligand causes X-linked immunodeficiency with hyper-IgM. Nature 1993;361:539–41.

[45] DeSanto JP, Bonnefoy JY, Gauchat JF, Fischer A, de Saint Basile G. CD40 ligand mutations in X-linked immunodeficiency with hyper-IgM. Nature 1993;361:541–3.

[46] Aruffo A, Farrington M, Hollenbaugh D, Li X, Milatovich A, Nonoyama S, et al. The CD40 ligand, gp39, is defective in activated T cells from patients with X-linked hyper-IgM syndrome. Cell 1993;72:291–300.

[47] Ramesh N, Fuleihan R, Ramesh V, Lederman S, Yellin MJ, Sharma S, et al. Deletions in the ligand for CD40 in X-linked immunoglobulin deficiency with normal or elevated IgM (HIGMX-1). Int Immunol 1993;5:769–73.

[48] Shapira SK, Vercelli D, Jabara HH, Fu SM, Geha RS. Molecular analysis of the induction of immunoglobulin E synthesis in human B cells by interleukin 4 and engagement of CD40 antigen. J Exp Med 1992;175:289–92.

[49] Splawski JB, Fu SM, Lipsky PE. Immunoregulatory role of CD40 in human B cell differentiation. J Immunol 1993;150:1276–85.

[50] Grabstein KH, Maliszexshi CR, Shanebeck K, Sato TA, Spriggs MK, Fanslow WC, et al. The regulation of T cell-dependent antibody formation in vitro by CD40 ligand and IL-2. J Immunol 1993;150:3141–7.

[51] Nonoyama S, Hollenbaugh D, Aruffo A, Ledbetter JA, Ochs HD. B cell activation via CD40 is required for specific antibody production by antigen-stimulated human B cells. J Exp Med 1993; 178:1097–102.

[52] Lederman S, Yellin MJ, Cleary AM, Pernis A, Inghirami G, Cohn LE, et al. T-BAM/CD40-L on helper T lymphocytes augments lymphokine-induced B cell Ig isotype switch recombination and rescues B cells from programmed cell death. J Immunol 1994;152:2163–71.

[53] Klaus SL, Pinchuk LM, Ochs HD, Law C-L, Fanslow WC, Armitage RJ, et al. Costimulation through CD28 enhances T cell-dependent B cell activation via CD40–CD40L interaction. J Immunol 1994;152:5643–52.

[54] Schattner E, Elkon KB, Tumang J, Crow MK, Friedman SM. Signaling through the B cell antigen CD40 induces Apo-1 expression on human B lymphocytes and facilitates malignant B cell death. J Exp Med 1995;182:1557–65.

[55] Caux C, Massacrier C, Vanbervliet B, Dubois B, Van Kooten C, Durand I. Activation of human dendritic cells through CD40 cross-linking. J Exp Med 1994;180(4):1263–72.

[56] Alderson MR, Armitage RJ, Tough TW, Strockbine L, Fanslow WC, Spirggs MK. CD40 expression by human monocytes: regulation by cytokines and activation of monocytes by the ligand for CD40. J Exp Med 1993;178:669–74.

[57] Kobayashi N, Nagumo H, Agematsu K. IL-10 enhances B-cell IgE synthesis by promoting differentiation into plasma cells, a process that is inhibited by CD27/CD70 interaction. Clin Exp Immunol 2002;129(3):446–52.

[58] Kumar-Sinha C, Varambally S, Sreekumar A, Chinnaiyan AM. Molecular cross-talk between the TRAIL and interferon signaling pathways. J Biol Chem 2002;277(1):575–85.

[59] Cerutti A, Schaffer A, Goodwin RG, Shah S, Zan H, Ely S, et al. Engagement of CD153 (CD30 ligand) by CD30$^+$ T cells inhibits class switch DNA recombination and antibody production in human IgD$^+$IgM$^+$ B cells. J Immunol 2000;165(2):786–94.

[60] Pollard KM, Hultman P, Kono DH. Using single-gene deletions to identify checkpoints in the progression of systemic autoimmunity. Ann N Y Acad Sci 2003;987:236–9.

[61] Castigli E, Alt FW, Davidson L, Bottaro A, Mizoguchi E, Bhan AK, et al. CD40-deficient mice generated by recombination-activating gene-2-deficient blastocyst complementation. Proc Natl Acad Sci USA 1994;91(25):12135–9.

[62] Tafuri A, Shahinian A, Bladt F, Yoshinaga SK, Jordana M, Wakeham A, et al. ICOS is essential for effective T-helper-cell responses. Nature 2001;409(6816):105–9.

[63] Dong C, Juedes AE, Temann UA, Shresta S, Allison JP, Ruddle NH, et al. ICOS co-stimulatory receptor is essential for T-cell activation and function. Nature 2001;409(6816):97–101.

[64] Tivol EA, Borriello F, Schweitzer AN, Lynch WP, Bluestone JA, Sharpe AH. Loss of CTLA-4 leads to massive lymphoproliferation and fatal multiorgan tissue destruction, revealing a critical negative regulatory role of CTLA-4. Immunity 1995;3:541–7.

[65] Waterhouse P, Penninger JM, Timms E, Wakeham A, Shahinian A, Lee KP, et al. Lymphoproliferative disorders with early lethality in mice deficient in CTLA-4. Science 1995;270:985–8.

[66] Nishimura H, Nose M, Hiai H, Minato N, Honjo T. Development of lupus-like autoimmune diseases by disruption of the PD-1 gene encoding an ITIM motif-carrying immunoreceptor. Immunity 1999;11:141–51.

[67] Nishimura H, Okazaki T, Tanaka Y, Nakatani K, Hara M, Matsumori A, et al. Autoimmune dilated cardiomyopathy in PD-1 receptor-deficient mice. Science 2001;291:319–22.

[68] Mehling A, Loser K, Varga G, Metze D, Luger TA, Schwarz T, et al. Overexpression of CD40 ligand in murine epidermis results in chronic skin inflammation and systemic autoimmunity. J Exp Med 2001;194(5):615–28.

[69] Chu JL, Drappa J, Parnassa A, Elkon KB. The defect in Fas mRNA expression in MRL/lpr mice is associated with insertion of the retrotransposon, ETn. J Exp Med 1993;178(2):723–30.

[70] Hilliard B, Wilmen A, Seidel C, Liu TS, Goke R, Chen Y. Roles of TNF-related apoptosis-inducing ligand in experimental autoimmune encephalomyelitis. J Immunol 2001;166(2):1314–9.

[71] Koshy M, Berger D, Crow MK. Increased expression of CD40 ligand on systemic lupus erythematosus lymphocytes. J Clin Invest 1996;98(3):826–37.

[72] Desai-Mehta A, Lu L, Ramsey-Goldman R, Datta SK. Hyperexpression of CD40 ligand by B and T cells in human lupus and its role in pathogenic autoantibody production. J Clin Invest 1996;97(9):2063–73.

[73] Mohan C, Shi Y, Laman JD, Datta SK. Interaction between CD40 and its ligand gp39 in the development of murine lupus nephritis. J Immunol 1995;154(3):1470–80.

[74] Vakkalanka RK, Woo C, Kirou KA, Koshy M, Berger D, Crow MK. Elevated levels and functional capacity of soluble CD40 ligand in systemic lupus erythematosus sera. Arthritis Rheum 1999;42(5):871–81.

[75] Kato K, Santana-Sahagun E, Rassenti LZ, Weisman MH, Tamura N, Kobayashi S, et al. The soluble CD40 ligand sCD154 in systemic lupus erythematosus. J Clin Invest 1999;104(7): 947–55.

[76] Bijl M, Horst G, Limburg PC, Kallenberg CG. Expression of costimulatory molecules on peripheral blood lymphocytes of patients with systemic lupus erythematosus. Ann Rheum Dis 2001;60(5):523–6.

[77] Prokunina L, Castillejo-Lopez C, Oberg F, Gunnarsson I, Berg L, Magnusson V, et al. A regulatory polymorphism in PDCD1 is associated with susceptibility to systemic lupus erythematosus in humans. Nat Genet 2002;32(4):666–9.

[78] Pullmann Jr R, Lukac J, Skerenova M, Rovensky J, Hybenova J, Melus V, et al. Cytotoxic T lymphocyte antigen 4 (CTLA-4) dimorphism in patients with systemic lupus erythematosus. Clin Exp Rheumatol 1999;17(6):725–9.

[79] Hudson LL, Rocca K, Song YW, Pandey JP. CTLA-4 gene polymorphisms in systemic lupus erythematosus: a highly significant association with a determinant in the promoter region. Hum Genet 2002;111(4–5):452–5.

[80] Daikh DI, Finck BK, Linsley PS, Hollenbaugh D, Wofsy D. Long-term inhibition of murine lupus by brief simultaneous blockade of the B7/CD28 and CD40/gp39 costimulation pathways. J Immunol 1997;159(7):3104–8.

[81] Emery P. The therapeutic potential of costimulatory blockade with CTLA4Ig in rheumatoid arthritis. Expert Opin Investig Drugs 2003;12(4):673–81.

[82] Wang X, Huang W, Mihara M, Sinha J, Davidson A. Mechanism of action of combined short-term CTLA4Ig and anti-CD40 ligand in murine systemic lupus erythematosus. J Immunol 2002; 168(4):2046–53.

[83] Knoerzer DB, Karr RW, Schwartz BD, Mengle-Gaw LJ. Collagen-induced arthritis in the BB rat. Prevention of disease by treatment with CTLA-4-Ig. J Clin Invest 1995;96(2):987–93.

[84] Tiede I, Fritz G, Strand S, Poppe D, Dvorsky R, Strand D, et al. CD28-dependent Rac1 activation is the molecular target of azathioprine in primary human CD4$^+$ T lymphocytes. J Clin Invest 2003;111:1133–45.

[85] Kosuge H, Suzuki J, Gotoh R, Koga N, Ito H, Isobe M, et al. Induction of immunologic tolerance to cardiac allograft by simultaneous blockade of inducible co-stimulator and cytotoxic T-lymphocyte antigen 4 pathway. Transplantation 2003;75(8):1374–9.

[86] Foell J, Strahotin S, O'Neil SP, McCausland MM, Suwyn C, Haber M, et al. CD137 costimulatory T cell receptor engagement reverses acute disease in lupus-prone NZB x NZW F(1) mice. J Clin Invest 2003;111(10):1505–18.

[87] Kalled SL, Cutler AH, Datta SK, Thomas DW. Anti-CD40 ligand antibody treatment of SNF1 mice with established nephritis: preservation of kidney function. J Immunol 1998; 160(5):2158–65.

[88] Kalunian KC, Davis Jr JC, Merrill JT, Totoritis MC, Wofsy D, IDEC-131 Lupus Study Group. Treatment of systemic lupus erythematosus by inhibition of T cell costimulation with anti-CD154: a randomized, double-blind, placebo-controlled trial. Arthritis Rheum 2002;46(12): 3251–8.

[89] Huang W, Sinha J, Newman J, Reddy B, Budhai L, Furie R, et al. The effect of anti-CD40 ligand antibody on B cells in human systemic lupus erythematosus. Arthritis Rheum 2002; 46(6):1554–62.

RHEUMATIC
DISEASE CLINICS
OF NORTH AMERICA

ELSEVIER
SAUNDERS

Rheum Dis Clin N Am 30 (2004) 193–212

Apoptosis and immune responses to self

Jeannine S. Navratil, MS, Janice M. Sabatine, PhD,
Joseph M. Ahearn, MD*

Division of Rheumatology and Clinical Immunology, University of Pittsburgh School of Medicine–Lupus Center of Excellence, University of Pittsburgh Schools of the Health Sciences, Biomedical Science Tower, 3500 Terrace Street, Pittsburgh, PA 15261, USA

Many systemic autoimmune diseases share a common mystery: most of the autoantibodies that are produced in patients who have these diseases target proteins that are normally found inside the cell, many within the nucleus. How does the immune system become primed to recognize these intracellular antigens? After autoantibodies are produced, do they contribute to the pathogenesis of the disease, and if so, how do they access the proteins that they target? Clues to answering these questions are being uncovered by studying a normal cellular process that is designed to rid the body of "unwanted" cells, namely, apoptosis. Apoptosis, often referred to as "programmed cell death," is critical to the normal biologic function and maintenance of homeostasis in multicellular organisms. However, many of the molecular and cellular events that are specific to apoptosis generate a reservoir of self-antigens with the potential to initiate, and, possibly perpetuate, autoimmune conditions. In fact, many of the autoantigens that are targeted in systemic autoimmune diseases undergo apoptosis-specific changes (Table 1). In this article we review three major issues related to apoptosis and discuss how this information may shed some light on the mystery of autoimmunity. First, what are the changes that occur to many intracellular autoantigens during apoptosis? Second, how are potentially immunogenic apoptotic cells cleared under normal circumstances? Third, what are the normal consequences

This work was supported by The Lupus Foundation of Southeastern Pennsylvania, The Lupus Foundation of Pennsylvania, The Alliance for Lupus Research, and NIH R01-AR-4676402.

* Corresponding author.

E-mail address: joa8@pitt.edu (J.M. Ahearn).

Table 1

Autoantigens targeted in systemic autoimmune diseases that are altered during apoptosis

Autoantigen	Description	Disease specificity	Apoptosis-specific alteration	References
70 kD U1-RNP	Small nuclear ribonucleoprotein	SLE SSc MCTD	Redistribution/relocation Caspase cleavage Granzyme B cleavage Oxidative cleavage	[1–4]
Alanyl tRNA synthetase (PL-12)	tRNA synthetase	PM DM	Granzyme B cleavage	[3]
C1q	Complement protein	SLE HUVS	Membrane surface changes	[5,6]
CENP-B	Centromere protein	SSc	Granzyme B cleavage	[3,7]
CENP-C	Centromere protein	SSc	Granzyme B cleavage	[7]
DNA-PK	DNA-dependent protein kinase	SLE SSc Overlap	Redistribution/relocation Caspase cleavage Granzyme B cleavage	[8,9]
Fibrillarin	Nucleolar RNA-associated protein	SSc	Granzyme B cleavage	[3]
hnRNP C1 and C2	Heterogenous nuclear core proteins	SSc Psoriasis	Redistribution/relocation Caspase cleavage	[9,10]
Isoleucyl tRNA synthetase (OJ)	tRNA synthetase	PM DM	Granzyme B cleavage	[3]
Keratin	Intermediate filament protein	DLE	Redistribution/relocation Caspase cleavage	[11,12]
Ki-67	Cell proliferation-associated protein	SS	Caspase cleavage Granzyme B cleavage	[3]
M3R	Type 3 muscarinic acetylcholine receptor	SS	Granzyme B cleavage	[13]
Mi-2	DNA-dependent protein kinase	DM	Caspase cleavage Granzyme B cleavage	[3]
Nuclear lamins	Nuclear matrix protein	SLE APS	Caspase cleavage	[14,15]
NuMA	Nuclear matrix/mitotic apparatus protein	SS	Caspase cleavage Granzyme B cleavage	[8,16,17]
PARP	Poly(ADP-ribose) polymerase	SLE	Redistribution/relocation Caspase cleavage Granzyme B cleavage	[3,9,18]
PMS1	DNA mismatch repair enzyme	PM	Caspase cleavage Granzyme B cleavage	[3,19]
PMScl	Nucleolar antigen	SSc PM/SSc Overlap Raynaud's	Granzyme B cleavage	[3]
PS	Phosphatidyl serine	SLE APS	Membrane surface changes	[20]
RNA Pol I	RNA polymerase I	SLE SSc	Granzyme B cleavage Phosphorylation Oxidative cleavage	[3,21,22]
RNA Pol II	RNA polymerase II	SSc	Granzyme B cleavage	[3]
Sp1	Transcriptional activator	UCTD	Caspase cleavage	[23,24]

(continued on next page)

Table 1 (*continued*)

Autoantigen	Description	Disease specificity	Apoptosis-specific alteration	References
SR proteins	Serine/arginine–rich splicing factors	SLE	Phosphorylation	[25]
SRP-72	Signal recognition particle	SLE DM	Granzyme B cleavage Phosphorylation	[3,26]
SSA/Ro	Ribonucleoprotein	SLE SS	Redistribution/relocation Colocalization with viral antigens	[1,27]
SSB/La	Ribonucleoprotein	SLE SS	Redistribution/relocation Caspase cleavage Granzyme B cleavage Dephosphorylation	[1,3,28]
Topoisomerase I	DNA-associated protein	SSc PM	Caspase cleavage Granzyme B cleavage Oxidative cleavage	[3,21,29]
Topoisomerase II	DNA-associated protein	SLE Fibrosing alveolitis	Caspase cleavage	[29]
UBF/NOR-90	Nucleolar-associated autoantigen	SS SSc	Caspase cleavage Granzyme B cleavage Oxidative cleavage	[3,21,29]
α-Fodrin	Cytoskeletal protein	SS	Granzyme B cleavage	[13]
β$_2$-Glycoprotein-1	PS-binding protein	SLE APS	Membrane surface changes	[20]

Abbreviations: APS, antiphospholipid syndrome; DLE, discoid lupus erythematosus; DM, dermato-myositis; HUVS, hypocomplementemic urticarial vasculitis syndrome; MCTD, mixed connective tissue disease; PM, polymyositis; SLE, systemic lupus erythematosus; SS, Sjögren's syndrome; SSc, systemic sclerosis; UCTD, undifferentiated connective tissue disease.

of clearance, and what factors or defects in clearance could lead to the development of autoimmunity and disease pathogenesis?

Changes that occur to intracellular autoantigens during apoptosis

It has been suggested that apoptotic cells may be the source of autoantigens that break tolerance and drive the autoimmune response [1]. Evidence for this speculation comes from understanding what happens to intracellular contents during apoptosis. When a cell receives a signal to die, it initiates a complex series of events to package its contents for subsequent disposal [30–32]. Subcellular constituents become reorganized into smaller membrane compartments and relocated within the dying cell [33]. Intracellular proteases and kinases become activated to participate in this cellular dismantling process [30,32]. The potentially dangerous aspect of this reorganization and cellular dismantling may lie in the ultimate fate of the autoantigens. Where do they end up and what biochemical changes do they undergo?

Redistribution of autoantigens during apoptosis

Autoantigens that are normally sequestered inside a healthy cell may become available to prime the immune system when they are redistributed to the surface of apoptotic cells. Early evidence for this came in 1984 when LeFeber et al [34] observed that autoantibodies that were specific for the nuclear antigens SSA/Ro, RNP, and Sm, from patients who had systemic lupus erythematosus (SLE), bound to the surface of keratinocytes that were exposed to UV-B irradiation. It was later determined that these UV-B–exposed keratinocytes were undergoing apoptosis [35]. In 1994, Casciola-Rosen et al [1] demonstrated that during apoptosis nuclear autoantigens, as well as other intracellular autoantigens, become redistributed and concentrated within surface blebs on apoptotic keratinocytes. Furthermore, the autoantigens cluster in two types of blebs: small blebs that contain cytoplasmic components, including RNA and ribosomal endoplasmic reticulum, and larger blebs that contain nuclear components. Thus, autoantigens that are normally sequestered deep within a cell become concentrated in "packages" on the surface of apoptotic cells. These packages, once released, could prime an immune response to the antigens they contain if not cleared properly.

The redistribution of intracellular antigens into apoptotic blebs not only may prime the immune response, but also may make the antigens accessible to existing autoantibodies after an immune response has been generated. In fact, current evidence indicates that the latter situation can be pathogenic. Miranda et al [36] and Tran et al [37,38] showed that congenital heart block, a complication that can occur during pregnancy in women who have SLE, may be caused by maternal autoantibodies that target antigens on the surface of fetal apoptotic cardiocytes and results in inflammation and permanent tissue damage. It is conceivable that similar pathologic interactions could occur under other circumstances where autoantibodies may encounter apoptotic cells. For example, the binding of autoantibodies to UV-B–induced apoptotic keratinocytes may be the cause of multi-organ flares that occur after sun exposure in some patients who have SLE. This autoantibody-autoantigen interaction, which causes a cutaneous inflammatory response and tissue damage, could also reprime the autoimmune response and set the stage for a disease flare [39].

Redistribution of autoantigens during apoptosis also may create a situation where self-antigens are presented in a novel context. Rosen et al [27] demonstrated that when apoptosis is induced by Sindbis virus infection, viral antigens colocalize with autoantigens within surface blebs in a pattern that is consistent with the life cycle of the virus. The colocalization of viral and self-antigens could create a microenvironment that favors the formation of viral antigen-self-antigen complexes, thereby providing a novel immune context with the potential to break tolerance.

Biochemical alterations to autoantigens during apoptosis

Apoptosis is a complex series of molecular events that not only redistributes cellular constituents, but also alters many of them biochemically [30]. Such biochemical alterations that occur to autoantigens may produce altered "versions" of these proteins that are unique to apoptotic cells. For instance, a group of enzymes that are key mediators of apoptosis are the caspases, cysteine proteases that get their name from the aspartic acid residues that precede their cleavage sites [31]. Among the many caspase substrates are several autoantigens that, when cleaved during apoptosis, could potentially reveal immunocryptic epitopes [2,9,11,14–18,23,29].

Neoantigens also may be produced by altering the phosphorylation state of proteins. During apoptosis, some self-antigens are phosphorylated selectively by stress-activated protein kinases [25,26,40]. Researchers have shown that autoantibodies from patients who had SLE or mixed connective tissue disease specifically recognize these phosphorylated forms of autoantigens [22,40,41]. Furthermore, the autoantigen La is dephosphorylated during apoptosis, which might expose neoepitopes as well as affect its subcellular distribution [28].

Biochemical alterations to autoantigens may differ depending on how cellular death is induced and might generate distinct immunogenic epitopes for the same antigen. For example, the 70-kD subunit of the U1 small nuclear ribonucleoprotein (U1-70-kD snRNP) is targeted by patients who have cutaneous manifestations of lupus, Raynaud's phenomenon, and scleroderma [4,21]. It is possible, however, that the autoantibodies that are produced against this autoantigen in each disease state are directed at distinct epitopes generated through processes specific to the pathogenesis of the disease. Reversible ischemia-reperfusion, also known as Raynaud's phenomenon, occurs repeatedly in patients who have scleroderma and may result in the production of reactive oxygen species that cleave autoantigens in cellular locations where metals might become concentrated, such as the nucleolus [42]. In fact, autoantibodies from patients who have Raynaud's phenomenon recognize oxidatively cleaved U1-70-kD snRNP [4]. Conversely, autoantibodies from patients who have lupus skin disease selectively recognize U1-70-kD snRNP cleavage fragments that are produced during apoptosis [4], which may be induced in the keratinocytes of these patients by UV-B exposure. This phenomenon may explain how clinically distinct autoimmune disorders can have common autoantigen targets and suggests that the cause and pathogenesis of an autoimmune disease may be reflected in the epitopes of the targeted autoantigens. Furthermore, once generated, autoantibodies may react with the altered autoantigens that are produced by these distinct events, thereby contributing to the pathogenesis of the disease and refueling autoimmunity.

In addition to considering that the same autoantigen may be biochemically altered to produce different antigenic epitopes, we also must consider that not all apoptotic cells generate the same immunogenic self-antigens. Consequently, some apoptotic cells may have a greater potential for breaking tolerance. Cytotoxic T lymphocytes (CTL) induce apoptosis in their target cells through Fas/Fas ligand interactions [43], as well as through the action of serine proteases contained within CTL granules. Granzyme B is one such serine protease that is involved in the induction of apoptosis in CTL targets [44,45] and is known to cleave several autoantigens [3,7,8,13,19]. In fact, most autoantigens that are targeted in human systemic autoimmune diseases are cleaved by granzyme B during CTL-induced apoptosis [3]. Furthermore, the resulting cleavage fragments are unique to apoptosis that is induced by granzyme B [3]. This finding may provide an important clue to understand how CTL-induced apoptosis-altered autoantigens may have a greater potential for breaking tolerance. Many of the alterations to self-antigens that occur during apoptosis are ubiquitous to the process and occur when T and B lymphocytes are selected during central tolerance. It is conceivable, therefore, that such fragments or altered antigens could be tolerized. Because the autoantigen fragments that are generated by granzyme B are produced only during CTL-induced apoptosis, it is unlikely that such fragments would be tolerized. Therefore, it is possible that lymphocytes that could react to those fragments still may exist. In addition, because CTL targets are often virus-infected cells, the granzyme B–generated fragments may be presented in context with viral antigens [27], which would provide yet another unique challenge to self tolerance. This possibility is intriguing, because it suggests that a specific apoptotic event, such as viral infection, may be responsible for initiating autoimmunity or for stimulating autoimmune flares.

Surface changes that occur during apoptosis

In addition to the intracellular changes that occur during apoptosis, changes also occur on the membrane surface. These changes have the potential to create an immunogenic and antigenic environment. Phosphatidylserine (PS), a negatively charged membrane phospholipid that is normally distributed on the intracellular portion of the membrane, is redistributed to the outer membrane early in apoptosis [46,47]. Here, it has the potential to bind to several autoantigens, such as β2-glycoprotein-I and annexin V [20,48]. Formation of complexes between these proteins and PS, or other phospholipids on the surface of apoptotic cells, could increase the immunogenicity of the apoptotic cell [49] and result in the generation of antiphospholipid antibodies [48,50]. In a recent study, mice had been immunized with β2-glycoprotein-I-bound apoptotic cells or with vesicles of various phospholipids complexed with β2-glycoprotein-I produced antiphospholipid antibodies [50,51]. Furthermore, antiphospholipid antibodies are known to target apoptotic cells [52,53], which could induce an inflammatory response, as well as opsonize apoptotic cells and greatly enhance their immunogenicity [54].

C1q is another molecule that may affect the immunogenicity of an apoptotic cell by binding to its altered surface. Recently, we showed that C1q, the first component of the classical pathway of complement, binds to the surface of apoptotic cells [5,6]. C1q is an autoantigen that often is targeted by patients who have SLE and hypocomplementemic urticarial vasculitis syndrome [55,56]. In a scenario that allows apoptotic cells to become immunogens, bound C1q could become part of the autoantigen complex of the apoptotic cell, thereby generating an anti-C1q antibody response.

Apoptotic cells are immunogenic

In the preceding paragraphs we discussed how the changes that occur to intracellular constituents and membrane phospholipid distribution during apoptosis may contribute to autoimmunity. Do apoptotic cells actually participate in generating an immune response? Evidence from several studies suggests that apoptotic cells are potentially immunogenic. Antigen presenting cells, such as dendritic cells (DCs) that phagocytize apoptotic cells, were shown to cross-present the antigens thus acquired to T cells [57–64]. In addition, mice that were immunized with large doses of apoptotic cells produced antibodies to intracellular autoantigens and the autoantigens are those that are typically targeted in systemic autoimmune diseases [51,65,66]. These findings imply a potentially important role for apoptotic cells in the development of autoimmunity.

Signals for the recognition and clearance of apoptotic cells

Despite the potential for provoking an autoimmune response, apoptotic cells are eliminated and processed in vivo, under normal circumstances, in such a way as to avoid self-priming. The process by which apoptotic cells are recognized and cleared is complex and involves several recognition signals on the apoptotic cell that are recognized by a variety of phagocytic receptors [67–69]. Anything that may perturb normal recognition and clearance could lead to the development of autoimmunity.

Recognition of phosphatidylserine on apoptotic cells

Recognition of apoptotic cells by phagocytes is probably a key factor in clearance. Researchers have identified a receptor on macrophages, as well as on "nonprofessional" phagocytes, such as fibroblasts and epithelial cells, that seems to recognize PS on apoptotic cells [70] and mediate their uptake [71]. Under normal circumstances, uptake of apoptotic cells by macrophages induces the production of antiinflammatory cytokines, such as transforming growth factor (TGF)-β, and downregulates inflammatory cytokine production [72]. Ligation of the PS receptor produces a similar antiinflammatory response in macrophages [70,73]. These findings suggest that PS recognition not only promotes uptake of apoptotic cells by macrophages, but also may play a role in maintaining a non-inflammatory environment for that uptake [73].

Binding of extracellular molecules to the newly exposed PS also may facilitate recognition and uptake of the apoptotic cell. One molecule that was shown to enhance binding of macrophages to PS is the protein product of growth arrest–specific gene 6 (GAS6). GAS6 mediates the binding of PS on apoptotic cells to the receptor tyrosine kinase Mer on macrophages [74,75]. Recent evidence suggests a role for Mer in mediating clearance of apoptotic cells. Mice that lack a functional Mer protein exhibit less clearance of apoptotic cells than do wild type mice because of defective phagocytosis by macrophages [76]. These Mer-deficient mice also spontaneously develop serologic manifestations of systemic lupus, including the development of autoantibodies to chromatin, IgG, and DNA, and they develop renal disease [77]. Mer also was shown to downregulate the production of inflammatory cytokines, such as tumor necrosis factor (TNF)-α, by macrophages [78]. Therefore, it is possible that defects in Mer lead to diminished or delayed clearance of apoptotic cells and to an increased potential for an inflammatory environment in which apoptotic cells are processed [77]. Such an environment could tip the balance between maintaining tolerance and stimulating an immune response.

Components of the classical complement pathway

There is considerable evidence that components of the classical pathway of complement may provide important recognition signals for clearance of apoptotic cells. We demonstrated that C1q, the first component of the classical pathway, binds directly to surface blebs that are generated by apoptotic keratinocytes [5]. We subsequently showed that this interaction is not restricted to keratinocytes, but that it occurs in vascular endothelial cells and peripheral blood mononuclear cells, which suggests that it probably occurs with all cells that are undergoing apoptosis [6]. The hypothesis that C1q participates in the clearance of apoptotic cells also is supported by studies of C1q-deficient mice [79,80]. The accumulation of apoptotic bodies in the glomeruli of these mice suggested that apoptotic cell clearance by macrophages is impaired or delayed. The C1q-deficient mice also spontaneously develop antinuclear antibodies and glomerulonephritis [79], which suggests that C1q is necessary not only for clearance, but also for maintaining tolerance and protecting against development of autoimmunity.

Evidence from humans also supports a role for complement in protection against autoimmunity. The strongest genetic risk factor for the development of SLE is a complete deficiency in the early components of the classical pathway, C1, C4, and C2 [81]. This association is hierarchical; the earlier the component is in the pathway the more strongly its deficiency is related to the occurrence and severity of disease. For example, the highest degree of association and most severe autoimmune phenotype are associated with deficiency of components of the C1 complex, C1q, C1r, or C1s. This observation may reflect a requirement for the classical pathway during recognition and clearance of potentially antigenic apoptotic cells.

Although the specific role of C1q has not been determined, there seem to be at least two ways in which it may be involved in the recognition and clearance of apoptotic cells. First, C1q may interact directly with specific receptors. C1q is a large (450 kD) glycoprotein with six globular head domains and a collagen-like tail domain [82]. We have shown that the globular domains of C1q bind to the surface of apoptotic cells [6]. This observation suggests that potential receptors that are involved in the subsequent recognition of bound C1q are specific for the collagen-like tail domain of the molecule. One such receptor may be C1qR$_P$ (CD93), a molecule that may enhance C1q-mediated phagocytosis and is expressed on macrophages, endothelial cells, and platelets [83]. Another molecule that is known to bind to the collagen-like region of C1q is calreticulin [84]. Although calreticulin is not a membrane protein, a recent study showed that it may be involved in C1q-mediated uptake of apoptotic cells [85]. Those investigators suggested that calreticulin acts as an adaptor molecule by binding to C1q that is present on the surface of apoptotic cells and interacts with CD91 on the surface of macrophages, thereby inducing uptake. Complement receptor type-1 (CR1; CD35) also was shown to bind to the collagen-like domain of C1q [86]. C1q that is bound to the surface of apoptotic cells may interact directly with such receptors on macrophages, DCs, and lymphocytes, as well as on other cells that are capable of participating in this clearance process.

The second mechanism by which C1q may mediate recognition and clearance of apoptotic cells and substructures is by activating the classical complement pathway and consequently providing additional ligands whereby apoptotic cells may be recognized and cleared. The globular heads of C1q that bind to apoptotic cells are the same domains that bind to Fc regions within antigen-antibody complexes. Therefore, C1q that is bound to apoptotic cells may be in a conformation that leads to classical pathway activation. Participation of C1r, C1s, C4, and C2 in recognition and clearance is consistent with the observation that deficiency of any classical pathway component can lead to development of SLE [81]. Also supporting this hypothesis are observations of C4- and C3-derived ligands on apoptotic cells in vitro [87,88] and in vivo [89]. In addition, reports indicate that mice that are deficient in C4 have defective macrophage-mediated clearance of apoptotic cells, although this defect is not as severe as that observed in mice that are deficient in C1q [80]. These findings suggest that although the requirement for C4 is not as stringent as that for C1q, the efficiency of clearance of apoptotic cells is decreased when C4 is not present. The potential for C4 to enhance the efficiency of C1q receptor–mediated clearance of apoptotic cells is supported by a recent study that demonstrated that C4 enhanced binding of C1q to CR1 [90].

Activation of complement on the surface of apoptotic cells seems to contradict the hypothesis that clearance of apoptotic cells under normal circumstances is a noninflammatory process. Certainly, uncontrolled activation of complement culminates in the formation of the membrane attack complex (MAC), subsequent cell lysis, and the generation of the potent inflammatory mediator, C5a. Experimental evidence from our studies and those of other investigators, however, indicates that complement activation on apoptotic cells is limited to deposition of ligands that are generated during the early recognition events of the pathway and does not result in C5 activation, C5a production, or MAC formation [88,91,92]. We demonstrated that deposition of C4- and C3-derived ligands is accompanied by a downregulation in expression of membrane-bound regulators of complement activation proteins decay-accelerating factor (DAF) and membrane cofactor protein (MCP) on the surface of apoptotic cells [88]. These molecules regulate early events in complement activation and their downregulation permits ligand deposition. The expression of CD59, which prevents the formation of MAC, remains unchanged, however [88]. In addition, results from a recent study by Gershov et al [91] indicated that C-reactive protein, an acute phase serum protein, binds to apoptotic cells, augments classical pathway activation, and prevents MAC formation. These data suggest that complement activation occurs in a limited and noninflammatory fashion on the surface of apoptotic cells and results in the deposition of complement-derived ligands that may participate in the recognition and clearance process.

Evidence supports the hypothesis that deposition of complement-derived ligands on apoptotic cells augments clearance. Mevorach et al [92] demonstrated that apoptotic cell clearance is mediated by macrophage receptors that are specific for iC3b, CR3, and CR4. In addition, a recent study indicated that the presence of iC3b on apoptotic cells mediates clearance by DCs and may play a role in tolerization [93]. Other complement receptors, such as CR1, also may be involved. CR1 is the only receptor that specifically recognizes C1q [86] and C3- and C4-derived ligands [94]. Interestingly CR1 polymorphisms and defects in expression are associated with SLE [95].

Apoptotic cell clearance: ignorance, tolerance, or autoimmunity?

When potentially immunogenic apoptotic cells are cleared, there are three major consequences. The first consequence is that the self-antigens that the cells contain are "ignored" by the immune system. This is probably the most frequent outcome and most likely occurs when apoptotic cells are cleared by macrophages or by "nonprofessional" phagocytes in tissues. The second consequence is that apoptotic cell clearance results in active tolerization to those self-antigens. There is recent evidence that "sampling" of apoptotic cells by DCs plays a major role in maintaining peripheral tolerance [96]. The third consequence is that apoptotic cell clearance results in the processing and presentation of self-antigens and the development of a pathogenic autoimmune response. Several factors may govern which outcome occurs: the efficiency of clearance, the cells that mediate clearance, and the environment in which clearance occurs.

Immune ignorance

Clearance of apoptotic cells by macrophages may result in immune ignorance. A major function of macrophages is to defend the host against infection by foreign microbes, such as bacteria. Upon ingestion of "foreign" particles, macrophages secrete inflammatory cytokines, such as TNF-α, to recruit other immune cells to the area and to promote a specific immune response to the invader. It seems ironic, therefore, that when macrophages ingest apoptotic cells, they do not produce an inflammatory response, but instead secrete antiinflammatory and immunosuppressive cytokines, such as TGF-β1 [72]. This apparently dichotomous response seems to be governed by the recognition signals that the macrophage "sees" that allow it to differentiate a foreign particle from a self particle [68,69]. Recognition signals that indicate "foreign invader" induce an inflammatory response, whereas signals that indicate "self" induce an antiinflammatory response. One such "self" signal is the exposure of PS on the surface of the apoptotic cell. Ligation of the PS receptor [70,73], as well as the binding of PS to Mer [78] on macrophages, results in an antiinflammatory response. Another "self" recognition signal may be the limited activation of complement that has been demonstrated on apoptotic cells [88,91,92]; consequently, the complement-mediated recognition of apoptotic cells by CR3 and CR4 does not trigger an inflammatory response in macrophages [92,97]. The noninflammatory clearance of apoptotic cells by macrophages does not result in an immune response; therefore, the self-antigens that are contained by the apoptotic cells are "ignored."

Peripheral tolerance

The clearance of apoptotic cells by immature DCs might result in the active suppression of potentially self-reactive lymphocytes as part of the process of peripheral tolerance. Proposing such a hypothesis may seem surprising, because DCs have been the long-accepted champions of antigen presentation and were shown recently to present antigens that they acquire from apoptotic cells to CD8+ T cells in what is now termed "cross priming" [58]. Several characteristics make DCs potent antigen-presenting cells for CD8+ and CD4+ T cells. They express high levels of T-cell costimulatory molecules, such as CD80 and CD86, on their surface and they are able to synthesize cytokines that are essential to T-cell development, such as interleukin (IL)-12, IL-15, and IL-18 [98]. Not all DCs are alike, however [99]. Whether a DC becomes immunostimulatory or tolerance inducing depends on where it is in its life cycle and what types of stimulation it encounters along the way [96,100,101].

A model for how DCs may maintain peripheral tolerance was proposed by Steinman et al [96] and was developed further by other investigators [100]. In this model, DC precursors circulate through the blood and travel through tissues, taking up apoptotic cells that they encounter. They travel to the lymphoid organs [102] where the self-antigens that they acquired from apoptotic cells are presented to T cells in the absence of costimulatory molecules, which results in tolerance to those antigens [96]. This scenario is believed to occur when DCs encounter apoptotic cells in the absence of inflammatory stimuli, such as TNF-α, interferon (IFN)-α (from virus-infected cells), or inflammatory products, such as bacterial lipopolysaccharide [101]. It also is likely that production of antiinflammatory (TGF-β1) and immunosuppressive (IL-10) cytokines by macrophages in the vicinity plays a role in keeping DCs in a "tolerant" state. In addition, there is evidence that signals that are received by DCs from the surface of the apoptotic cell may affect DC maturation. In a recent study, immature DCs that ingested apoptotic cells that were opsonized with the complement-derived ligand, iC3b, downregulated expression of CD86 and MHC class II molecules [93]. This finding suggests that the presence of complement on apoptotic cells may help to maintain tolerance by inducing an immunosuppressive rather than immunostimulatory phenotype in DCs. How multiple signals that influence maturation of DCs, as well as how DCs either turn on and turn off an immune response, is of considerable interest and has been addressed in detail by other investigators [96,100,101,103,104]. It seems that DCs play an important role in maintaining tolerance to apoptosis-generated self-antigens when they encounter apoptotic cells in the absence of inflammatory stimuli and present the acquired antigens to T cells in a manner that actively avoids the development of autoimmunity.

Autoimmunity

Under normal circumstances, apoptotic cells are recognized by macrophages and immature DCs as nondangerous "self" particles. Ingestion by macrophages results in no response and ingestion by immature DC results in tolerance, the active suppression of a potential response (Fig. 1a). For these processes to proceed correctly, proper recognition signals on apoptotic cells are crucial. Alterations or deficiencies in these signals could induce an immune response by allowing macrophages and DCs to respond as if the apoptotic cells were foreign invaders. The complement proteins, C1q, iC3b, and C4, on apoptotic cells may participate as recognition signals for macrophages or DCs [5,6,88,92]. In their absence, macrophage recognition of apoptotic cells may be delayed which causes less efficient uptake. Consequently, other proteins, such as β2-glycoprotein-I or annexin V, might have an opportunity to bind to the apoptotic cell surface [20,48]. Both of these proteins increased the immunogenicity of apoptotic cells [49–51], possibly by providing "foreign invader" signals to macrophages. After the apoptotic cells are recognized as foreign, the macrophages release inflammatory cytokines, such as TNF-α, and create an inflammatory environment in which the apoptotic cells are cleared (Fig. 1b). When immature DCs are present, the inflammatory environment induces them to mature and express costimulatory molecules that enable them to present autoantigens that they acquire from apoptotic cells to T cells, thereby activating an autoimmune response. Furthermore, the presence of iC3b on apoptotic cells was shown to downregulate DC expression of costimulatory and antigen presenting molecules. Therefore, a deficiency of iC3b on apoptotic cells could delay recognition and promote an inflammatory environment that favors DC maturation and self-antigen presentation [93]. This model may explain how and why deficiencies in complement proteins are strongly associated with autoimmune diseases.

Defects in macrophage receptors for these "self" recognition signals also may compromise clearance. Defects in Mer, for example, delay apoptotic cell clearance by macrophages [76]; this delay could lead to the aforementioned scenario. Mer also plays a role in downregulating production of the inflammatory cytokine TNF-α by macrophages. Therefore, macrophages that lack a functional Mer protein would fail to recognize "self" recognition signals on apoptotic cells and

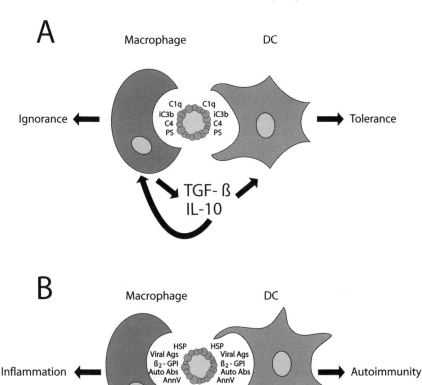

Fig. 1. Recognition signals may govern the immune response to apoptotic cells. (*A*) Under normal circumstances recognition signals, such as PS or the complement proteins, C1q, C4, or iC3b, on apoptotic cells may induce macrophages (*left*) or DCs (*right*) to respond to apoptotic cells as nonthreatening "self." In this scenario, macrophages that clear apoptotic cells secrete antiinflammatory cytokines, such as TGF-β and IL-10, and do not stimulate an immune response (ignorance). Immature DCs that clear apoptotic cells in the absence of inflammatory stimuli do not mature and do not express costimulatory molecules. (*B*) In contrast, when clearance is delayed or autoantibodies are already present, changes occur that allow the binding or expression of alternative recognition signals such as β2-glycoprotein-I (β2-GPI), annexin V (AnnV), heat shock proteins (HSPs), viral antigens (viral Ags), or existing autoantibodies (auto Abs) on apoptotic cells, that may induce macrophages or DCs to respond to apoptotic cells as "foreign invaders." In this scenario, macrophages clearing apoptotic cells secrete inflammatory mediators, such as TNF-α and stimulate an autoimmune response.

would contribute to an inflammatory environment [78]. Such a scenario would result in the cycle that leads to the development of an autoimmune response and may explain why Mer-deficient mice develop autoimmunity [77].

We discussed how a delay in clearance may allow apoptotic cells to bind proteins, such as β2-glycoprotein-I or annexin V, that increase immunogenicity. A delay in apoptotic cell clearance also could allow the apoptotic cells to progress to postapoptotic necrosis. Late-stage apoptotic cells were shown to induce macrophages to release proinflammatory cytokines [105], which stimulate an immune response by DCs [63]. It is questionable, however, whether the postapoptotic cells ever exist in vivo. It is likely that they never reach the necrotic stage. There is probably more than one mechanism for recognition and clearance of apoptotic cells; when one fails there is another that is still functional. Under these circumstances, recognition and clearance may not be optimally efficient, but apoptic cells likely operate as efficiently as they would normally and be cleared before they reached the necrotic stage. In a situation where the load of apoptotic cells is unusually high and clearance is already compromised, macrophages may be overwhelmed and postapoptotic necrosis might occur [106].

In addition to alterations or deficiencies in normal recognition signals, apoptotic cells can express other molecules that may misdirect macrophages and DCs toward an inflammatory response. For example, heat shock proteins (HSP), which are expressed on the surface of apoptotic cells that are stressed before they are signaled to undergo apoptosis, may induce an inflammatory response in macrophages and DCs [107]. Another example may be found in virus-infected cells. When virus-infected cells undergo apoptosis, either induced by the virus itself or by the CTL that recognize them, an environment could be generated that also would favor activation and antigen presentation. Such an environment could include production of cytokines, such as IFN-α, or antibody-opsonization of viral antigens that remain on the surface of the apoptotic cell, which could signal "foreign invader" [27].

With so many participants involved in apoptotic cell clearance, there are likely many "contingency plans" that keep the system working in the event of a failure in one or two mechanisms. Autoimmunity probably is not caused by a single breach in the system, but undoubtedly requires repeated incidents of defective clearance to generate autoreactive cells. If tolerance has been broken and autoantibodies have been generated, however, the autoantibodies may opsonize apoptotic cells and quickly change their appearance. Macrophages now see "self" as "foreign invader," which would reprime the autoimmune response [52,54,108]. Autoantibodies that are able to access and recognize autoantigens that are generated by apoptotic cells can accelerate this misidentification and immunostimulation, thus repriming and refueling the autoimmune disease.

Summary

The mystery that surrounds autoimmunity revolves around how the immune system of patients who have systemic autoimmune diseases becomes primed to recognize intracellular antigens, how the autoantibodies thus produced contribute to the pathogenesis of the disease, and how those autoantibodies access their target proteins. By examining the mechanisms that are involved in the normal cellular process of apoptosis, we are beginning to unravel this mystery. The intracellular autoantigen targets of many systemic autoimmune diseases become altered during apoptosis in ways that may change how they are perceived by the immune system. High concentrations of self-antigens, or in the case of viral infection, complexes of foreign and self-antigens, are packaged during generation of apoptotic cells. The packages also may contain altered fragments of self-antigens that have not been encountered previously by the immune system. Under normal circumstances, apoptotic cells are cleared rapidly by macrophages and DCs. The normal consequence of that clearance is that the apoptosis-altered self-antigens are either ignored by the immune system or tolerance to those antigens is maintained. Clearance is achieved through complex mechanisms that enable macrophages and DCs to recognize apoptotic cells as nonthreatening "self" particles. Defects in this process that cause a delay in clearance could change the appearance of apoptotic cells and cause them to be recognized as "foreign invaders," thereby stimulating an inflammatory response that, in turn, activates an immune response to self-antigens. By studying the mechanisms that are involved in recognition and clearance of apoptotic cells, we are uncovering clues to the defects that may underlie the development of systemic autoimmunity.

Acknowledgments

We would like to thank Jason Brickner for his expert help in creating Fig. 1.

References

[1] Casciola-Rosen LA, Anhalt G, Rosen A. Autoantigens targeted in systemic lupus erythematosus are clustered in two populations of surface structures on apoptotic keratinocytes. J Exp Med 1994;179:1317–30.

[2] Casciola-Rosen LA, Miller DK, Anhalt GJ, Rosen A. Specific cleavage of the 70-kDa protein component of the U1 small nuclear ribonucleoprotein is a characteristic biochemical feature of apoptotic cell death. J Biol Chem 1994;269:30757–60.

[3] Casciola-Rosen LA, Andrade F, Ulanet D, Wong WB, Rosen A. Cleavage by granzyme B is strongly predictive of autoantigen status. implications for initiation of autoimmunity. J Exp Med 1999;190:815–25.

[4] Greidinger EL, Casciola-Rosen L, Morris SM, Hoffman RW, Rosen A. Autoantibody recognition of distinctly modified forms of the U1–70-kd antigen is associated with different clinical disease manifestations. Arthritis Rheum 2000;43:881–8.

[5] Korb LC, Ahearn JM. C1q binds directly and specifically to surface blebs of apoptotic human keratinocytes. Complement deficiency and systemic lupus erythematosus revisited. J Immunol 1997;158:4525–8.

[6] Navratil JS, Watkins SC, Wisnieski JJ, Ahearn JM. The globular heads of C1q specifically recognize surface blebs of apoptotic vascular endothelial cells. J Immunol 2001;166:3231–9.

[7] Schachna L, Wigley FM, Morris S, Gelber AC, Rosen A, Casciola-Rosen L. Recognition of granzyme B-generated autoantigen fragments in scleroderma patients with ischemic digital loss. Arthritis Rheum 2002;46:1873–84.

[8] Andrade F, Roy S, Nicholson D, Thornberry N, Rosen A, Casciola-Rosen L. Granzyme B directly and efficiently cleaves several downstream caspase substrates: implications for CTL-induced apoptosis. Immunity 1998;8:451–60.

[9] Casciola-Rosen LA, Anhalt GJ, Rosen A. DNA-dependent protein kinase is one of a subset of autoantigens specifically cleaved early during apoptosis. J Exp Med 1995;182:1625–34.

[10] Stanek D, Vencovsky J, Kafková J, Raska I. Heterogeneous nuclear RNP C1 and C2 core proteins are targets for an autoantibody found in the serum of a patient with systemic sclerosis and psoriatic arthritis. Arthritis Rhem 1997;40:2172–7.

[11] Caulin C, Salvesen G, Oshima R. Caspase cleavage of keratin 18 and reorganization of intermediate filaments during epithelial cells apoptosis. J Cell Biol 1997;138:1379–94.

[12] Grubauer G, Romani N, Kofler H, Stanzl U, Fritsch P, Hintner H. Apoptotic keratin bodies as autoantigens causing the production of IgM-anti-keratin intermediate filament autoantibodies. J Invest Dermatol 1986;87:466–71.

[13] Nagaraju K, Cox A, Casciola-Rosen L, Rosen A. Novel fragments of the Sjögren's syndrome autoantigens α-fodrin and type 3 muscarinic acetylcholine receptor generated during cytotoxic lymphocyte granule-induced cell death. Arthritis Rheum 2001;44:2376–86.

[14] Neamati N, Fernandez A, Wright S, Kiefer J, McConkey DJ. Degradation of lamin B1 precedes oligonucleosomal DNA fragmentation in apoptotic thymocytes and isolated thymocyte nuclei. J Immunol 1995;154:3788–95.

[15] Oberhammer FA, Hochegger K, Froschl G, Tiefenbacher R, Pavelka M. Chromatin condensation during apoptosis is accompanied by degradation of lamin A + B without enhanced activation of cdc2 kinase. J Cell Biol 1994;126:827–37.

[16] Hsu HL, Yeh NH. Dynamic changes of NuMA during the cell cycle and possible appearance of a truncated form of NuMA during apoptosis. J Cell Sci 1996;109:277–88.

[17] Weaver VM, Carson CE, Walker PR, Chaly N, Lach B, Raymond Y, et al. Degradation of nuclear matrix and DNA cleavage in apoptotic thymocytes. J Cell Sci 1996;109:45–56.

[18] Lazebnik YA, Kaufmann SH, Desnoyers S, Poirier GG, Earnshaw WC. Cleavage of poly(ADP-ribose) polymerase by a proteinase with properties like ICE. Nature 1994;371: 346–7.

[19] Casciola-Rosen LA, Pluta AF, Cox AE, Morris S, Wigley FM, Petri M, et al. The DNA mismatch repair enzyme PMS1 is a myositis-specific autoantigen. Arthritis Rheum 2001;44:389–96.

[20] Casciola-Rosen L, Rosen A, Petri M, Schlissel M. Surface blebs on apoptotic cells are sites of enhanced procoagulant activity: implications for coagulation events and antigenic spread in systemic lupus erythematosus. Proc Natl Acad Sci USA 1996;93:1624–9.

[21] Casciola-Rosen L, Wigley F, Rosen A. Scleroderma autoantigens are uniquely fragmented by metal-catalyzed oxidation reactions: implications for pathogenesis. J Exp Med 1997;185: 71–9.

[22] Stetler D, Jacob S. Phosphorylation of RNA polymerase I augments its interaction with autoantibodies of systemic lupus erythematosus patients. J Biol Chem 1984;259:13629–32.

[23] Piedrafita F, Pfahl M. Retinoid-induced apoptosis and Sp1 cleavage occur independently of transcription and require caspase activation. Mol Cell Biol 1997;17:6348–58.

[24] Spain TA, Sun R, Gradzka M, Lin SF, Craft J, Miller G. The transcriptional activator Sp1, a novel autoantigen. Arthritis Rheum 1997;40:1085–95.

[25] Utz PJ, Hottelet M, van Venrooij W, Anderson P. Association of phosphorylated serine/arginine (SR) proteins and the U1-small nuclear ribonuclear protein (snRNP) autoantigen complex accompanies apoptotic cell death. J Exp Med 1998;187:547–60.

[26] Utz PJ, Hottelet M, Le TM, Kim SJ, Geiger ME, van Venrooij WJ, et al. The 72-kDa component of signal recognition particle is cleaved during apoptosis. J Biol Chem 1998;273:35362–70.

[27] Rosen A, Casciola-Rosen L, Ahearn J. Novel packages of viral and self-antigens are generated during apoptosis. J Exp Med 1995;181:1557–61.

[28] Rutjes SA, Utz PJ, van der Heijden A, Broekhuis C, van Venrooij WJ, Pruijn GJM. The La(SS-B) autoantigen, a key protein in RNA biogenesis, is dephosphorylated and cleave early during apoptosis. Cell Death Differ 1999;6:976–86.

[29] Casiano CA, Martin SJ, Green DR, Tan EM. Selective cleavage of nuclear autoantigens during CD95 (Fas/APO-1)-mediated T cell apoptosis. J Exp Med 1996;184:765–70.

[30] Hengartner MO. The biochemistry of apoptosis. Nature 2000;407:770–6.

[31] Thornberry NA. Caspases: enemies within. Science 1998;281:1312–6.

[32] Utz PJ, Anderson P. Life and death decisions: regulation of apoptosis by proteolysis of signaling molecules. Cell Death Differ 2000;7:589–602.

[33] Kerr J, Wyllie A, Currie A. Apoptosis: a basic biological phenomenon with wide-ranging implications in tissue kinetics. Br J Cancer 1972;26:239–57.

[34] LeFeber WP, Norris DA, Ryan SR, Huff JC, Lee LA, Kubo M, et al. Ultraviolet light induces binding of antibodies to selected nuclear antigens on cultured human keratinocytes. J Clin Invest 1984;74:1545–51.

[35] Young AR. The sunburn cell. Photodermatol 1987;4:127–34.

[36] Miranda ME, Tseng C, Rashbaum W, Ochs RL, Casiano CA, DiDonato F, et al. Accessibility of SSA/Ro and SSB/La antigens to maternal autoantibodies in apoptotic human fetal cardiac myocytes. J Immunol 1998;161:5061–9.

[37] Tran HB, Macardle PJ, Hiscock J, Cavill D, Bradley J, Buyon JP, et al. Anti-La/SSB antibodies transported across the placenta bind apoptotic cells in fetal organs targeted in neonatal lupus. Arthritis Rheum 2002;46:1572–9.

[38] Tran HB, Ohlsson M, Beroukas D, Hiscock J, Bradley J, Buyon JP, et al. Subcellular redistribution of La/SSB autoantigen during physiologic apoptosis in the fetal mouse heart and conduction system: a clue to the pathogenesis of congenital heart block. Arthritis Rheum 2002;46:202–8.

[39] Navratil JS, Ahearn JM. Apoptosis, clearance mechanisms, and the development of systemic lupus erythematosus. Current Rheum Reports 2001;3:191–8.

[40] Utz PJ, Hottelet M, Schur PH, Anderson P. Proteins phosphorylated during stress-induced apoptosis are common targets for autoantibody production in patients with systemic lupus erythematosus. J Exp Med 1997;185:843–54.

[41] Kamachi M, Le TM, Kim SJ, Geiger ME, Anderson P, Utz PJ. Human autoimmune sera as molecular probes for the identification of an autoantigen kinase signaling pathway. J Exp Med 2002;196:1213–25.

[42] Rosen A, Casciola-Rosen L, Wigley F. Role of metal-catalyzed oxidation reactions in the early pathogenesis of scleroderma. Curr Opin Rheumatol 1997;9:538–43.

[43] Van Parijs L, Abbas AK. Homeostasis and self-tolerance in the immune system: turning lymphocytes off. Science 1998;280:243–8.

[44] Heusel JW, Wesselschmidt RL, Shresta S, Russell JH, Ley TJ. Cytotoxic lymphocytes require granzyme B for the rapid induction of DNA fragmentation and apoptosis in allogeneic target cells. Cell 1994;76:977–87.

[45] Shi L, Kam CM, Powers JC, Aebersold R, Greenberg AH. Purification of three cytotoxic lymphocyte granule serine proteases that induce apoptosis through distinct substrate and target cell interactions. J Exp Med 1992;176:1521–9.

[46] Fadok VA, Voelker DR, Campbell PA, Cohen JJ, Bratton DL, Henson PM. Exposure of phosphatidylserine on the surface of apoptotic lymphocytes triggers specific recognition and removal by macrophages. J Immunol 1992;148:2207–16.

[47] Martin SJ, Reutelingsperger CPM, McGahon AJ, Rader JA, van Schie RCAA, LaFace DM, et al. Early redistribution of plasma membrane phosphatidylserine is a general feature of apoptosis regardless of the initiating stimulus: inhibition by overexpression of bcl-2 and Abl. J Exp Med 1995;182:2257–65.

[48] Andrade F, Casciola-Rosen L, Rosen A. Apoptosis in systemic lupus erythematosus. Clinical implications. Rheum Dis Clin North Am 2000;26:215–27.

[49] Stach CM, Turnay X, Voll RE, Kern PM, Kolowos W, Beyer TD, et al. Treatment with annexin V increases immunogenicity of apoptotic human T-cells in Balbc mice. Cell Death Differ 2000;7:911–5.

[50] Subang R, Levine JS, Janoff AS, Davidson SMK, Taraschi TF, Koike T, et al. Phospholipid-bound β2-glycoprotein I induces the production of anti-phospholipid antibodies. J Autoimmun 2000;15:21–32.

[51] Levine JS, Subang R, Koh JS, Rauch J. Induction of anti-phospholipid antibodies by β2-glycoprotein-I bound to apoptotic thymocytes. J Autoimmun 1998;11:413–24.

[52] Manfredi AA, Rovere P, Galati G, Heltai S, Bozzolo E, Soldini L, et al. Apoptotic cell clearance in systemic lupus erythematosus. I. Opsonization by antiphospholipid antibodies. Arthritis Rheum 1998;41:205–14.

[53] Price BE, Rauch J, Shia MA, Walsh MT, Lieberthal W, Gilligan HM, et al. Antiphospholipid autoantibodies bind to apoptotic, but not viable, thymocytes in a β2-glycoprotein I-dependent manner. J Immunol 1996;157:2201–8.

[54] Rovere P, Sabbadini MG, Vallinoto C, Fascio U, Rescigno M, Crosti M, et al. Dendritic cell presentation of antigens from apoptotic cells in a proinflammatory context: role of opsonizing anti-β2-glycoprotein I antibodies. Arthritis Rheum 1999;42:1412–20.

[55] Wener MH, Uwatoko S, Mannik M. Antibodies to the collagen-like region of C1q in sera of patients with autoimmune rheumatic diseases. Arthritis Rheum 1989;32:544–51.

[56] Wisnieski JJ, Baer AN, Christensen J, Cupps TR, Flagg DN, Jones JV, et al. Hypocomplementemic urticarial vasculitis syndrome: clinical and serologic findings in 18 patients. Medicine 1995;74:24–41.

[57] Albert ML, Pearce SFA, Francisco LM, Sauter B, Roy P, Silverstein RL, et al. Immature dendritic cells phagocytose apoptotic cells via αVβ5 and CD36, and cross-present antigens to cytotoxic T lymphocytes. J Exp Med 1998;188:1359–68.

[58] Albert ML, Sauter B, Bhardwaj N. Dendritic cells acquire antigen from apoptotic cells and induce class I-restricted CTLs. Nature 1998;392:86–9.

[59] Henry F, Boisteau O, Bretaudeau L, Lieubeau B, Meflah K, Gregoire M. Antigen-presenting cells that phagocytose apoptotic tumor-derived cells are potent tumor vaccines. Cancer Res 1999;59:3329–32.

[60] Hoffmann TK, Meidenbauer N, Dworacki G, Kanaya H, Whiteside TL. Generation of tumor-specific T lymphocytes by cross-priming with human dendritic cells ingesting apoptotic tumor cells. Cancer Res 2000;60:3542–9.

[61] Larsson M, Fonteneau J-F, Somersan S, Sanders C, Bickham K, Thomas EK, et al. Efficiency of cross presentation of vaccinia virus-derived antigens by human dendritic cells. Eur J Immunol 2001;31:3432–42.

[62] Ronchetti A, Iezzi G, Crosti MC, Garancini MP, Protti MP, Bellone M. Role of antigen-presenting cells in cross-priming of cytotoxic T lymphocytes by apoptotic cells. J Leukoc Biol 1999;66:247–51.

[63] Rovere P, Sabbadini MG, Vallinoto C, Fascio U, Zimmermann VS, Bondanza A, et al. Delayed clearance of apoptotic lymphoma cells allows cross-presentation of intracellular antigens by mature dendritic cells. J Leukoc Biol 1999;66:345–9.

[64] Zhao XQ, Huang XL, Gupta P, Borowski L, Fan Z, Watkins SC, et al. Induction of anti-human immunodeficiency virus type 1 (HIV-1) CD8+ and CD4+ T-cell reactivity by dendritic cells loaded with HIV-1 X4-infected apoptotic cells. J Virol 2002;76:3007–14.

[65] Gensler TJ, Hottelet M, Zhang C, Schlossman S, Anderson P, Utz PJ. Monoclonal antibodies derived from BALB/c mice immunized with apoptotic jurkat T cells recognize known autoantigens. J Autoimmun 2001;16:59–69.

[66] Mevorach D, Zhou JL, Song X, Elkon KB. Systemic exposure to irradiated apoptotic cells induces autoantibody production. J Exp Med 1998;188:387–92.

[67] Manfredi AA, Iannacone M, D'Auria F, Rovere-Querini P. The disposal of dying cells in living tissues. Apoptosis 2002;7:153–61.

[68] Savill J, Fadok V. Corpse clearance defines the meaning of cell death. Nature 2000;407:784–8.

[69] Savill J, Dransfield I, Gregory C, Haslett C. A blast from the past: clearance of apoptotic cells regulates immune responses. Nat Rev Immunol 2002;2:965–75.

[70] Fadok VA, Bratton DL, Rose DM, Pearson A, Ezekewitz RAB, Henson PM. A receptor for phosphatidylserine-specific clearance of apoptotic cells. Nature 2000;405:85–90.

[71] Hoffmann PR, deCathelineau AM, Ogden CA, Leverrier Y, Bratton DL, Daleke DL, et al. Phosphatidylserine (PS) induces PS receptor-mediated macropinocytosis and promotes clearance of apoptotic cells. J Cell Biol 2001;155:649–59.

[72] Fadok VA, Bratton DL, Konowal A, Freed PW, Westcott JY, Henson PM. Macrophages that

have ingested apoptotic cells in vitro inhibit proinflammatory cytokine production through autocrine/paracrine mechanisms involving TGF-β, PGE2, and PAF. J Clin Invest 1998;101: 890–8.

[73] Huynh M-LN, Fadok VA, Henson PM. Phosphatidylserine-dependent ingestion of apoptotic cells promotes TGF-[beta]1 secretion and the resolution of inflammation. J Clin Invest 2002; 109:41–50.

[74] Nagata K, Ohashi K, Nakano T, Arita H, Zong C, Hanafusa H, et al. Identification of the product o growth arrest-specific gene 6 as a common ligand for Axl, Sky, and Mer receptor tyrosine kinases. J Biol Chem 1996;271:30022–7.

[75] Nakano T, Ishimoto Y, Kishino J, Umeda M, Inoue K, Nagata K, et al. Cell adhesion to phosphatidylserine mediated by a product of growth arrest-specific gene 6. J Biol Chem 1997;272: 29411–4.

[76] Scott RS, McMahon EJ, Pops SM, Reap EA, Caricchio R, Cohen PL, et al. Phagocytosis and clearance of apoptotic cells is mediated by Mer. Nature 2001;411:207–11.

[77] Cohen PL, Caricchio R, Abraham V, Camenisch TD, Jennette JC, Roubey RAS, et al. Delayed apoptotic cell clearance and lupus-like autoimmunity in mice lacking the c-mer membrane tyrosine kinase. J Exp Med 2002;196:135–40.

[78] Camenisch TD, Koller BH, Earp HS, Matsushima GK. A novel receptor tyrosine kinase, Mer, inhibits TNF-α production and lipopolysaccharide-induced endotoxic shock. J Immunol 1999; 162:3498–503.

[79] Botto M, Dell'Agnola C, Bygrave AE, Thompson EM, Cook HT, Petry F, et al. Homozygous C1q deficiency causes glomerulonephritis associated with multiple apoptotic bodies. Nat Genet 1998;19:56–9.

[80] Taylor PR, Carugati A, Fadok VA, Cook HT, Andrews M, Carroll MC, et al. A hierarchical role for classical pathway complement proteins in the clearance of apoptotic cells in vivo. J Exp Med 2000;192:359–66.

[81] Walport MJ, Davies KA, Morley BJ, Botto M. Complement deficiency and autoimmunity. Ann N Y Acad Sci 1997;815:267–81.

[82] Reid KB, Porter RR. Subunit composition and structure of subcomponent C1q of the first component of human complement. Biochem J 1976;155:19–23.

[83] Nepomuceno RR, Tenner AJ. C1qRp, the C1q receptor that enhances phagocytosis, is detected specifically in human cells of myeloid lineage, endothelial cells, and platelets. J Immunol 1998; 160:1929–35.

[84] Malhotra R, Thail S, Reid KBM, Sim RB. Human leukocyte C1q receptor binds other soluble proteins with collagen domains. J Exp Med 1990;172:955–9.

[85] Ogden CA, deCathelineau A, Hoffmann PR, Bratton D, Ghebrehiwet B, Fadok VA, et al. C1q and mannose binding lectin engagement of cell surface calreticulin and CD91 initiates macropinocytosis and uptake of apoptotic cells. J Exp Med 2001;194:781–95.

[86] Klickstein LB, Barbashov SF, Liu T, Jack RM, Nicholson-Weller A. Complement receptor type I (CR1, CD35) is a receptor for C1q. Immunity 1997;7:345–55.

[87] Nauta AJ, Trouw LA, Daha MR, Tijsma O, Nieuwland R, Schwaeble WJ, et al. Direct binding of C1q to apoptotic cells and cell blebs induces complement activation. Eur J Immunol 2002; 32:1726–36.

[88] Navratil JS, Zurowski NB, Ahearn JM. Apoptotic endothelial cells and PBMC are tagged specifically by C3- and C4-derived ligands during membrane loss of RCA proteins: implications for immune tolerance and pathogenesis of SLE [abstract]. Immunopharmacology 2000; 49:36.

[89] Zurowski NB, Navratil JS, Ursu S, Nosce R, Ahearn JA. Ultraviolet B (UVB) induces apoptosis and deposition of C3- and C4- derived ligands on primary human and murine keratinocytes in vivo: implications for immune tolerance and the pathogenesis of SLE [abstract]. Immunopharmacology 2000;49:36.

[90] Tas SW, Klickstein LB, Barbashov S, Nicholson-Weller A. C1q and C4b bind simultaneously to CR1 and additively support erythrocyte adhesion. J Immunol 1999;163:5056–63.

[91] Gershov D, Kim SJ, Brot N, Elkon KB. C-reactive protein binds to apoptotic cells, protects the cells from assembly of the terminal complement components, and sustains an antiinflammatory innate immune response: implications for systemic autoimmunity. J Exp Med 2000; 192:1353–63.

[92] Mevorach D, Mascarenhas JO, Gershov D, Elkon KB. Complement-dependent clearance of apoptotic cells by human macrophages. J Exp Med 1998;188:2313–20.

[93] Verbovetski I, Bychkov H, Trahtemberg U, Shapira I, Hareuveni M, Ben-Tal O, et al. Opsonization of apoptotic cells by autologous iC3b facilitates clearance by immature dendritic cells, down-regulates DR and CD86, and up-regulates CC chemokine receptor 7. J Exp Med 2002;196:1553–61.

[94] Ahearn JM, Rosengard AM. Complement receptors. In: Volanakis JE, Frank MM, editors. The human complement system in health and disease. New York: Marcel Dekker, Inc; 1998. p. 167–202.

[95] Walport MJ, Lachmann PJ. Erythrocyte complement receptor type 1, immune complexes and the rheumatic diseases. Arthritis Rheum 1987;31:153–8.

[96] Steinman RM, Turley S, Mellman I, Inaba K. The induction of tolerance by dendritic cells that have captured apoptotic cells. J Exp Med 2000;191:411–6.

[97] Wright SD, Silverstien SC. Receptors for C3b and C3bi promote phagocytosis but not the release of toxic oxygen from human phagocytes. J Exp Med 1983;158:2016–23.

[98] Bhardwaj N. Processing and presentation of antigens by dendritic cells: implications for vaccines. Trends Mol Med 2001;7:388–94.

[99] Liu Y-J. Dendritic cell subsets and lineages, and their functions in innate and adaptive immunity. Cell 2001;106:259–62.

[100] Albert ML, Jegathesam M, Darnell RB. Dendritic cell maturation is required for the cross-tolerization of CD8 + T cells. Nat Immunol 2001;2:1010–7.

[101] Sauter B, Albert ML, Francisco L, Larsson M, Somersan S, Bhardwaj N. Consequences of cell death: exposure to necrotic tumor cells, but not primary tissue cells or apoptotic cells, induces the maturation of immunostimulatory dendritic cells. J Exp Med 2000;191:423–33.

[102] Huang FP, Platt N, Wykes M, Major JR, Powell TJ, Jenkins CD, et al. A discrete subpopulation of dendritic cells transports apoptotic intestinal epithelial cells to T cell areas of mesenteric lymph nodes. J Exp Med 2000;191:435–44.

[103] Fonteneau J-F, Larsson M, Bhardwaj N. Dendritic cell-dead cell interactions: implications and relevance for immunotherapy. J Immunother 2001;24:294–304.

[104] Mellman I, Steinman RM. Dendritic cells: specialized and regulated antigen processing machines. Cell 2001;106:255–8.

[105] Stern M, Savill J, Haslett C. Human monocyte derived macrophage phagocytosis of senescent eosinophils undergoing apoptosis. Am J Pathol 1996;149:911–6.

[106] Ronchetti A, Rovere P, Iezzi G, Galati G, Heltai S, Protti MP, et al. Immunogenicity of apoptotic cells in vivo: role of antigen load, antigen-presenting cells, and cytokines. J Immunol 1999; 163:130–6.

[107] Feng H, Zeng Y, Whitesell L, Katsanis E. Stressed apoptotic tumor cells express heat shock proteins and elicit tumor-specific immunity. Blood 2001;97:3505–12.

[108] Levine JS, Koh JS, Subang R, Rauch J. Apoptotic cells as immunogen and antigen in the antiphospholipid syndrome. Exp Mol Pathol 1999;66:82–98.

ELSEVIER
SAUNDERS

RHEUMATIC
DISEASE CLINICS
OF NORTH AMERICA

Rheum Dis Clin N Am 30 (2004) 213–227

The genetics of autoimmune-mediated rheumatic diseases: clinical and biologic implications

Robert Winchester, MD

*Division of Autoimmune and Molecular Diseases, Departments of Pediatrics and Medicine,
Columbia University School of Medicine, 630 West 168th Street, PH4-477, New York, NY 10032, USA*

Knowledge of the genetic basis of the autoimmune-mediated rheumatic diseases enhances our understanding of the disease process and provides useful insights that range from guiding choices in therapy, through identifying family members at risk, to explaining the nature and character of the disease to patients. This article emphasizes the interpretation of the meaning and significance of the genetic aspects of susceptibility to these autoimmune diseases. This article is concerned with the contrast between the mechanisms that are involved in the adaptive immune response based on T- and B-cell clonal recognition and proliferation, versus those of the innate immune system based on the use of stereotyped pathogen-specific receptors. For reasons of space, only selected diseases are discussed, but the principles are applicable to virtually all of the autoimmune-mediated rheumatic diseases.

Some features of the genetics of autoimmune-mediated rheumatic diseases

Familial aggregation

The finding that the increased risk of a given autoimmune rheumatic disease is present almost exclusively in blood relatives of the index case emphasizes that a genetic, not environmental, effect is responsible for the aggregation [1]. The degree to which cases are found among blood relatives of an index case who has an autoimmune-mediated rheumatic disease varies considerably according to the disease. Familial aggregation is marked for some rheumatic diseases, like systemic lupus erythematosus (SLE) and the spondylarthritides, such as psoriatic arthritis or

This work was supported by a NIH grant, U19AI46132 (Autoimmunity Centers of Excellence) and by a grant from the National Psoriasis Foundation.

E-mail address: rjw8@columbia.edu

ankylosing spondylitis, where the index case in approximately one in four or five families will have an affected parent, sibling, or child [2,3]. Conversely, for other rheumatic diseases, like rheumatoid arthritis (RA), familial aggregation is uncommon and usually is difficult to observe within the scope of a single clinic or a single practice [4]. The result is that most cases of RA seem sporadic and lack any genetic element [5]. For this reason, national or international studies are required to examine the genetics of RA so that a sufficient number of families who have multiple cases can be identified for a meaningful linkage-based survey [6]. At the clinical level, finding other affected family members often provides valuable insight into the precise diagnosis of the disorder.

The frequency of the disease in blood relatives of the index case divided by the population prevalence of the disease in a sample that is ethnically matched to the index case is one of the simplest measures of the strength of the genetic contribution [7]. This ratio, the recurrence risk, is approximately 4 for RA and approaches 50 to 100 for SLE and the spondylarthritides, which emphasizes the higher evident heritability of the later.

If one attempts to classify the mode of inheritance of the common autoimmune-mediated rheumatic diseases from examining the pattern of affected individuals in a family, the results form no simple Mendelian pattern, and accordingly, the inheritance is termed "complex." Some families that have multiple cases exhibit parent-to-child transmission that suggests a dominant mode, whereas other families have several affected siblings that are compatible with a recessive mode of transmission. The largest proportion of families has only one affected member and appears sporadic, as illustrated in Fig. 1.

A critical issue in formal genetic studies of the autoimmune-mediated rheumatic diseases is that there is complete uniformity in the way that the index case for each family is identified. This process of index case ascertainment has a major,

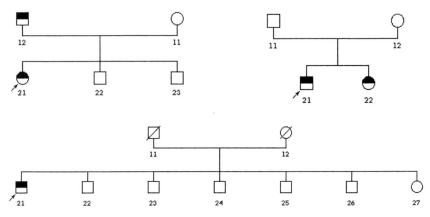

Fig. 1. Three nuclear pedigrees that illustrate various modes of inheritance of psoriatic arthritis. In the lower pedigree, psoriatic arthritis is sporadic in occurrence. In the upper left pedigree, the inheritance seems to be dominant, whereas in the upper right pedigree the mode of inheritance seems to be recessive. The partly shaded squares and circles represent males and females affected with psoriatic arthritis, respectively.

and sometimes unsuspected, influence on the genetic question being asked. For example, if one were interested in the relative frequencies of SLE and discoid lupus, the result might vary considerably depending on whether one began as-certaining cases with demonstrable SLE or began ascertaining cases of discoid lupus. Similarly, if one was interested in the frequency of psoriatic arthritis and psoriasis in families, the result varies considerably depending on whether one began with cases of psoriatic arthritis and asked how many relatives had psoria-sis, versus a study that began by ascertainment of those who had psoriasis and determined how many relatives had psoriatic arthritis.

Concordance between identical twins

The extent of concordance between the two members of an identical twinship re-emphasizes the existence of a determining genetic element [1]. Moreover, the extent of the concordance mirrors the recurrence risk found in familial aggrega-tion. Even among individuals with diseases with high recurrence risks (eg, lupus), the percentage of concordant twins is only 25% to 50% and is nearly 10-fold lower in RA. This implies that the genetic effect predisposes to, but does not determine, the development of the rheumatic disease. Clearly, some nongermline genetic event must occur to convert the predisposition or susceptibility into a disease [5]. Epidemiologic studies do not identify any evident single environmental factor that could account for this effect, however. Conversely, the importance of stochastic events in the formation of the T-cell repertoire and in the generation of the adaptive immune response offers a somatic genetic explanation for the source of this effect [5]. Thus, the main lessons from identical twins are that a genetic basis is present and necessary but not sufficient for the development of disease and that a nongermline effect is operating.

The actual percentages of concordance vary among studies for several reasons. Among them, is the issue of ascertainment, because the ascertainment of the second case influences the frequency reported for concordance. Ascertainment depends on the sensitivity of the criteria that are used for diagnosis; the more stringent published criteria for classification, although appropriately rigorous for their designed purpose, lack sensitivity for this type of application. Conversely, a factor that tends to raise the concordance rate is a lowering in the threshold for disease detection because the presence of symptoms in one twin enhances the likelihood of diagnosis in the other. Additionally, the length of time after the diagnosis of disease in the first twin that the second twin is observed for the development of disease is another major variable; the twins would not be expected to develop the disease simultaneously and accurate ascertainment re-quire a multiple-year follow-up observational period.

Low penetrance rates for genetic susceptibility

The concordance rate is an approximate measure of the penetrance of the particular autoimmune-mediated rheumatic disease or how frequently the disease

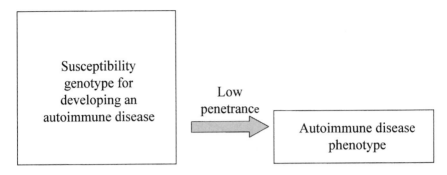

Fig. 2. The proportion of the population that inherits susceptibility genes is much greater than the proportion that manifests the autoimmune disease as a phenotype because of low penetrance of the trait, which is likely due to stochastic events in the formation of the T-cell repertoires and possibly influenced by environmental factors.

susceptibility genotype results in a disease phenotype (Fig. 2). In contrast to the lower penetrance rates of autoimmune disease, the penetrance of genetic diseases that involve a mutant gene, such as those that result in an enzymatic or structural defect, usually approaches 100%. The possible immunologic basis of the low penetrance of autoimmune-mediated rheumatic disease is discussed in the last section on T-cell repertoire. Because nonidentical twins and siblings, in general, typically have an additional genetic difference from each other, the penetrance rate that is observed in a typical family is slightly lower than that of identical twins. Based on the number of individuals who are positive for HLA-B27 and develop Reiter's syndrome during an epidemic of, for example, shigella enteritis, the penetrance of epidemic Reiter's syndrome or reactive arthritis following infection of an individual who is positive for HLA-B27 approaches or exceeds 50% and it seems to be the most penetrant autoimmune-mediated rheumatic disease with the greatest penetrance. The practical impact of the low penetrance of autoimmune-mediated rheumatic disease in dealing with family members is that genetic counseling must stress the implication of the low penetrance and how inheritance of these diseases differs from many, much more highly penetrant genetic diseases that involve mutant genes. Conversely, guidance to a family where there are members that are HLA-B27 might include attention to avoiding situations that favor enteric infection that operate at higher penetrance.

Identification of major histocompatibility complex genes that are involved in determining the predisposition to autoimmune-mediated rheumatic disease

Two general approaches used to identify the genes that are involved in determining the predisposition to autoimmune-mediated rheumatic disease [8]. One approach is used if a candidate gene is known that is likely involved in a pathway that leads to the autoimmune process. Typically, a case control format is used that direct evaluates the frequency of a particular allele of the candidate gene in cases and matched controls. The second, and less sensitive, approach is used if there is no a priori candidate gene and a genome-wide search is made based on linkage between the inheritance of a disease trait and several marker genes or polymorphisms. Typically, the second approach involves affected sibling pairs more often and is aimed at detecting the gene in common among all affected sibling pairs.

Major histocompatibility complex genes are a major genetic determinant of autoimmune-mediated rheumatic disease

The search for a genetic basis of autoimmune diseases began with the candidate gene approach that is based on the importance of the major histocompatibility complex (MHC) in regulating graft rejection and the hypothesis that one allele among the multiplicity of HLA alleles might correlate with proclivity to develop a rheumatic disease. Fig. 3 depicts the schematic organization of the MHC. In 1973, ankylosing spondylitis was shown to be associated with HLA-B27 [9]. The landmark observation was followed by the demonstration that Reiter's syndrome, an immune response to certain gram-negative bacteria, also was associated with HLA-B27. This was the first example in humans of the genetic control of an immune response to a bacterium by MHC genes [10]. Shortly thereafter, the class II MHC genes were described; in the subsequent years, most of the remaining autoimmune-mediated rheumatic diseases were shown to be associated with different alleles of MHC class II genes, notably alleles of the HLA-DR locus [11].

The first striking feature about the MHC class I and II genes is the extremely high number of functionally different alleles—several hundred for each locus [12,13]. Most of the molecules that are encoded by these alleles have different

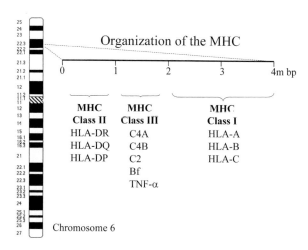

Fig. 3. Organization of the major histocompatibility complex (MHC). The MHC is located on the short arm of chromosome 6 and is divided into three principal regions that consist of MHC class I, class II, and class III genes. The HLA loci are located in the MHC class I and class II regions. There are several hundred genes in the MHC, of which a major proportion are concerned with immune responsiveness. Bf, factor B; TNF-α, tumor necrosis factor-α.

peptide-binding properties and present distinct peptide repertoires to the T cell. The apparent evolutionary drive that accounts for the state of the MHC in the human population reflects the survival advantage of multiple MHC alleles, multiple loci that encode homologous genes, and general heterozygosity of MHC alleles. This is directly attributable to the survival advantage of these polymorphisms in dealing with infections by microorganisms, because a microorganism that has adapted to one individual's immune environment is forced to confront a different adaptive immune environment in the next individual. This is the advantage that the adaptive immune system has over the innate immune system.

The second feature about the MHC class I and II genes is that they operate during development and subsequently to select a complementary repertoire of T cells that specifically recognize self peptides from a vast repertoire of somatically-generated T-cell clones. The MHC molecules and the self-peptides that they contain participate in editing the repertoire to eliminate overtly self-aggressive clones, but leave the bulk of the self-selected T-cell repertoire intact. These two features make understanding how MHC molecules operate to cause autoimmune disease a major challenge.

Physiologic nature of the immune response in autoimmune disease

The finding that different MHC alleles determined susceptibility to different autoimmune diseases was a major clue in understanding the biologic basis of rheumatic diseases and provided several central insights. The significance of these associations is an emerging line of study and much remains to be discovered. Following the confirmatory demonstration that the MHC alleles that predispose to autoimmune-mediated rheumatic disease were identical in sequence to those found in large numbers of healthy individuals [4], it was evident that the immunologic basis of the autoimmune response was rooted deeply in the self-recognition that characterizes a physiologic, normal immune response. Thus, the MHC alleles that are responsible for susceptibility to autoimmune disease are not abnormal, nor are they somatically mutated, as is the case in many malignancies.

Although a comprehensive explanation of the processes that lead to autoimmune disease still is not available, major insights have been gained. One of these is that the widespread use of self-reactivity or autorecognition by MHC molecules is the basis of the formation of the normal adaptive immune system

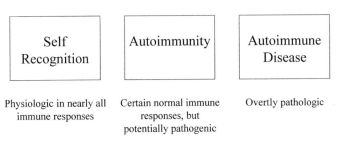

Fig. 4. Three levels of self-reactivity in the T- cell repertoire.

and not the exclusive property of an autoimmune response. This changed the perception of autorecognition that lies at the heart of autoimmune disease from a distinct abnormality that was summarized in Ehrlich's term "horror autotoxicus" to a key physiologic element in normal immune recognition. In this sense, autoimmune diseases are much less the result of differences in kind from the normal immune response than differences in degree. Three levels of self-reactivity in the T-cell repertoire are distinguished in Fig. 4.

Self-recognition

Multiple lines of evidence support the physiologic nature of self-recognition in the adaptive immune response. Because the T-cell repertoire is selected positively on self-peptides that are presented in the context of one's particular MHC molecules, the T-cell repertoire is inherently self-directed. Any T-cell clone that made a response to a non-self-peptide, no matter how exotic, was selected on a self-peptide that was presented in the context of one's own MHC molecules.

Moreover, the process of self-recognition does not stop with formation of the T-cell repertoire, but also is critical for maintenance of T cells in the peripheral repertoire, particularly naïve T cells that requires continual interaction with self-MHC molecules. Murine and in vitro experiments demonstrated that the peptide-specific T-cell receptors (TCRs) of T-cell clones were constantly engaged by self-peptide presented by self-MHC molecules [14–16]. This is reflected by the physiologic enhanced phosphorylation state of the CD3ζ-chain and other signaling components of the clonal TCRs in the absence of engagement by nonself-peptides and the loss of this phosphorylation in animals in where this engagement by self-MHC is limited. The examination of the phosphorylation state is a promising area for study that may shed additional light on events in autoimmunity.

Autoimmunity

There is increasing evidence that limited autoimmunity that involves recognition of self-antigens may develop during the course of physiologic immune responses that does not result in intrinsic ongoing injury to self-tissues. This may occur through transient activation of a variety of T-cell or B-cell clones in the immune response. The subsequent elimination or downregulation of this auto-immune response can occur through elimination of the pathogen or other antigens that drive the immune response or through the action of several regulatory or suppressive circuits.

Autoimmune disease

The development of an autoimmune disease involves a change in autoreactivity from being a means to support the development of an effective immune response to nonself-peptides to an immune response in which self-peptides or antigens are the targets. Extensive clinical investigation showed that the central characteristic of an autoimmune-mediated rheumatic disease is that the immune response that underlies and is responsible for the disease essentially is indistinguishable from an adaptive immune response to a persisting nonself-antigen;

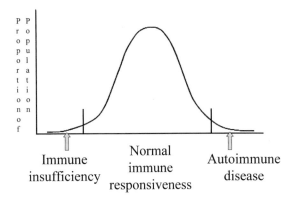

Fig. 5. A hypothetical subdivision of the population into the large majority that has an effective immune system and two tails that have either an insufficient immune response or an autoimmune disease.

the obvious difference is that the autoimmune response is targeted to a self-antigen [5]. The significance of this for the clinician cannot be overemphasized; the therapy must attenuate the inflammation of the autoimmune response without unacceptably decreasing otherwise indistinguishable physiologic immune responses.

From the perspective of MHC biology it seems that the consequences of adaptive immunity for an individual ranges from immune insufficiency through autoimmune disease; most of the population exhibits an immune system that is perfectly attuned to their pathogen environment (Fig. 5). It is likely that several genes and stochastic events account for the dispersion of individuals along the x-axis of the graph. Moreover, it is unlikely that a single gene will be identified that will displace qualitatively an individual's immune system into frank autoimmune disease. Autoimmune diseases are not uncommon and affect approximately 5% of the population, which accounts for the tail at the right of the curve. In this view, autoimmune disease is a necessary concomitant of the existence of an adaptive immune response.

Distribution of target autoantigen determines nature of autoimmune disease

As in virtually all other adaptive immune responses, T-cell recognition regulates the autoimmune response. This is the case whether the dominant immune response is primarily antibody or mainly cell mediated. The finding that different MHC alleles predispose to different diseases emphasized that the recognition of distinct peptides by T-cells presented by these differing MHC molecules is critical to development of each disease. It also emphasized the nearly unique character of each individual's T-cell repertoire and recognition properties. This fact reflects the central element in the adaptive immune response—presentation of a peptide by MHC and recognition of peptide by a T-cell clone.

The specific character of the autoimmune disease is determined by the distribution and biology of the antigens that are recognized by the immune response. Although there is limited knowledge about the precise driving peptide that is recognized by T cells that regulate the autoimmune response in each of the autoimmune-mediated rheumatic diseases, it is clear that differences in the target of the immune response result in clinically different autoimmune diseases. In SLE, the autoimmune response cannot eliminate the widely distributed nuclear autoantigens that are essential to cell function. The persistence, wide distribution, and soluble nature of these autoantigens largely determine why the disease is classified as a rheumatic disorder. Conversely, peptides from musculoskeletal-specific antigens seem to be targets in some autoimmune rheumatic disorders, such as polymyositis. Insulin-dependent diabetes mellitus is the prototype of an immune response to lineage-specific gene products on the pancreatic β-cell, where the immune response eliminates the target lineage. The spondylarthritis disorders also seem to be driven by the recognition of a lineage-specific peptide that is expressed by fibroblasts, but here, the lineage persists and leads to sustained inflammation. The precise molecular nature of the driving peptide is largely unknown for all autoimmune-mediated rheumatic diseases. In some diseases, the presence of autoantibodies led to the identification of autoantigenic target, but the nature of the peptides that are recognized by T cells are not well-delineated.

Classification of autoimmune-mediated rheumatic diseases according to major histocompatibility complex class

A utilitarian classification of autoimmune-mediated rheumatic diseases into MHC class I or class II–associated disorders can be developed according to the class of the MHC molecule that primarily is involved in susceptibility (Fig. 6). For example, susceptibility to the development of the spondylitis group of diseases, including ankylosing spondylitis, Reiter's syndrome, reactive arthritis, undifferentiated spondylarthritis, psoriatic arthritis, and related disorders, is associated with the inheritance of particular class I MHC alleles, notably HLA-B27 and the additional group of psoriatic susceptibility alleles that include HLA-B13, B57, that are in linkage disequilibrium with HLA-Cw6 [3]. These MHC class I–associated disorders are characterized by a T-cell–mediated pathogenesis without evident participation of autoantibodies. Because the CD8 T-cell repertoire recognizes peptides that are presented by MHC class 1 molecules, this suggests that the critical immune recognition event that underlies the class I–

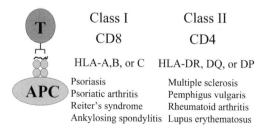

Fig. 6. Classification of autoimmune diseases according to the class of the MHC molecule allele and lineage of autoantigen-specific T cells. APC, antigen-presenting cell.

associated autoimmune diseases involves a CD8 T cell. Support for this was provided by the observation that most of these disorders are unaffected by the profound, but selective, CD4 depletion that occurs in advanced AIDS [3], Conversely, other autoimmune-mediated rheumatic diseases, such as SLE and RA, are associated with particular class II alleles, HLA-DR2 or DR3 and HLA-DR4 or DR1, respectively. These disorders are characterized by the variable presence and importance of autoantibodies, which suggests the presence of CD4 T-cell–mediated help to B cells. Furthermore, also consistent with an immune recognition event that is centered on the CD4 T cell in their pathogenesis, diseases that are associated with particular class II alleles typically abate in advanced AIDS. This classification of autoimmune disease suggests that the driving T-cell clone in class II–associated diseases are CD4 in lineage, whereas the clones that drive the class I–associated diseases are CD8 in lineage. The class II–associated diseases are further subdivided according to whether the CD4 T cells primarily provide help to B cells and preside over the development of autoantibodies or participate in cell-mediated immunity. Inherent in this classification is the fact that different peptides seen by TCR are critical to the development of each disease.

Why are particular alleles associated with different autoimmune-mediated rheumatic diseases?

MHC molecules function by binding peptides with well-defined motifs. Because specific peptides are presented only by the particular allelic MHC molecules and recognized by clonal specific TCR, the ability of a given MHC allelic molecule to present a particular peptide is critical to the development of each disease. Although the nature of the peptide that drives each disease remains unknown, the existence of the different HLA associations is the strongest evidence to support the distinct nature of a peptide or peptides for each disease. As an example, one explanation for the association of HLA-B27 with the spondylarthritis group of diseases is that the peptide-binding pocket of the HLA-B27 molecule binds peptides nine amino acids in length by anchoring side chains at position 2 and the C terminus that preferentially contain a positively charged amino acid such as arginine. This binding motif favors the binding of a particular peptide that becomes the target of the immune response that results in a spondylarthritis. Fig. 7 is a schematic illustration of the peptide-binding pockets of a MHC class I molecule. The different abilities of HLA-B alleles to bind different peptides is illustrated by a protein, such as an HIV-1 envelope variant, where 15 peptides that are contained in the protein can bind the HLA-B27 molecule, 6 different peptides can bind the HLA-B7 peptides with a proline at position 2 and a leucine at the C terminus, and no peptide from this protein can bind HLA-B35 because it binds peptides with a proline at position 2 and a tyrosine at the C terminus. Thus, the immune response in the person who is positive for HLA-B27 has the opportunity to identify 15 peptides, while the person who is positive for B7 can identify 6 peptides within this HIV-1 envelope protein. In contrast, in the HLA-B35-positive person the presence of the HIV envelope

TCR

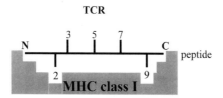

Fig. 7. Peptides bind to a MHC class I molecule through two principal pockets in the MHC molecule. Rules for peptide binding to MHC class I molecules: peptides are usually nine amino acids in length; always oriented with NH2 terminus to the left; most often are anchored by interactions of the side chains of their second (P2) and ninth (P9) amino acids to MHC pockets that confer specificity for amino acids with similar physical properties (eg, size, charge, hydrophobicity).

protein is not recognized. This view suggests that HLA-B27 molecules, through particular anchor residues, bind a given self-peptide, perhaps derived from a molecule that is expressed on fibroblast lineage cells efficiently and selectively. Although a peptide must be presented by the MHC molecule to be recognized by a T-cell clone, not all presented peptides are well-recognized by T-cell clones Generally, the peptides that are well-recognized are immunodominant or sub-dominant peptides.

Insight into the importance of specific alleles, such as HLA-DRB1*0401 and not broader HLA types or specificities, such as HLA-DR4, is provided by the study of the molecular basis of susceptibility to RA. The difference in suscepti-bility to RA and pemphigus vulgaris (PV) illustrates the importance of seemingly subtle differences between alleles in influencing the development of an autoim-mune disease. The puzzling association of HLA-DR4 with RA that is found in some populations, but not others, is reviewed in [4]. The frequency of HLA-DR4 in patients who have RA who were seen at university clinics across North America, northern Europe, and eastern Asia is approximately 60% to 75%, whereas 10% to 15% of unaffected controls were positive. Conversely, in Israel, surrounding Mediterranean countries, and India the frequency of HLA-DR4 in patients who had RA was a lower than in the unaffected controls. Meanwhile, in those latter regions the preponderance of the patients who had RA were positive for HLA DR1 and the frequency of HLA-DR1 is increased in those with RA compared with controls. In contrast, pemphigus vulgaris is associated primarily with HLA-DR4 in the latter countries but is not associated with HLA-DR4 in North America, northern Europe, and western Asia. The first clue to this disparate set of findings is that HLA-DR4 is mainly encoded by the DRB1*0401 and *0404 alleles in North America and northern Europe and by the *0405 alleles in eastern Asia. DRB1*0402 and *0403 are the dominant HLA-DR4–encoding alleles in Israel, the surrounding Mediterranean countries, and India.

There is a minimal, but important, structural difference between the two sets of HLA-DR4 alleles that are found in the different ethnic or racial groups. The differences explain their behavior in terms of disease susceptibility [4] (Table 1). The association of alleles that encode the HLA-DR4 specificity with RA is found only with DRB1*0401, *0404, and *0405 alleles, where the allele encodes a

Table 1
Features of MHC alleles that are responsible for disease susceptibility

Allele	Sequence in β-chain P4 rim			Charge of amino acids			Disease association	
	70	71	74				RA	PV
DRB1*0401	Gln	Lys	Ala	Neu	Pos	Neu	Yes	No
DRB1*0402	Asp	Glu	Ala	Neg	Neg	Neu	No	Yes
DRB1*0404	Gln	Arg	Ala	Neu	Pos	Neu	Yes	No
DRB1*0405	Gln	Arg	Ala	Neu	Pos	Neu	Yes	No

positively-charged amino acid in the stretch of residues around positions 70 to 74 on the DRB chain. The PV association with HLA-DR4 is found mainly with DRB1*0402 and *0403 where negatively-charged amino acids are coded by the allele in the same region. This region forms part of the rim of the P4 pocket that binds the fourth amino acid side-chain of the peptide that is contained in the MHC groove. The consensus motif L Q K/R A (leu, gln, lys / arg, ala) is encoded by nearly all of the alleles that confer susceptibility to the development of RA. This motif also is found in most of the alleles that have the HLA-DR1 specificity, which accounts for the association of HLA-DR1 alleles with RA in Israel, India, and other parts of the world. The DR1 sequence (DRB1*0101) is different from the DRB1*0401 sequence at multiple locations that are relevant to peptide binding, except where they encode the consensus motif L Q K/R A. A motif of neutral and positively-charged amino acids in the MHC molecule around the rim of the P4 pocket by itself is sufficient to confer susceptibility to RA when it is encoded by any allele at the DRB1 locus. When this association was discovered a little more than a decade ago, this common region was termed quaintly the "shared epitope"; the term is still used. The peptide-binding properties of the P4 pocket imply that peptides that are bound to molecules that bear the consensus P4 motif L Q K/R A, contain a negatively-charged amino acid at P4. Therefore, the repertoire of self-peptides that is used to select the T-cell repertoire when bound to DRB1*0401 molecule contain val-XXX-asp-X-gln, whereas the repertoire of self-peptides that is used to select the T-cell repertoire when bound to DRB1*0402 molecule contain val-XXX-arg-X-gln. Although we know the specificity of a portion of the peptide that binds to the DRB1*0401 molecule, the remaining sequence of the peptide that drives RA is unknown. In the case of PV, studies identified desmoglein 3 as the target of the autoantibodies that mediate the blistering skin disease. Candidate peptides that fit the aforementioned motif have been identified in desmoglein, which suggests that they drive the CD4 T-cell component of this autoimmune disease [17].

The role of the T-cell repertoire in autoimmune disease

Effector events

In an autoimmune disease that is mediated primarily by autoantibodies, the CD4 T-cell that is critically involved in recognition of self-peptides primarily functions in the germinal center of lymph nodes where it collaborates with a B cell that is the precursor to the autoantibody-producing plasma cell. In those autoimmune diseases where T cells participate in, or primarily mediate, tissue injury, the inflammatory site is infiltrated by several T-cell clones; among these, a few consist of the driving effector T-cell clones that recognize the self-peptides that are the target of the adaptive immune response that underlies the disease. The clones may expand notably in this response. In the process of recognizing self-peptides, the driving clones elaborate chemokines and cytokines, as well as express a variety of cell surface activation molecules. Thus, they recruit several different T cells into the inflammatory site based on the clones' expression of chemokine receptors, but not necessarily according to clonal TCR specificity. Characterization of the nature of the T-cell infiltrate in the site of inflammation is an active and increasingly informative area of clinical investigation that is necessary to understand the immune processes that occur in the inflammatory site. This involves techniques to identify the antigenic specificity of the infiltrating T-cell clones as well as describing the complexity of the repertoire at the level of the structure of the TCR $\alpha\beta$ chains through genomic-sequencing techniques. Increasingly, there is evidence for the presence of widespread degeneracy in the clones that are involved in the immune or autoimmune response and multiple examples of incorporation of bystander clones that are not cognitively relevant to inciting peptide. Many of the bystander clones are directed to peptides that are completely irrelevant to the disease, such as those directed to Epstein-Barr virus peptides or stress proteins (eg, heat shock peptides). The activation of these clones in the site of inflammation implies that they participate in the totality of the injury process, although they are not related cognitively to the driving clones. Another feature of inflammatory sites is the extensive chemokine-mediated recruitment of nonproliferating T-cell clones that do not seem to be activated, but provide a measure for the totality of the intensity of the immune response. Another feature of an inflammatory site is that mesenchymal cells respond to the presence of inflammation by the sustained secretion of additional proinflammatory cytokines in a modulatory process that progressively removes many of the phenomena that sustain inflammation far from the driving T-cell clones [18].

Postdevelopmental maturation of the repertoire

The delayed appearance of autoimmune disease implies the operation of a time-dependent process that ultimately results in the development of the disease. The most likely basis for this outcome is in the nature of specific events that are involved in maturation of the T-cell repertoire. Although extensive attention has been directed to the development of the initial postthymic repertoire, less has been given to the postdevelopmental maturation of the repertoire that occurs over several years. One lesson from the modest concordance rates between identical twins that is relevant to this point is that stochastic generation and maturation of the TCR repertoire is important to development of the TCR repertoire. This is likely an incremental and accumulative process. This leads to the proposal

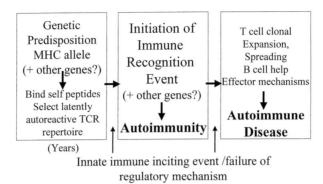

Fig. 8. Hypothetical stages of progression to the development of an autoimmune disease. Auto-recognition and some limited immunity are physiologic.

that there are stages in the development of autoimmunity, and, ultimately, auto-immune disease (Fig. 8). Progression through these stages seems to depend on stochastic events that most likely occur in the somatically-generated lymphocyte repertoires, without the presence of an epidemiologically uniform event, such as a specific infection.

In this way, the development of an autoimmune disease seems to be the consequence of a string of bad luck that involves inheritance of MHC genes that set the stage for the recognition of particular self-peptides, positive selection of the clones that are capable of recognizing the presented peptide in the thymus, and failure of the clone to be eliminated during negative selection in the thymus or peripherally. Through chance-specific and nonspecific stimulation in a process that takes many years, the T-cell clone becomes activated and expanded. Ultimately, the clone is enabled to recognize self-peptides without exogenous support. We hypothesized a model where several stages of clonal expansion and repertoire alteration eventually result in the development of an autoimmune disease [5].

The triggering events that are involved in finally moving a T cell from physiologic self-recognition, through autoimmunity, to development of the pattern of sustained activation that underlies autoimmune disease, remain largely un-known. Hypotheses that involve molecular mimicry have been proposed for several years without overly convincing evidence. Because the innate immune system specifies many of the critical immune recognition events that are re-sponsible for activation of T-cell clones in the physiologic adaptive immune response, it is likely that mechanisms that involve innate immune activation mechanisms of the adaptive immune system underlie the development of T-cell clone reactivity that are responsible for the clinical appearance of autoimmune disease. Dendritic or natural killer (NK) cells and CD8 T cells with NK receptors are particularly likely mediators of innate immunity that are suited by their physiologic function to serve the function of activating proliferation of T cells [19,20]. Lastly, the concept of tolerance and its loss that were developed to explain events in allograft acceptance may not be wholly appropriate to introduce into the genesis of autoimmunity in view of the intrinsic self-recognition that characterizes physiologic immune recognition and the transition from physiologic to pathologic self-recognition. The notion of tolerance is relevant when applied to selectively reducing the activity of an autoreactive clone. New developments in the field of inducing specific clonal tolerance are awaited as alternatives to the more general types of repertoire-wide nontolerizing immune suppression that currently are used for autoimmune disease.

References

[1] Winchester R. Genetics of autoimmune diseases. Curr Opin Immunol 1989;1:199–204.

[2] Winchester RJ, Lahita RG. Genetic susceptibility to SLE. In: Lahita R, editor. Systemic lupus erythematosus. New York: John Wiley & Sons; 1986. p. 81–118.

[3] Winchester R. Psoriatic arthritis. In: Fitzpatrick TB, Eisen AZ, Wolff K, Freedberg IM, Austen FF, editors. Dermatology in general medicine. New York: McGraw-Hill; 2002. p. 427–35.

[4] Winchester R. The molecular basis of susceptibility to rheumatoid arthritis. Adv Immunol 1994; 56:389–466.

[5] Ollier W, Winchester R. The germline and genetic somatic basis for rheumatoid arthritis. Curr Dir Autoimmun 1999;1:166–93.

[6] Seldin MF, Amos CI, Ward R, et al. The genetics revolution and the assault on rheumatoid arthritis. Arthritis Rheum 1999;42:1071–9.

[7] Risch N. Assessing the role of HLA-linked and unlinked determinants of disease. Am J Hum Genet 1987;40:1–14.

[8] Risch N, Merikangas K. The future of genetic studies of complex human diseases. Science 1996; 273:1516–7.

[9] Brewerton DA, Hart FD, Nicholls A, et al. Ankylosing spondylitis and HLA-27. Lancet 1973; 1:904–7.

[10] Brewerton DA, Caffrey M, Nicholls A, et al. Reiter's disease and HLA 27. Lancet 1973;2:996–8.

[11] Winchester R, Kunkel HG. The human Ia system. Adv Immunol 1979;28:221–92.

[12] Trowsdale J. MHC. Res Immunol 1997;148:425–6.

[13] Little AM, Parham P. Polymorphism and evolution of HLA class I and II genes and molecules. Rev Immunogenet 1999;1:105–23.

[14] Sloan-Lancaster J, Shaw AS, Rothbard JB, et al. Partial T cell signaling: altered phospho-zeta and lack of zap70 recruitment in APL-induced T cell anergy. Cell 1994;79:913–22.

[15] Witherden D, van Oers N, Waltzinger C, et al. Tetracycline-controllable selection of CD4(+) T cells: half-life and survival signals in the absence of major histocompatibility complex class II molecules. J Exp Med 2000;191:355–64.

[16] Tanchot C, Lemonnier FA, Perarnau B, et al. Differential requirements for survival and proliferation of CD8 naive or memory T cells. Science 1997;276:2057–62.

[17] Wucherpfennig KW, Yu B, Bhol K, et al. Structural basis for major histocompatibility complex (MHC)-linked susceptibility to autoimmunity: charged residues of a single MHC binding pocket confer selective presentation of self-peptides in pemphigus vulgaris. Proc Natl Acad Sci USA 1995;92:11935–9.

[18] Gulko PS, Seki T, Winchester R. Fibroblast-like synoviocytes: their intrinsic and modified phenotypes and their potential role in the pathogenesis of rheumatoid arthritis. In: Firestein G, Panayi G, Wollheim F, editors. Rheumatoid arthritis frontiers in pathogenesis and treatment. Oxford (UK): Oxford University Press; 2000. p. 123–45.

[19] Steinman RM, Inaba K, Turley S, et al. Antigen capture, processing, and presentation by dendritic cells: recent cell biological studies. Hum Immunol 1999;60:562–7.

[20] Jabri B, Selby JM, Negulescu H, et al. TCR specificity dictates CD94/NKG2A expression by human CTL. Immunity 2002;17:487–99.

ELSEVIER
SAUNDERS

Rheum Dis Clin N Am 30 (2004) 229–235

RHEUMATIC
DISEASE CLINICS
OF NORTH AMERICA

Index

Note: Page numbers of article titles are in **bold face** type.

A

Adhesion molecules, endothelial cell
  interactions with, 99–103, 107–108

Anaphylotoxin, complement-derived, 4–5

Anergy
  B lymphocyte function in, 163
  T lymphocyte function in, 151–152

Angiogenesis
  endothelium role in
    clinical perspectives of, 107–108
    pathophysiology of, 104–107
  in rheumatoid arthritis, 44–45
  inhibitors of, 106–107

Angioneurotic edema, hereditary, complement
  deficiencies in, 9

Ankylosing spondylitis
  cytokines in, 46
  familial aggregation of, 214

Annexin 1, lipoxin interactions with, 88

Antigen-presenting cells
  B lymphocytes as, 168
  costimulatory molecule interaction with,
    177–181
  in T-lymphocyte activation, 143–145
  T lymphocytes as, 136–138

Antiphospholipid antibodies
  in apoptosis, 198
  treatment of, 11–12

Apoptosis, **193–212**
  autoantigens in
    biochemical alterations to,
      197–198
    description of, 193–195
    redistribution during, 196
    surface changes in, 198–199
  cells in
    autoimmunity and, 204–206
    autoreactive T lymphocytes, 152
    clearance of, 202–206
    immune ignorance of, 202–203

peripheral tolerance of, 203–204
  recognition of, 199–202
complement in, 7–8
phagocytosis after, 25
T-cell receptor signaling and, 145–146

Arachidonic acid, lipoxin formation from,
  71–75

Arteritis, giant cell, 54–55

Arthritis
  collagen-induced, treatment of, 12
  psoriatic
    cytokines in, 46
    familial aggregation of, 213–214
  reactive, cytokines in, 46
  rheumatoid. *See* Rheumatoid arthritis.

Aspirin-triggered lipoxins
  actions of, 73–75, 79–81
  agonists of, 75
  formation of, in disease, 78
  in proinflammatory gene expression,
    86–87
  overview of, 68–71
  receptors for, 83–87
  therapies related to, 87–90

Autacoids, in inflammation resolution. *See*
  Inflammation, resolution of, endogenous
  small molecules for.

Autoantigens
  distribution of, autoimmune disease
    nature and, 220–221
  in apoptosis
    biochemical alterations to,
      197–198
    description of, 193–195
    redistribution during, 196
    surface changes in, 198–199

Autoimmune disease
  apoptosis dysregulation in, 204–206
  B lymphocytes in, 167–168
  classification of, versus major
    histocompatibility class, 221–222

0889-857X/04/$ – see front matter © 2004 Elsevier Inc. All rights reserved.
doi:10.1016/S0889-857X(04)00010-9

Your *Clinics* subscription just got better!

You can now access the FULL TEXT of this publication online at no additional cost! Activate your online subscription today and receive...

- Full text of all issues from 2002 to the present
- Photographs, tables, illustrations, and references
- Comprehensive search capabilities
- Links to MEDLINE and Elsevier journals

Activate Your Online Access Today!

Plus, you can also sign up for E-alerts of upcoming issues or articles that interest you, and take advantage of exclusive access to bonus features!

To activate your individual online subscription:

1. Visit our website at **www.TheClinics.com**.

2. Click on "Register" at the top of the page, and follow the instructions.

3. To activate your account, you will need your subscriber account number, which you can find on your mailing label (note: the number of digits in your subscriber account number varies from six to ten digits). See the sample below where the subscriber account number has been circled.

This is your subscriber account number

```
****************************************3-DIGIT 001
FEB00   J0167   C7   (123456-89)  10/00   Q: 1

J.H. DOE, MD
531 MAIN ST
CENTER CITY, NY  10001-001
```

4. That's it! Your online access to the most trusted source for clinical reviews is now available.

theclinics.com

ELSEVIER

Changing Your Address?

Make sure your subscription changes too! When you notify us of your new address, you can help make our job easier by including an exact copy of your Clinics label number with your old address (see illustration below.) This number identifies you to our computer system and will speed the processing of your address change. Please be sure this label number accompanies your old address and your corrected address—you can send an old Clinics label with your number on it or just copy it exactly and send it to the address listed below.

We appreciate your help in our attempt to give you continuous coverage. Thank you.

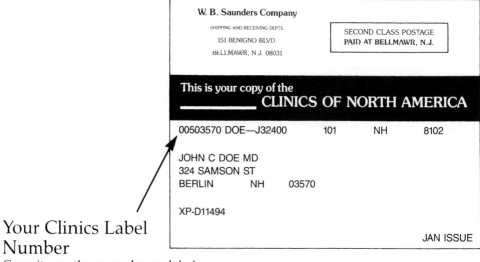

Your Clinics Label Number

Copy it exactly or send your label along with your address to:
W.B. Saunders Company, Customer Service
Orlando, FL 32887-4800
Call Toll Free 1-800-654-2452

Please allow four to six weeks for delivery of new subscriptions and for processing address changes.

YES! Please start my subscription to the **CLINICS** checked below with the ❏ first issue of the calendar year or ❏ current issues. If not completely satisfied with my first issue, I may write "cancel" on the invoice and return it within 30 days at no further obligation.

Please Print:

Name _____

Address_____

City_____ State _____ ZIP _____

Method of Payment

❏ Check (payable to **Elsevier**; add the applicable sales tax for your area)

❏ VISA　　　❏ MasterCard　　　❏ AmEx　　　❏ Bill me

Card number _____ Exp. date _____

Signature _____

Staple this to your purchase order to expedite delivery

❏ **Adolescent Medicine Clinics**
　❏ Quarterly　　$92
　❏ Institutions　$121

❏ **Anesthesiology**
　❏ Quarterly　　$167
　❏ Institutions　$230
　❏ *Residents　$84

❏ **Cardiology**
　❏ Quarterly　　$161
　❏ Institutions　$246
　❏ *Residents　$81

❏ **Chest Medicine**
　❏ Quarterly　　$179
　❏ Institutions　$260

❏ **Child and Adolescent Psychiatry**
　❏ Quarterly　　$167
　❏ Institutions　$243
　❏ *Residents　$81

❏ **Critical Care**
　❏ Quarterly　　$161
　❏ Institutions　$243
　❏ *Residents　$81

❏ **Dental**
　❏ Quarterly　　$145
　❏ Institutions　$221

❏ **Emergency Medicine**
　❏ Quarterly　　$162
　❏ Institutions　$243
　　❏ Send CME info

❏ **Facial Plastic Surgery**
　❏ Quarterly　　$191
　❏ Institutions　$280

❏ **Foot and Ankle**
　Quarterly　　$153
　Institutions　$212

❏ **Gastroenterology**
　❏ Quarterly　　$183
　❏ Institutions　$256

❏ **Gastrointestinal Endoscopy**
　❏ Quarterly　　$183
　❏ Institutions　$256

❏ **Hand**
　❏ Quarterly　　$196
　❏ Institutions　$291

❏ **Hematology/Oncology**
　❏ Bimonthly　　$199
　❏ Institutions　$286

❏ **Immunology & Allergy**
　❏ Quarterly　　$162
　❏ Institutions　$243

❏ **Infectious Disease**
　❏ Quarterly　　$159
　❏ Institutions　$248

❏ **Clinics in Liver Disease**
　❏ Quarterly　　$161
　❏ Institutions　$214

❏ **Medical**
　❏ Bimonthly　　$130
　❏ Institutions　$209
　❏ *Residents　$65
　　❏ Send CME info

❏ **MRI**
　❏ Quarterly　　$184
　❏ Institutions　$265
　　❏ Send CME info

❏ **Neuroimaging**
　❏ Quarterly　　$184
　❏ Institutions　$265
　　❏ Send CME inf0

❏ **Neurologic**
　❏ Quarterly　　$169
　❏ Institutions　$267

❏ **Obstetrics & Gynecology**
　❏ Quarterly　　$168
　❏ Institutions　$263

❏ **Occupational and Environmental Medicine**
　❏ Quarterly　　$114
　❏ Institutions　$152
　❏ *Residents　$57

❏ **Ophthalmology**
　❏ Quarterly　　$184
　❏ Institutions　$297

❏ **Oral & Maxillofacial Surgery**
　❏ Quarterly　　$172
　❏ Institutions　$255
　❏ *Residents　$81

❏ **Orthopedic**
　❏ Quarterly　　$175
　❏ Institutions　$269
　❏ *Residents　$88

❏ **Otolaryngologic**
　❏ Bimonthly　　$195
　❏ Institutions　$321

❏ **Pediatric**
　❏ Bimonthly　　$129
　❏ Institutions　$226
　❏ *Residents　$65
　　❏ Send CME info

❏ **Perinatology**
　❏ Quarterly　　$148
　❏ Institutions　$217
　　❏ Send CME inf0

❏ **Plastic Surgery**
　❏ Quarterly　　$233
　❏ Institutions　$346

❏ **Podiatric Medicine & Surgery**
　❏ Quarterly　　$160
　❏ Institutions　$243

❏ **Primary Care**
　❏ Quarterly　　$131
　❏ Institutions　$203

❏ **Psychiatric**
　❏ Quarterly　　$165
　❏ Institutions　$263

❏ **Radiologic**
　❏ Bimonthly　　$213
　❏ Institutions　$302
　❏ *Residents　$107
　　❏ Send CME info

❏ **Sports Medicine**
　❏ Quarterly　　$174
　❏ Institutions　$253

❏ **Surgical**
　❏ Bimonthly　　$183
　❏ Institutions　$273
　❏ *Residents　$92

❏ **Urologic**
　❏ Quarterly　　$186
　❏ Institutions　$280
　　❏ Send CME info

BUSINESS REPLY MAIL

FIRST-CLASS MAIL   PERMIT NO 7135   ORLANDO FL

POSTAGE WILL BE PAID BY ADDRESSEE

PERIODICALS ORDER FULFILLMENT DEPT
ELSEVIER
6277 SEA HARBOR DR
ORLANDO FL 32821-9816